National Commission for
Health Education Credentialing, Inc.

Credentialing Excellence in Health Education

The Health Education Specialist: A Companion Guide for Professional Excellence

Sixth Edition

National Commission for
Health Education Credentialing, Inc.

Published by: National Commission for Health Education Credentialing, Inc.
                1541 Alta Drive, Suite 303
                Whitehall, PA 18052-5642
                Local phone: (484) 223-0770
                Phone: (888) NCHEC-4-U, (888) 624-3248
                Fax: (800) 813-0727
                www.nchec.org

ISBN 0-9652570-5-3

ACKNOWLEDGMENTS

In 1992, Sigred G. Deeds, DrPH, CHES, authored the original edition of *The Health Education Specialist: A Self-Study Guide for Professional Competence*. Her work was based on 25 years' experience in a variety of health education settings. In 1995, Dr. Deeds donated her book to the National Commission for Health Education Credentialing, Inc.

This edition marks the sixth revision to Dr. Deeds' original work. The fifth edition was revised by Amos O. Aduroja, PhD, CHES; Carolyn Cox, PhD, CHES; Judith Luebke, PhD, CHES; Lisa Roth-Edwards, MPH, CHES; Jiunn-Jye Sheu, MSPH, PhD, CHES; Jody R. Steinhardt, MPH, CHES; and Kelly Wilson, PhD, CHES. Previous editions were revised by Michael Cleary, EdD, CHES; Brad Neiger, PhD, CHES; Kathleen Middleton, MS, CHES; and Joanna Hayden, PhD, CHES; with the help of numerous volunteers.

The difference in this companion guide is that it is based on the results of the Health Educator Job Analysis-2010. The resultant revised Areas of Responsibility, Competencies, and Sub-competencies identified in that project have been incorporated into this companion guide, and additional material on the new and revised Competencies has been included. For the first time, this publication is including both entry- and advanced-level Competencies and Sub-competencies. In addition, the sample questions have been reviewed and revised; and questions have been added to reflect the new material.

The sixth edition of *Health Education Specialist: A Companion Guide for Professional Excellence* was compiled with efforts of health education specialists with expertise and experience in the Seven Areas of Responsibility identified in this companion guide. The authors refined and added to previous editions. Much gratitude to the editor, Leonard Jack, Jr., PhD, MSc, CHES and co-editors, Melissa Grim, PhD, CHES and Kelly Wilson, PhD, CHES for their tireless work to meet short deadlines in order to release this publication in a timely manner.

Sincere appreciation and recognition is extended to Carolyn Cox, PhD, CHES, for reviewing and assisting in polishing several drafts of practice examination questions. Special thanks also to students in the Department of Health and Human Performance at Texas State University who provided assistance to Kelly Wilson, PhD, CHES with verifying references were properly cited throughout the companion guide.

Editor:
Leonard Jack, Jr., PhD, MSc, CHES

Co-Editors:
Melissa Grim, PhD, CHES
Kelly Wilson, PhD, CHES

Contributing Authors:

Chapter I: Assess Needs, Assets, and Capacity for Health Education
Tung-Sung "Sam" Tseng, DrPH, MS, CHES
Melissa Grim, PhD, CHES

Chapter II: Plan Health Education
Angela Mickalide, PhD, CHES

Chapter III: Implement Health Education
Katherine Wilson, PhD, CHES
Christopher N. Thomas, MS, CHES

Chapter IV: Conduct Evaluation and Research Related to Health Education
Maurice "Bud" Martin, PhD, CHES
Dennis Kamholtz, PhD, CHES

Chapter V: Administer and Manage Health Education
Chris Arthur, PhD, CHES
Patricia A. Frye, DrPH, MPA, CHES

Chapter VI: Serve As Health Education Resource Person
Cam Escoffery, PhD, MPH, CHES

Chapter VII: Communicate and Advocate for Health and Health Education
Rebecca Reeve, PhD, CHES
Donna Beal, MPH, CHES
Leonard Jack, Jr, PhD, MSc, CHES

Study Guide Task Force and Reviewers:
Kelly Wilson, PhD, CHES, Chair
Judith Luebke, PhD, CHES
Carol Cox, PhD, CHES
Lori Elmore, MPH, CHES

Additional Reviewers:
Linda Lysoby, MS, CHES, CAE
Kimberly Sanders, BS

Copy Editors:
Melissa Rehrig, MPH, CHES
Emily Gunnels, MS

TABLE OF CONTENTS

INTRODUCTION

The purpose of this book is to guide health education specialists in advancing their knowledge and skills in the field of health education at both entry-and advanced-levels of practice. This sixth edition, *The Health Education Specialist: A Companion Guide for Professional Excellence*, has purposefully changed the title of the document to encompass the terms "companion guide" rather than "study guide." While the companion guide may be used to help individuals prepare for the national examination for either the Certified Health Education Specialist (CHES) or Master Certified Health Education Specialist (MCHES) credentials, it can also be used as a professional development tool. The *Health Education Specialist: A Companion Guide for Professional Excellence* can be used to help assess health education knowledge and direct continuing education studies. Employers can encourage their employees to use this book as a tool to determine whether additional professional development in specific areas is needed. Instructors in professional preparation programs may find the format and organization of this book to be a useful supplement to textbooks and classroom lectures. Students enrolled in health education professional preparation programs can utilize this guide as an excellent reference source. It should be understood that relying on this book as the only resource for studying for the CHES or MCHES exams is strongly discouraged.

The *Health Education Specialist: A Companion Guide for Professional Excellence* is organized to follow the Seven Areas of Responsibility, their related Competencies and Sub-competencies at both entry and advanced levels as delineated in *A Competency Based Framework for Health Education Specialists - 2010* (National Commission for Health Education Credentialing, Inc. [NCHEC], Society for Public Health Education [SOPHE], & American Association for Health Education [AAHE], 2010a). That framework is based on the Health Educator Job Analysis-2010 (NCHEC et al., 2010b), an 18-month project to update, refine and validate the model of health education practice. The updated model comprises 223 Sub-competencies, organized into 34 Competencies within seven major Areas of Responsibility. Of the Sub-competencies, 61 were validated as advanced-level only. The HEJA-2010 study expanded upon the previous Competency Update Project (CUP) (Gilmore, Olson, Taub, & Connell, 2005), which first provided a model of three levels of practice (entry, advanced 1, and advanced 2) with each subsequent level building upon the previous level(s).

Extensive research involving health education specialists across the nation has verified the existence of entry-and advanced-levels of health education practice with the differentiation at five years of experience. In 2009, it was released that the NCHEC Board of Commissioners voted to implement an advanced-level of certification. This proves to be an exciting time for the profession of health education and for health education specialists – which was carefully considered in this edition of the guide.

Like earlier versions, the HEJA-2010 model includes Responsibilities, Competencies and Sub-competencies that are considered generic and independent of the setting in which the health education specialist works (NCHEC et al., 2010b). The CHES examination addresses only those Competencies and Sub-competencies that were identified in the HEJA-2010 as entry-level. The MCHES examination addresses all of the Competencies and Sub-competencies, regardless of level. Additional details regarding the role and history of credentialing can be found in Chapter VII of *The Health Education Specialist: A Companion Guide for Professional Excellence*.

HOW TO USE THIS BOOK

This book can be used to identify areas of practice that may require further study using nationally recognized scholarly references. Whether for purposes of exam preparation, part of academic preparation or for professional development activities, study should not be limited to this one resource. Those preparing for the CHES or MCHES exam are reminded that these exams are national competency-based tests that measure the possession, application and interpretation of knowledge related to the Seven Areas of Responsibility. Further, the information included in this companion guide cannot be considered exhaustive by the reader. Additional optional readings that may also assist in supporting study are listed on the NCHEC Web site www.nchec.org.

Many Certified Health Education Specialists (CHES) who used previous NCHEC study guides reported that using the guide as a basic resource for a study group was very helpful. Using a discussion format to work through the practice questions was reported as a useful way to prepare not only for the exam but also for professional development activities.

As a starting point to assist in identifying gaps in one's formal preparation for health education practice, a *Self-Assessment for Health Education Specialists: Perceived Competence* tool is included in the companion guide and follows the Introduction. After the self-assessment exercise, it may be helpful to review each chapter and note any other apparent weaknesses. Each chapter follows a logical organization: Area of Responsibility, followed by the role of a health education specialist relative to the Responsibility, examples of each role in the practice setting, key terms, and information germane to each of the corresponding Competencies and Sub-competencies. It is important to note that while key terms may appear in more than one chapter, the users are advised that definitions within chapters may vary given the context in which it is being used.

Throughout the *Health Education Specialist: A Companion Guide for Professional Excellence*, there is a graphic differentiation between entry-level and advanced-level Sub-competencies. The advanced-level content is distinguished by this symbol ▨. Also, in some places, the editors felt that it was important to note that although the Sub-competency was advanced-level, content within the text was not beyond the scope of an entry-level health education specialist. The entry- and advanced – level text is differentiated by this symbol ◻ ▨. After reviewing the material in each chapter, it may be beneficial to complete the practice questions. Practice entry-level questions are located in Appendix C and practice advanced-level questions are packaged separately.

The content of this publication reflects consensus about a common core of professional preparation leading to entry-and advanced-level practice as a health education specialist. This publication should be considered a supplemental tool, and not a primary source, for identifying areas of practice that may require further study using nationally recognized scholarly references. Study and preparation for the CHES and MCHES exams should not be limited to *The Health Education Specialist: A Companion Guide for Professional Excellence*.

SELF-ASSESSMENT FOR HEALTH EDUCATION SPECIALISTS: PERCEIVED COMPETENCE

The competency statements in this assessment describe the broadly defined skills that a qualified entry-level, generic, health education specialist is expected to be able to demonstrate, at least at minimum levels. To assess individual skill level for each competency statement, rate each competency from 1 to 4, with 1 indicating not competent and 4 indicating very competent.

Area of Responsibility I:
ASSESS NEEDS, ASSETS, AND CAPACITY FOR HEALTH EDUCATION

The health education specialist can:

COMPETENCY 1.1: Plan Assessment Process

		Not Competent			Very Competent
1.1.1	Identify existing and needed resources to conduct assessments	1	2	3	4
1.1.2	⫫ Identify stakeholders to participate in the assessment process	1	2	3	4
1.1.3	Apply theories and models to develop assessment strategies	1	2	3	4
1.1.4	Develop plans for data collection, analysis, and interpretation	1	2	3	4
1.1.5	⫫ Engage stakeholders to participate in the assessment process	1	2	3	4
1.1.6	Integrate research designs, methods, and instruments into assessment plans	1	2	3	4

COMPETENCY 1.2: Access Existing Information and Data Related to Health

1.2.1	Identify sources of data related to health	1	2	3	4
1.2.2	Critique sources of health information using theory and evidence from the literature	1	2	3	4
1.2.3	Select valid sources of information about health	1	2	3	4
1.2.4	Identify gaps in data using theories and assessment models	1	2	3	4
1.2.5	Establish collaborative relationships and agreements that facilitate access to data	1	2	3	4
1.2.6	Conduct searches of existing databases for specific health-related data	1	2	3	4

COMPETENCY 1.3: Collect Quantitative and/or Qualitative Data Related to Health

1.3.1	Collect primary and/or secondary data	1	2	3	4
1.3.2	Integrate primary data with secondary data	1	2	3	4
1.3.3	Identify data collection instruments and methods	1	2	3	4
1.3.4	Develop data collection instruments and methods	1	2	3	4
1.3.5	Train personnel and stakeholders regarding data collection	1	2	3	4
1.3.6	Use data collection instruments and methods	1	2	3	4
1.3.7	Employ ethical standards when collecting data	1	2	3	4

COMPETENCY 1.4: Examine Relationships Among Behavioral, Environmental and Genetic Factors That Enhance or Compromise Health

1.4.1	Identify factors that influence health behaviors	1	2	3	4
1.4.2	Analyze factors that influence health behaviors	1	2	3	4
1.4.3	Identify factors that enhance or compromise health	1	2	3	4
1.4.4	Analyze factors that enhance or compromise health	1	2	3	4

Key: ⬛ Entry ⫫ Advanced – level information

COMPETENCY 1.5: Examine Factors That Influence the Learning Process

		Not Competent		Very Competent	
1.5.1	Identify factors that foster or hinder the learning process	1	2	3	4
1.5.2	▧ Analyze factors that foster or hinder the learning process	1	2	3	4
1.5.3	Identify factors that foster or hinder attitudes and belief	1	2	3	4
1.5.4	Analyze factors that foster or hinder attitudes and beliefs	1	2	3	4
1.5.5	▧ Identify factors that foster or hinder skill building	1	2	3	4
1.5.6	▧ Analyze factors that foster or hinder skill building	1	2	3	4

COMPTENCY 1.6: Examine Factors That Enhance or Compromise the Process of Health Education

1.6.1	Determine the extent of available health education programs, interventions, and policies	1	2	3	4
1.6.2	Assess the quality of available health education programs, interventions, and policies	1	2	3	4
1.6.3	Identify existing and potential partners for the provision of health education services	1	2	3	4
1.6.4	Assess social, environmental, and political conditions that may impact health education	1	2	3	4
1.6.5	Analyze the capacity for developing needed health education	1	2	3	4
1.6.6	Assess the need for resources to foster health education	1	2	3	4

COMPETENCY 1.7: Infer Needs for Health Education Based on Assessment Findings

1.7.1	Analyze assessment findings	1	2	3	4
1.7.2	▧ Synthesize assessment findings	1	2	3	4
1.7.3	Prioritize health education needs	1	2	3	4
1.7.4	Identify emerging health education needs	1	2	3	4
1.7.5	Report assessment findings	1	2	3	4

Area of Responsibility II:

PLAN HEALTH EDUCATION

COMPETENCY 2.1: Involve Priority Populations and Other Stakeholders in the Planning Process

2.1.1	Incorporate principles of community organization	1	2	3	4
2.1.2	Identify priority populations and other stakeholders	1	2	3	4
2.1.3	Communicate need for health education to priority populations and other stakeholders	1	2	3	4
2.1.4	Develop collaborative efforts among priority populations and other stakeholders	1	2	3	4
2.1.5	Elicit input from priority populations and other stakeholders	1	2	3	4
2.1.6	Obtain commitments from priority populations and other stakeholders	1	2	3	4

Key: ▢ Entry ▧ Advanced – level information

SELF-ASSESSMENT FOR HEALTH EDUCATION SPECIALISTS: PERCEIVED COMPETENCE

COMPETENCY 2.2: Develop Goals and Objectives

		Not Competent		Very Competent	
2.2.1	ⅠⅠ Use assessment results to inform the planning process	1	2	3	4
2.2.2	Identify desired outcomes utilizing the needs assessment results	1	2	3	4
2.2.3	ⅠⅠ ◻ Select planning model(s) for health education	1	2	3	4
2.2.4	ⅠⅠ Develop goal statements	1	2	3	4
2.2.5	ⅠⅠ Formulate specific, measurable, attainable, realistic and time-sensitive objectives	1	2	3	4
2.2.6	Assess resources needed to achieve objectives	1	2	3	4

COMPETENCY 2.3: Select or Design Strategies and Interventions

2.3.1	ⅠⅠ Assess efficacy of various strategies to ensure consistency with objectives	1	2	3	4
2.3.2	Design theory-based strategies and interventions to achieve stated objectives	1	2	3	4
2.3.3	◻ ⅠⅠ Select a variety of strategies and interventions to achieve stated objectives	1	2	3	4
2.3.4	Comply with legal and ethical principles in designing strategies and interventions	1	2	3	4
2.3.5	Apply principles of cultural competence in selecting and designing strategies and interventions	1	2	3	4
2.3.6	Pilot test strategies and interventions	1	2	3	4

COMPETENCY 2.4: Develop a Scope and Sequence for the Delivery of Health Education

2.4.1	Determine the range of health education needed to achieve goals and objectives	1	2	3	4
2.4.2	Select resources required to implement health education	1	2	3	4
2.4.3	Use logic models to guide the planning process	1	2	3	4
2.4.4	ⅠⅠ Organize health education into a logical sequence	1	2	3	4
2.4.5	ⅠⅠ Develop a timeline for the delivery of health education	1	2	3	4
2.4.6	Analyze the opportunity for integrating health education into other programs				
2.4.7	Develop a process for integrating health education into other programs	1	2	3	4

COMPETENCY 2.5: Address Factors That Affect Implementation

2.5.1	Identify factors that foster or hinder implementation	1	2	3	4
2.5.2	Analyze factors that foster or hinder implementation	1	2	3	4
2.5.3	Use findings of pilot to refine implementation plans as needed	1	2	3	4
2.5.4	Develop a conducive learning environment	1	2	3	4

Key: ◻ Entry ⅠⅠ Advanced – level information

SELF-ASSESSMENT FOR HEALTH EDUCATION SPECIALISTS: PERCEIVED COMPETENCE

Area of Responsibility III:

IMPLEMENT HEALTH EDUCATION

COMPETENCY 3.1: Implement a Plan of Action

		Not Competent		Very Competent	
3.1.1	Assess readiness for implementation	1	2	3	4
3.1.2	Collect baseline data	1	2	3	4
3.1.3	Use strategies to ensure cultural competence in implementing health education plans	1	2	3	4
3.1.4	Use a variety of strategies to deliver a plan of action	1	2	3	4
3.1.5	Promote plan of action	1	2	3	4
3.1.6	Apply theories and models of implementation	1	2	3	4
3.1.7	Launch plan of action	1	2	3	4

COMPETENCY 3.2: Monitor Implementation of Health Education

3.2.1	Monitor progress in accordance with timeline	1	2	3	4
3.2.2	Assess progress in achieving objectives	1	2	3	4
3.2.3	Modify plan of action as needed	1	2	3	4
3.2.4	Monitor use of resources	1	2	3	4
3.2.5	Monitor compliance with legal and ethical principles	1	2	3	4

COMPETENCY 3.3: Train Individuals Involved in Implementation of Health Education

3.3.1	Select training participants needed for implementation	1	2	3	4
3.3.2	▨ Identify training needs	1	2	3	4
3.3.3	▨ Develop training objectives	1	2	3	4
3.3.4	▨ Create training using best practices	1	2	3	4
3.3.5	Demonstrate a wide range of training strategies	1	2	3	4
3.3.6	Deliver training	1	2	3	4
3.3.7	▨ Evaluate training	1	2	3	4
3.3.8	▨ Use evaluation findings to plan future training	1	2	3	4

Area of Responsibility IV:

CONDUCT EVALUATION AND RESEARCH RELATED TO HEALTH EDUCATION

COMPETENCY 4.1: Develop Evaluation/Research Plan

4.1.1	▨ Create purpose statement	1	2	3	4
4.1.2	▨ Develop evaluation/research questions	1	2	3	4
4.1.3	Assess feasibility of conducting evaluation/research	1	2	3	4
4.1.4	Critique evaluation and research methods and findings found in the related literature	1	2	3	4
4.1.5	Synthesize information found in the literature	1	2	3	4
4.1.6	Assess the merits and limitations of qualitative and quantitative data collection for evaluation	1	2	3	4

Key: ◻ Entry ▨ Advanced – level information

SELF-ASSESSMENT FOR HEALTH EDUCATION SPECIALISTS: PERCEIVED COMPETENCE

	Not Competent		Very Competent	
4.1.7 ⅗ Assess the merits and limitations of qualitative and quantitative data collection for research	1	2	3	4
4.1.8 Identify existing data collection instruments	1	2	3	4
4.1.9 Critique existing data collection instruments for evaluation	1	2	3	4
4.1.10 ⅗ Critique existing data collection instruments for research	1	2	3	4
4.1.11 ⅗ Create a logic model to guide the evaluation process	1	2	3	4
4.1.12 Develop data analysis plan for evaluation	1	2	3	4
4.1.13 ⅗ Develop data analysis plan for research	1	2	3	4
4.1.14 Apply ethical standards in developing the evaluation/research plan	1	2	3	4

COMPETENCY 4.2: Design Instruments to Collect Evaluation and Research Data

	Not Competent		Very Competent	
4.2.1 Identify useable questions from existing instruments	1	2	3	4
4.2.2 Write new items to be used in data collection for evaluation	1	2	3	4
4.2.3 ⅗ Write new items to be used in data collection for research	1	2	3	4
4.2.4 Establish validity of data collection instruments	1	2	3	4
4.2.5 Establish reliability of data collection instruments	1	2	3	4

COMPETENCY 4.3: Collect and Analyze Evaluation/Research Data

	Not Competent		Very Competent	
4.3.1 Collect data based on the evaluation/research plan	1	2	3	4
4.3.2 Monitor data collection and management	1	2	3	4
4.3.3 Analyze data using descriptive statistics	1	2	3	4
4.3.4 Analyze data using inferential and/or other advanced statistical methods	1	2	3	4
4.3.5 Analyze data using qualitative methods	1	2	3	4
4.3.6 Apply ethical standards in collecting and analyzing data	1	2	3	4

COMPETENCY 4.4: Interpret Results of the Evaluation/Research

	Not Competent		Very Competent	
4.4.1 Compare results to evaluation/research questions	1	2	3	4
4.4.2 Compare results to other findings from evaluation	1	2	3	4
4.4.3 Propose possible explanations of findings	1	2	3	4
4.4.4 Identify possible limitations of findings	1	2	3	4
4.4.5 Develop recommendations based on results	1	2	3	4

COMPETENCY 4.5: Apply Findings From Evaluation/Research

	Not Competent		Very Competent	
4.5.1 Communicate findings to stakeholders	1	2	3	4
4.5.2 ⅗ Evaluate feasibility of implementing recommendations from evaluation	1	2	3	4
4.5.3 Apply evaluation findings in policy analysis and program development	1	2	3	4
4.5.4 ⅗ Disseminate research findings through professional conference presentations	1	2	3	4

Key: ☐ Entry ⅗ Advanced – level information

SELF-ASSESSMENT FOR HEALTH EDUCATION SPECIALISTS: PERCEIVED COMPETENCE

Area of Responsibility V:

ADMINISTER AND MANAGE HEALTH EDUCATION

COMPETENCY 5.1: Manage Fiscal Resources

		Not Competent		Very Competent	
5.1.1	Identify fiscal and other resources	1	2	3	4
5.1.2	Prepare requests/proposals to obtain fiscal resources	1	2	3	4
5.1.3	Develop budgets to support health education efforts	1	2	3	4
5.1.4	Manage program budgets	1	2	3	4
5.1.5	Prepare budget reports	1	2	3	4
5.1.6	Demonstrate ethical behavior in managing fiscal resources	1	2	3	4

COMPETENCY 5.2: Obtain Acceptance and Support for Programs

5.2.1	Use communication strategies to obtain program support	1	2	3	4
5.2.2	Facilitate cooperation among stakeholders responsible for health education	1	2	3	4
5.2.3	Prepare reports to obtain and/or maintain program support	1	2	3	4
5.2.4	Synthesize data for purposes of reporting	1	2	3	4
5.2.5	Provide support for individuals who deliver professional development opportunities	1	2	3	4
5.2.6	Explain how program goals align with organizational structure, mission, and goals	1	2	3	4

COMPETENCY 5.3: Demonstrate Leadership

5.3.1	Conduct strategic planning	1	2	3	4
5.3.2	Analyze an organization's culture in relationship to health education goals	1	2	3	4
5.3.3	Promote collaboration among stakeholders	1	2	3	4
5.3.4	Develop strategies to reinforce or change organizational culture to achieve health education goals	1	2	3	4
5.3.5	Comply with existing laws and regulations	1	2	3	4
5.3.6	Adhere to ethical standards of the profession	1	2	3	4
5.3.7	Facilitate efforts to achieve organizational mission	1	2	3	4
5.3.8	Analyze the need for a systems approach to change	1	2	3	4
5.3.9	Facilitate needed changes to organizational cultures	1	2	3	4

COMPETENCY 5.4: Manage Human Resources

5.4.1	Develop volunteer opportunities	1	2	3	4
5.4.2	Demonstrate leadership skills in managing human resources	1	2	3	4
5.4.3	Apply human resource policies consistent with relevant laws and regulations	1	2	3	4
5.4.4	Evaluate qualifications of staff and volunteers needed for programs	1	2	3	4
5.4.5	Recruit volunteers and staff	1	2	3	4
5.4.6	Employ conflict resolution strategies	1	2	3	4
5.4.7	Apply appropriate methods for team development	1	2	3	4
5.4.8	Model professional practices and ethical behavior	1	2	3	4

Key: ☐ Entry ⦚ Advanced – level information

	Not Competent		Very Competent	
5.4.9 ⚞ Develop strategies to enhance staff and volunteers' career development	1	2	3	4
5.4.10 ⚞ Implement strategies to enhance staff and volunteers' career development	1	2	3	4
5.4.11 Evaluate performance of staff and volunteers	1	2	3	4

COMPETENCY 5.5: Facilitate Partnerships in Support of Health Education

5.5.1 ⚞ Identify potential partner(s)	1	2	3	4
5.5.2 ⚞ Assess capacity of potential partner(s) to meet program goals	1	2	3	4
5.5.3 Facilitate partner relationship(s)	1	2	3	4
5.5.4 ⚞ Elicit feedback from partner(s)	1	2	3	4
5.5.5 ⚞ Evaluate feasibility of continuing partnership	1	2	3	4

Area of Responsibility VI:

SERVE AS A HEALTH EDUCATION RESOURCE PERSON

COMPETENCY 6.1: Obtain and Disseminate Health-Related Information

6.1.1 Assess information needs	1	2	3	4
6.1.2 Identify valid information resources	1	2	3	4
6.1.3 Critique resource materials for accuracy, relevance, and timeliness	1	2	3	4
6.1.4 Convey health-related information to priority populations	1	2	3	4
6.1.5 Convey health-related information to key stakeholders	1	2	3	4

COMPETENCY 6.2: Provide Training

6.2.1. ⚞ Analyze requests for training	1	2	3	4
6.2.2 ⚞ Prioritize requests for training	1	2	3	4
6.2.3 Identify priority populations	1	2	3	4
6.2.4 ⚞ Assess needs for training	1	2	3	4
6.2.5 ⚞ Identify existing resources that meet training needs	1	2	3	4
6.2.6 ▢ ⚞ Use learning theory to develop or adapt training programs	1	2	3	4
6.2.7 ⚞ Develop training plan	1	2	3	4
6.2.8 ⚞ Implement training sessions and programs	1	2	3	4
6.2.9 ⚞ Use a variety of resources and strategies	1	2	3	4
6.2.10 ⚞ Evaluate impact of training programs	1	2	3	4

COMPETENCY 6.3: Serve as a Health Education Consultant

6.3.1 Assess needs for assistance	1	2	3	4
6.3.2 Prioritize requests for assistance	1	2	3	4
6.3.3 Define parameters of effective consultative relationships	1	2	3	4
6.3.4 Establish consultative relationships	1	2	3	4

Key: ▢ Entry ⚞ Advanced – level information

SELF-ASSESSMENT FOR HEALTH EDUCATION SPECIALISTS: PERCEIVED COMPETENCE

		Not Competent		Very Competent	
6.3.5 ▨ Provide expert assistance		1	2	3	4
6.3.6 Facilitate collaborative efforts to achieve program goals		1	2	3	4
6.3.7 ▨ Evaluate the effectiveness of the expert assistance provided		1	2	3	4
6.3.8 Apply ethical principles in consultative relationships		1	2	3	4

Area of Responsibility VII:
COMMUNICATE AND ADVOCATE FOR HEALTH AND HEALTH EDUCATION

COMPETENCY 7.1: Assess and Prioritize Health Information and Advocacy Needs

7.1.1 Identify current and emerging issues that may influence health and health education	1	2	3	4
7.1.2 Access accurate resources related to identified issues	1	2	3	4
7.1.3 Analyze the impact of existing and proposed policies on health	1	2	3	4
7.1.4 Analyze factors that influence decision-makers	1	2	3	4

COMPETENCY 7.2: Identify and Develop a Variety of Communication Strategies, Methods, and Techniques

7.2.1 Create messages using communication theories and models	1	2	3	4
7.2.2 Tailor messages to priority populations	1	2	3	4
7.2.3 Incorporate images to enhance messages	1	2	3	4
7.2.4 Select effective methods or channels for communicating to priority populations	1	2	3	4
7.2.5 Pilot test messages and delivery methods with priority populations	1	2	3	4
7.2.6 Revise messages based on pilot feedback	1	2	3	4

COMPETENCY 7.3: Deliver Messages Using a Variety of Strategies, Methods and Techniques

7.3.1 Use techniques that empower individuals and communities to improve their health	1	2	3	4
7.3.2 Employ technology to communicate to priority populations	1	2	3	4
7.3.3 Evaluate the delivery of communication strategies, methods, and techniques	1	2	3	4

COMPETENCY 7.4: Engage in Health Education Advocacy

7.4.1 Engage stakeholders in advocacy	1	2	3	4
7.4.2 Develop an advocacy plan in compliance with local, state, and/or federal policies and procedures	1	2	3	4
7.4.3 Comply with organizational policies related to participating in advocacy	1	2	3	4
7.4.4 Communicate the impact of health and health education on organizational and socio-ecological factors	1	2	3	4
7.4.5 Use data to support advocacy messages	1	2	3	4
7.4.6 Implement advocacy plans	1	2	3	4

Key: ▢ Entry ▨ Advanced – level information

	Not Competent		Very Competent	
7.4.7 Incorporate media and technology in advocacy	1	2	3	4
7.4.8 Participate in advocacy initiatives	1	2	3	4
7.4.9 ◣ Lead advocacy initiatives	1	2	3	4
7.4.10 ◣ Evaluate advocacy efforts	1	2	3	4

COMPETENCY 7.5: Influence Policy to Promote Health

7.5.1 ◣ Use evaluation and research findings in policy analysis	1	2	3	4
7.5.2 Identify the significance and implications of health policy for individuals, groups, and communities	1	2	3	4
7.5.3 Advocate for health-related policies, regulations, laws, or rules	1	2	3	4
7.5.4 ◣ Use evidence-based research to develop policies to promote health	1	2	3	4
7.5.5 Employ policy and media advocacy techniques to influence decision-makers	1	2	3	4

COMPETENCY 7.6: Promote the Health Education Profession

7.6.1 Develop a personal plan for professional growth and service	1	2	3	4
7.6.2 Describe state-of-the-art health education practice	1	2	3	4
7.6.3 Explain the major responsibilities of the health education specialist in the practice of health education	1	2	3	4
7.6.4 Explain the role of health education associations in advancing the profession	1	2	3	4
7.6.5 Explain the benefits of participating in professional organizations	1	2	3	4
7.6.6 Facilitate professional growth of self and others	1	2	3	4
7.6.7 Explain the history of the health education profession and its current and future implications for professional practice	1	2	3	4
7.6.8 Explain the role of credentialing in the promotion of the health education profession	1	2	3	4
7.6.9 Engage in professional development activities	1	2	3	4
7.6.10 Serve as a mentor to others	1	2	3	4
7.6.11 Develop materials that contribute to the professional literature	1	2	3	4
7.6.12 Engage in service to advance the health education profession	1	2	3	4

Key: ◻ Entry ◣ Advanced – level information

CHAPTER I

Area of Responsibility I
Assess Needs, Assets, and Capacity for Health Education

1.1: Plan Assessment Process
Sub-competencies:
1.1.1   Identify existing and needed resources to conduct assessments
1.1.2   ▧ Identify stakeholders to participate in the assessment process
1.1.3   Apply theories and models to develop assessment strategies
1.1.4   Develop plans for data collection, analysis, and interpretation
1.1.5   ▧ Engage stakeholders to participate in the assessment process
1.1.6   Integrate research designs, methods, and instruments into assessment plans

1.2: Access existing information and data related to health
Sub-competencies:
1.2.1   Identify sources of data related to health
1.2.2   Critique sources of health information using theory and evidence from the literature
1.2.3   Select valid sources of information about health
1.2.4   Identify gaps in data using theories and assessment models
1.2.5   Establish collaborative relationships and agreements that facilitate access to data
1.2.6   Conduct searches of existing databases for specific health-related data

1.3: Collect quantitative and/or qualitative data related to health
Sub-competencies:
1.3.1   Collect primary and/or secondary data
1.3.2   Integrate primary data with secondary data
1.3.3   Identify data collection instruments and methods
1.3.4   Develop data collection instruments and methods
1.3.5   Train personnel and stakeholders regarding data collection
1.3.6   Use data collection instruments and methods
1.3.7   Employ ethical standards when collecting data

1.4: Examine relationships among behavioral, environmental, and genetic factors that enhance or compromise health
Sub-competencies:
1.4.1   Identify factors that influence health behaviors
1.4.2   Analyze factors that influence health behaviors
1.4.3   Identify factors that enhance or compromise health
1.4.4   Analyze factors that enhance or compromise health

Key: ▢ Entry ▧ Advanced – level information

1.5: Examine factors that influence the learning process

Sub-competencies:

1.5.1   Identify factors that foster or hinder the learning process
1.5.2   ▌▌Analyze factors that foster or hinder the learning process
1.5.3   Identify factors that foster or hinder attitudes and beliefs
1.5.4   Analyze factors that foster or hinder attitudes and beliefs
1.5.5   ▌▌Identify factors that foster or hinder skill building
1.5.6   ▌▌Analyze factors that foster or hinder skill building

1.6: Examine factors that enhance or compromise the process of health education

Sub-competencies:

1.6.1   Determine the extent of available health education programs, interventions, and policies
1.6.2   Assess the quality of available health education programs, interventions, and policies
1.6.3   Identify existing and potential partners for the provision of health education
1.6.4   Assess social, environmental, and political conditions that may impact health education
1.6.5   Analyze the capacity for developing needed health education
1.6.6   Assess the need for resources to foster health education

1.7: Infer needs for health education based on assessment findings

Sub-competencies:

1.7.1   Analyze assessment findings
1.7.2   ▌▌Synthesize assessment findings
1.7.3   Prioritize health education needs
1.7.4   Identify emerging health education needs
1.7.5   Report assessment findings

The Role

The primary purpose of a needs assessment is to gather information to determine what health education activities are appropriate in a given setting. Needs may be basic—that is, essential to the comfort and well-being of every human being (food, water, warmth, oxygen, etc.)—or indicators of a gap between conditions as they are and as they ought to be. Although the term "problem" is frequently used interchangeably with "need" in health education, strictly speaking they are different. A health problem is defined as a potential or real threat to physical or emotional well-being.

Needs assessment is the systematic, planned collection of information about the health knowledge, perceptions, attitudes, motivation, and practices of individuals or groups and the quality of the socioeconomic environment in which they live. Logically, assessment of needs should precede program planning. This process provides data that determines whether a health education program is justified, and if so, what its nature and emphasis ought to be.

To successfully conduct a needs assessment, it is necessary to identify health-related databases and valid sources of data. It is also necessary to be able to gather data with appropriate instruments, apply survey techniques, and identify behaviors that influence health. Determining the extent of existing services and gaps in the provision of services is critical, along with the ability to analyze data and determine priorities for health education (NCHEC, 2010a).

Settings

The following text describes how a needs assessment is used in different practice settings (NCHEC et al., 2010a).

Community Setting. The health education specialist in the community setting relies on many sources of current data, such as health planning agencies, public health departments, census reports, and interviews with community leaders and members of the priority population. Data provides information about perceived health needs. If specific behaviors or health practices are causally linked to the incidence of major health problems, then a health education program may be planned to motivate and facilitate voluntary, desirable changes in those behaviors.

School (K-12) Setting. In the school setting, local, state, and national data are used to determine the scope and sequence of curricula and to identify strengths and weaknesses to aid in developing a Coordinated School Health Program. National-level and state-level data may be considered and utilized, but local data are essential to good curriculum planning. Information about health knowledge, attitudes, skills, and practices can be gathered directly from students and used to improve health instruction, school policies, and the school environment. Information gathered from parents, administrators, and school health personnel by a "Healthy School Team," consisting of representatives from each of the eight components of the Coordinated School Health Program, will assist in identifying potential gaps in creating a healthy school community.

Health Care Setting. In the health care setting, complaints by health professionals about a growing number of emergency room visits, for example, might lead the health education specialist to survey records to determine whether the problem is general or limited to patients with particular kinds of emergencies or with situational needs (e.g., patients without adequate health insurance or with limited access to primary care physicians). An assessment of the reasons for this trend would help to determine what services or policies could help to improve the situation.

Business/Industry Setting. In the workplace, a health education specialist might work with medical professionals to analyze data that can be used to identify health needs of the workers, for example, data about health insurance claims, absenteeism and its causes, types of accidents and severity of injuries, and compensation claims. In addition, a health education specialist in this setting should survey employees to discover their felt needs and interests. Analysis of these data would indicate priority needs for health promotion programs.

College/University Setting. In the college or university setting, health education specialists are often involved in assessing student performance in meeting state and national standards in order to maintain accreditation. Tracking students' progress in meeting the standards, assessing the learning environment, and linking the two are important for revising the curriculum and meeting accreditation requirements.

Key: ☐ Entry ⟍⟍ Advanced – level information

University Health Services Setting. The health education specialist who practices in student health services works side-by-side with clinical practitioners. The health education specialist assesses the health needs of students, staff, and faculty through the use of focus groups, surveys, and interviews. In the assessment process, it is important to develop avenues for obtaining information on perceptions, attitudes, practices, and felt needs in addition to health problems and practices.

Key Terms

O━━ **Needs assessment** is the systematic identification of needs within a population and determination of the degree to which those needs are being met (McKenzie, Neiger, & Thackeray, 2009).

O━━ **Primary data** are data gathered by the health education specialist directly from or about the individual or population of interest. These data answer questions related to the specific needs assessment. Primary data are often collected by means of surveys, interviews, focus groups, and direct observation (McKenzie et al., 2009).

O━━ **Secondary data** are data that have already been collected by others that may or may not be directly gathered from the individual or population being assessed. Examples include existing research published in peer-reviewed journals and/or datasets, such as the US Census, Vital Records and Disease Registries (Gilmore & Campbell, 2005).

O━━ **Stakeholders** may be involved in program operations as program manager, program staff, partners, funding agencies, coalition members or those served or affected by the program/project including patients, clients, advocacy groups and community members (Centers for Disease Control and Prevention [CDC], 1999).

Competency 1.1:
Plan Assessment Process

A **needs assessment** is a process by which health education specialists gather information regarding health needs and desires of a population. In order to conduct a thorough needs assessment health education specialists must carefully plan for the needs assessment process, including assessing resources, locating existing data, collecting data, and using research methods to guide data collection.

1.1.1   Identify existing and needed resources to conduct assessments

Needs assessment is the systematic identification of needs within a population and determination of the degree to which those needs are being met (McKenzie et al., 2009). It is how the program planner identifies and measures gaps between what is and what ought to be. Some educators refer to service needs and service demands or wants (Windsor, Clark, Boyd, & Goodman, 2004). Service needs are those things health professionals believe a given population must have or be able to do in order to resolve a health problem. Service demands are those things people say they must have or be able to do in order to resolve their health problem. Both service needs and service demands are important. Many different approaches can be used to conduct a needs assessment. Often, the needs assessment may be limited by lack of time, personnel, and/or

Key: ▢ Entry ⋀ Advanced – level information

money. However, conducting a needs assessment is a critical step for health education programs. McKenzie et al. (2009) identified the following six-step process for conducting a needs assessment:

1. determine the scope of work and the purpose for the needs assessment;
2. gather the data;
3. analyze the data;
4. identify any factors linked to the health problem;
5. identify the focus for the program; and
6. validate the need before continuing with the planning process.

1.1.2 ⫫ Identify stakeholders to participate in the assessment process

Stakeholders are those who affect change and those who are affected by it. Identifying both types of stakeholders will allow health education specialists to develop relationships with stakeholders, to help create an effective team to conduct a needs assessment, as well as to help with the development, implementation, and evaluation of programs.

1.1.3 Apply theories and models to develop assessment strategies

Theories are useful during the various stages of planning, implementing, and evaluating interventions. Program planners can use theories to shape the pursuit of answers to the questions of why, what, and how. In other words, theories can be used to guide the search for why people are not following public health and medical advice or not caring for themselves in healthy ways. They can help pinpoint what one needs to know before developing and organizing an intervention program. Theories can provide insight into how to shape program strategies to reach people and organizations and make an impact on them. They also help to identify what should be monitored, measured, and compared in a program evaluation (Glanz, Rimer, & Viswanath, 2008b).

The breadth and depth of information collected in needs assessments can vary, depending on the needs assessment model used. Issel (2009) identifies five models for conducting a needs assessment: epidemiological model, public health model, social model, asset model, and rapid model. The epidemiological model focuses on epidemiological data (death rates, prevalence rates, birth rates, etc). The public health model similarly attempts to quantify health problems and often uses epidemiological data. This model, however, can be more focused on a specific population and can be mindful of limitations of resources. Some planning models, such as PRECEDE-PROCEED, can be used as tools for this approach. Please refer to Chapter II for more information on selecting planning model(s) for health education. The social model investigates social or political issues that influence health. The asset model focuses on the strengths of a community, organization, or population and looks to find ways to use existing assets to improve health. The rapid model is a framework that is used when time and money are lacking for a needs assessment. It offers some basic information, but is often lacking in detail. These needs assessment models are not independent, and health education specialists might use several at once.

Some program planning models include one or more steps involved in collecting data for needs assessment. Some models, such as the PRECEDE-PROCEED model, are specific in the order and types of information that should be collected (McKenzie et al., 2009). Likewise, it is necessary to review behavior change models to understand the diverse influences on health and behaviors. Please refer to Chapter III for additional information on the factors that impact the implementation of health education programs. Since health and health behaviors are influenced by many factors, it is important to collect data on what is happening, but also why it is happening. It is important to identify both a planning model and an implementation model in this stage, as this will help to identify the types of data that need to be collected to fully understand the complex influences on health (Doyle, Ward, & Oomen-Early, 2010).

1.1.4 Develop plans for data collection, analysis, and interpretation

Health education specialists should develop a comprehensive data collection and analysis plan. The data collection and analysis plan might apply multiple approaches based on program needs. For example, the feasibility of collecting data among different subpopulations in order to identify disparities should be considered. In addition, the analysis plan should take into account potential bias results from data collection or analysis methods. Please refer to Chapter IV for a description of research methods.

1.1.5 \\ Engage stakeholders to participate in the assessment process

Increasing the involvement of stakeholders in the assessment process can not only result in an improved assessment but also increase the value of the results. Sometimes health education specialists or researchers might develop assessment plans using theories or their own experience; stakeholders can provide useful information or another way of gathering information that might be relevant in the current situation.

1.1.6 Integrate research designs, methods, and instruments into assessment plans

The design of evaluation or research is the grand scheme that delineates when and from whom data are collected. Methods indicate the way in which data are collected as part of the evaluation and typically consist of strategies (Issel, 2009). When conducting needs assessments, health education specialists need to be mindful of sampling techniques, basic research designs used to collect and compare data, methods of collecting data, the types of data needed to answer research questions, and the need for valid and reliable instruments to measure health status, behaviors, attitudes, beliefs, etc. How to apply proper study design with appropriate methods and instruments is a key issue of assessment plans. Please refer to Chapter IV for more information on research design and methods.

Competency 1.2:
Access Existing Information and Data Related to Health

A needs assessment is a critical part of program planning. Needs assessment allows the health education specialist to determine what health problems exist in a particular setting or with a particular group of people. To obtain health-related data, multiple methods should be used. **Primary data** are pieces of information the health education specialist collects to answer unique questions about the specific needs assessment. **Secondary data** have been collected previously for some other purpose and are available for use by others (McKenzie et al., 2009). It must be kept in mind that not all collection methods and sources are appropriate in all practice settings.

Key: ☐ Entry \\ Advanced – level information

ASSESS NEEDS, ASSETS, AND CAPACITY FOR HEALTH EDUCATION

1.2.1 Identify sources of data related to health

Health education specialists locate and obtain valid and reliable data pertaining to a specific population. Most health education specialists identify needs of the priority population through a review of the current literature. Literature databases are available in libraries (computer databases) and through the Internet. Please refer to Chapter VI for a description of literature databases. It is important that data refer to a population with characteristics similar to those of the priority population (McKenzie et al., 2009).

1.2.2 Critique sources of health information using theory and evidence from the literature

Valid and reliable data are necessary components to a thorough needs assessment. Health education specialists must be able to locate valid and reliable health information from a variety of sources if secondary data sources are to be used. If primary data are being collected on a specific population, health education specialists need to use or develop valid and reliable instruments to collect the data. If such instruments are used, this can allow for more meaningful comparisons of data to be made. This allows health education specialists to draw conclusions about needs for health programs.

In addition, information is commonly obtained from the Internet, computerized reference databases, CD-ROMs, books, and peer-reviewed journals. The technology field is constantly producing new innovations, and it is the role of the health education specialist to make sound decisions about the appropriateness and compatibility of the data. With knowledge from health behavior theories or models, the health education specialist can make realistic decisions to meet the needs of the priority population.

1.2.3 Select valid sources of information about health

There is an increasing demand for health information, and the health education specialist will find a variety of sources. The roles of the health education specialist include being a resource person and communicating information about the needs, concerns, and resources of the community. The health education specialist must also have the skills to evaluate sources of information, and the first step is to become a skeptical, critical consumer of health information.

1.2.4 Identify gaps in data using theories and assessment models

As data are analyzed during the needs assessment, it may become apparent there are little data regarding certain health problems, health behaviors, attitudes, beliefs, or other theoretical constructs related to health behaviors. This might lead to further data collection to gather this information, or it might lead to prioritization of health issues among a population based upon these gaps in data. Theories and models are useful for program planning, intervention and evaluation. In this stage, health education specialists can apply explanatory theories and models to identify gaps in data, to help understand why a health problem exists or to guide the search for modifiable factors (Glanz et al., 2008b).

Key: ◻ Entry ◣◣ Advanced – level information

1.2.5   Establish collaborative relationships and agreements that facilitate access to data

There are a variety of ways to gather needs assessment data, including primary data from the community or target population and secondary data from a literature review, federal or local health agencies. Through collaborative agreements with stakeholders, agencies, or data resources, health education specialists have been able to facilitate access to data.

1.2.6   Conduct searches of existing databases for specific health-related data

Computerized reference databases are accessible at most universities and public libraries. Some reference databases, such as those of the Behavioral Risk Factor Surveillance System (BRFSS), the National Library of Medicine's PubMed, and the Education Resources Information Center (ERIC), are accessible to the public at no charge. Many journals are published in electronic form (sometimes with free access, others for a fee), and most are also available in hard copy.

Competency 1.3:
Collect Quantitative and/or Qualitative Data Related to Health

To save valuable time and to produce resources that will help in planning a program for the priority population, it is critical for the health education specialist to conduct a needs assessment and collect health-related data from that population (Cottrell, Girvan, & McKenzie, 2009). Data collected for a needs assessment can be quantitative, qualitative, or both. Quantitative data are used to numerically describe what is occurring (Baumgartner & Hensley, 2006). Qualitative data are not numerical, and are usually descriptions of what is occurring or why it is occurring (Baumgartner & Hensley, 2006). Both types of data are valuable to health education specialists throughout the program planning, implementation, and evaluation process.

1.3.1   Collect primary and/or secondary data

Primary and secondary data can be collected through a variety of sources and methods.

Primary Data Sources

• Surveys are used to determine the knowledge, attitudes, beliefs, behaviors, skills, and health status of a priority population. Surveys should use well-constructed questionnaires that have been tested for validity and reliability, have a high response rate, and be administered to a valid sample. According to Aday and Cornelius (2006), a "good" survey correlates with "good" planning.

• Interviews are similar to surveys in that they can be conducted in a variety of ways. They can be completed by telephone, face-to-face, electronically, or in groups. Key informant interviews are conducted with individuals who have knowledge of and the ability to report on the needs of a corporation, hospital, or organization. All methods require trained interviewers to ensure consistency and accuracy and to conduct the interviews in an unbiased manner. Telephone interviews offer a relatively easy method of collecting data at moderate cost. They allow the interviewer to clarify questions, but do not have the advantage of visual cues the face-to-face method offers. Electronic (or Web-based) interviews are growing as a viable means of

Key: ☐ Entry ⋀ Advanced – level information

collecting data from a large number of individuals quickly and at low cost. However, the disadvantages—such as access to a limited population (only those with Internet access), lack of anonymity, and the fact that e-mails can easily be ignored—are difficult to overcome (McKenzie et al., 2009).

• Observations are used to gather data through direct surveillance of the population. Data collection is accomplished through watching and recording specific behaviors of the population being studied. At times, the observer becomes a part of the day-to-day activities. Examples of observations include watching factory workers for their use of safety equipment and/or precautions, observing the smoking behaviors of employees on a break, and checking food service workers' adherence to workplace health code regulations (McKenzie et al., 2009).

• Community forums are public meetings. They bring together people in a particular population to discuss their perceptions of the community's health problems. It is important to remember the silent majority may not speak out, while more vocal individuals' views may wrongly be seen as the group's views (McKenzie et al., 2009).

• Focus group techniques capitalize on communication among participants who are selected based on specific criteria. Individuals are invited to participate, and focus groups are typically led by a skilled facilitator. In many instances, the facilitator encourages the participants to talk to one another, ask questions, give examples, and provide comments regarding a particular topic. Focus groups are designed so that participants share opinions and explain the reasons underlying those opinions. The number of participants for focus groups varies depending on the intended outcome; a focus group can be as small as two people or as large as the facilitator can manage. Analysis of results can be challenging. It may be difficult to infer consensus, and the results may not be generalizable (Neutens & Rubinson, 2010).

• Nominal group process is a highly structured process in which a few representatives from the priority population are asked to respond to questions based on specific needs. It uses small groups of five to seven people, with each member of the group having an equal voice in the discussion and voting. All participants share their opinions by privately ranking the ideas proposed and then sharing this ranking with the group in round-robin fashion. This is a time-consuming process and may require a large meeting space, depending upon the number of people participating (Gilmore & Campbell, 2005; McKenzie et al., 2009).

• Delphi panel is a group process that generates consensus by using a series of mailed or e-mailed questionnaires. The process involves individuals from three groups: decision makers, staff, and program participants. A questionnaire containing one or two broad questions is sent to the entire group. Their answers are then analyzed. Based on the analysis of the responses, a second questionnaire with more specific questions is developed. This questionnaire is sent to the same group of respondents, their responses are analyzed, and another questionnaire is developed. On average, questionnaires are analyzed and sent out three to five times (Gilmore & Campbell, 2005).

• Self-assessment instruments can require people to answer questions about their health history, behavior, and screening results, such as blood pressure, cholesterol, height, and weight. These data are then compared against a database of individuals with similar characteristics, which provides a risk assessment

Key: ◘ Entry ⚏ Advanced – level information

for a number of diseases, as well as life expectancy. Other self-assessment techniques are performed by individuals to detect disease or disease risk. Examples of self-assessments include health assessments or health risk appraisals, breast self-examination, testicular self-examination, and self-monitoring for skin cancer (McKenzie et al., 2009).

• Community capacity inventory and community asset maps are tools for identifying community resources and issues. Community capacity inventory typically involves developing a written list of the skills and talents of individual community members and of the associations and other resources in the neighborhood as a whole. Simple survey, walking and windshield tours, interviews, community newspaper or directories, and other assessment methods can be used to gather information. Community asset maps are created by community members as they "map" local resources, abilities, and other building blocks for community growth and change. A community asset map is a visual representation of the physical assets of a community – library, playgrounds, schools, parks, and houses of worship – that may constitute important physical and social support structures for achieving community goals (Minkler & Wallerstein, 2008).

• Health education specialists may also rely on secondary data sources to gain important insight on community capacity, assets, and needs. Secondary data often involves gathering epidemiological data, such as incidence and/or prevalence rates, death rates, birth rates, and more.

Secondary Data Sources *(McKenzie et al., 2009):*

- *Federal Government agencies*
    - Centers for Disease Control and Prevention (CDC)
- Morbidity/Mortality Weekly Report (MMWR)
    - National Center for Health Statistics (NCHS)
- Vital records
    - United States Census Bureau
- Population, employment, income, family size, education, housing, and other social indicators
- The *Statistical Abstract of the United States* provides summary statistics of populations by metropolitan area, state, and the country as a whole, as well as information on health expenditures and health coverage (including Medicare and Medicaid), injuries, disability status, nutritional intakes and food consumption.
    - United States Department of Health and Human Services (USDHHS)
- Centers for Medicare and Medicaid Services (CMS)
- Health Resources Service Administration (HRSA)
- Social assistance programs
    - Social Security (SSA)

Key: ◘ Entry ▧ Advanced – level information

- *State and local agencies*
  - o County, city, and state health departments or related agencies
- Vital records, disease registries, police records, morbidity/mortality records, epidemiological studies, incident reports, safety surveys
- Behavioral Risk Factor Surveillance System (BRFSS) data
- Youth Risk Behavior Surveillance System (YRBSS) data

- *Nongovernment agencies and organizations*
  - o Health care system
- Hospital discharge data, emergency room visit data, injury/hospitalization records
  - o Disease-specific organizations, such as American Diabetes Association, American Heart Association, Arthritis Foundation, Susan B. Komen Breast Cancer Foundation

- *Existing records*
  - o Health data that are collected as a by-product of services, such as clinical records, data from immunization programs, data from water pollution control programs, clinical indicators, data from physicians' offices, data on absenteeism, and data from insurance claims

- *Literature*
  - o Peer-reviewed journals
  - o Published scientific studies and reports

1.3.2 Integrate primary data with secondary data

Data credibility can be improved by utilizing multiple methods for gathering data. It is also helpful to integrate primary and secondary data in order to obtain different, yet thorough perspectives on health needs, and to compare and contrast data from the target population with data from similar populations. This combination of data can help establish the rationale for the need of a program.

1.3.3 Identify data collection instruments and methods

Survey methods include mail, telephone, face-to-face and Internet surveys (Neutens & Rubinson, 2010). Table 1.1 highlights the advantages and disadvantages of each type of survey.

Table 1.1

Advantages and Disadvantages of Survey Methods

Method	Advantages	Disadvantages
Mail	•Eliminates interviewer bias •Greater assurance of anonymity •Allows respondent to complete at his/her convenience •Accessibility to a wide geographic region •Increases accuracy because respondent can consult records •Identical wording for all respondents •Promotes inter-rater reliability	•Lack of flexibility •Likelihood of unanswered questions •Low response rate •Inability to record spontaneous reactions or nonverbal responses •Lack of control over the order in which questions are answered •No guarantee of return by due date •Inability to use complex questionnaire format •Strong possibility of duplicate mailing •Fear of loss of anonymity
Telephone	•Cost savings compared with face-to-face survey •Faster than mail survey or personal interview •Accessibility to a wide geographic region •Increased monitoring and quality control	•Respondents may see the call as a hoax or disruption •Loss of visual component of reading the survey •Interviewer has little control; respondent can hang up at any time •Low response rates due to unlisted numbers, caller ID, reduced use of land lines, and "do not call" lists
Face-to-face	•Personalization of the survey to one participant •Flexibility for further probing •Higher response rates •Control over question order •Spontaneity and no possibility of help from others •Ability to use more complex questionnaires	•Expensive •Time-consuming •Increases interviewer bias •Lack of anonymity •Lack of standardization of questions •Difficulty in summarizing the findings
Web or Internet surveys	•Quick response •Low cost to administer •Data gathering process is automatic •Can be administered to a large number of participants •Forced-choice format	•Limited ability to monitor returned surveys •Can limit time frame within which respondent can access survey •Can force explicit choice response •Hardware and software can be costly •May not be anonymous

Key: ◻ Entry ◨ Advanced – level information

ASSESS NEEDS, ASSETS, AND CAPACITY FOR HEALTH EDUCATION

1.3.4 Develop data collection instruments and methods

The following steps are necessary in developing and implementing a fair and balanced survey.

Steps in Designing and Completing a Survey

1. *Planning the survey.* This step includes determining (a) survey objectives, (b) monetary resources, (c) time resources, and (d) personnel resources.
2. *Designing the survey.* A survey should be designed to accomplish the objectives and should reflect data needs, data collection techniques, and resources.
3. *Collecting the data.* The method chosen should match the survey objectives and fit resource constraints.
4. *Planning data analysis.* An appropriate method of data analysis, consistent with the type of data being collected and the goals of the needs assessment, should be chosen.
5. *Drawing the sample.* From the survey objectives and design come (a) the target population, (b) the sample size and selection, and (c) appropriate interviewers, if interviews are to be conducted.
6. *Constructing the questionnaire.* The questions formulated for a survey are of the utmost importance and require detailed attention. Use existing validated questions when possible. All questions should match the objectives.
7. *Pretesting the questionnaire.* The survey should be pretested with a sample comparable to the target population.
8. *Revising the questionnaire.* Revisions should be based on findings from the pretest. If there are extensive changes, a second pretest should be conducted.
9. *Administering the survey.* The method chosen (e.g., mail, E-mail, telephone) should fit the nature of the data to be gathered and the objectives of the survey.
10. *Preparing the data.* Data preparation includes coding the questions and responses for tabulation and designing contingent values (as necessary) to limit data entry errors.
11. *Verifying.* Data entered should be tested for accuracy and for errors in coding.
12. *Entering data.* The method of data entry will vary according to resources; the key is to use a software program that is user-friendly, that is advantageous for analysis, and that can be watched for errors.
13. *Tabulating.* A frequency count should be conducted to ascertain how many answers are in each of the categories for every question.
14. *Analyzing.* Analysis varies according to the purpose of the study, but it generally includes calculating percentages, averages, and relational indices and performing tests of significance.
15. *Recording and reporting.* The report should reflect all of the previous steps outlined including the objectives, hypotheses, reliability of results, and recommendations for action. Reports often include an executive summary of the methods and major findings for the study.

(Neutens & Rubinson, 2010)

1.3.5 Train personnel and stakeholders regarding data collection

Health education specialists train personnel and stakeholders regarding appropriate data collection methods, in order to ensure the quality of data. Standardizing the procedure of data collection with frequent monitoring of the process will help ensure collection of data is accurate, complete and conforms to program requirements.

Key: ☐ Entry ⫽ Advanced – level information

1.3.6 Use data collection instruments and methods

Each instrument and method has its own advantages and disadvantages. Health education specialists should use these instruments carefully to ensure the objective target will be reached.

1.3.7 Employ ethical standards when collecting data

The application of ethical principles to the data collection needs to be carefully considered. The following discussion focuses on the ethics of data collection (Issel, 2009).

- *Informed consent:* This is the agreement to voluntarily and willingly participate in a study based on a full disclosure of what constitutes participation in the study and what the risks and benefits involved in participation are.
- *Institutional Review Board (IRB):* IRBs are composed of researchers and community members or stakeholders who review proposed research for compliance with federal regulations governing research involving human subjects.
- *Health Insurance Portability and Accountability Act (HIPAA):* The purpose of HIPAA is to protect personal health information. In order for health data to be used, individual permission must be granted, with some exceptions (CDC, 2003b).

Competency 1.4:
Examine Relationships Among Behavioral, Environmental, and Genetic Factors that Enhance or Compromise Health

Planners need to identify and prioritize the behavioral, environmental, and social risk factors that are associated with health. Modifying these factors or determinants is pertinent to improving the health status of individuals and communities (McKenzie et al., 2009). The types and number of risk factors are as varied as influences themselves.

1.4.1 Identify factors that influence health behaviors

- *Behavioral (lifestyle) factors* are behaviors or actions of individuals, groups, or communities. Behavioral indicators may include compliance, consumption and utilization patterns, coping, preventive actions, and self-care (McKenzie et al., 2009).

- *Environmental factors* are determinants outside the individual that can be modified to support behavior, health, and quality of life. Examples of environmental factors include economic factors, physical factors, public services, and an individual's access to, affordability of, and equity in health services (McKenzie et al., 2009).

- *Individual factors* include educational, social, and cultural characteristics of the individual. Individual factors include a person's knowledge, attitudes, beliefs, and perceptions related to health. An individual's culture, religious or spiritual beliefs, and skill set must be considered when assessing influences on health behavior (McKenzie et al., 2009; Turnock, 2004).

Key: ◻ Entry \\\\ Advanced – level information

ASSESS NEEDS, ASSETS, AND CAPACITY FOR HEALTH EDUCATION

1.4.2 Analyze factors that influence health behaviors

According to ecological models, behavior has multiple influences including factors at the intrapersonal, interpersonal, organizational, community and public policy levels. Influences on behaviors interact across these different levels (Sallis, Owen & Fisher, 2008). Once the health behavior has been determined, and factors that influence the behavior have been identified, there is a need to gather more information to know how these factors influence the behavior. Health education specialists will need to weigh the importance and changeability of the factors against available resources for the program.

1.4.3 Identify factors that enhance or compromise health

Health is influenced by a variety of different factors. According to Turnock (2004), traditional categories of factors include biological factors (from genetic endowment to aging), environmental factors (from food, air, and water to communicable diseases), lifestyle factors (from diet to injury avoidance and sexual behaviors), psychosocial factors (from poverty to stress, personality, and cultural factors), and the use of and access to health-related services. These various components are often interrelated, and their combined effect influences the likelihood of disease, functional capacity, health behavior, and well-being.

1.4.4 Analyze factors that enhance or compromise health

Once the factors that enhance or compromise health have been identified, there is a need to gather more information about how these factors influence health. Health education specialists can use data gathered from the needs assessment, data from the literature indicating risk factors and determinants of health, and data collected from surveys (for example, Youth Risk Behavior Surveillance System, Behavioral Risk Factor Surveillance System) to identify which factors are most important and changeable in order to determine the goals and objectives of the health promotion program.

Competency 1.5:
Examine Factors that Influence the Learning Process

People learn in different ways – what works for one individual or group does not always work for everyone. Therefore, it is important to understand the learning process to select methods for delivering health education and to tailor health messages in ways that are appropriate for an individual or group.

1.5.1 Identify factors that foster or hinder the learning process

In the needs assessment, health education specialists need to identify multiple influences on health and behaviors. One such influence is knowledge. During this stage, it is important to discover the knowledge base of a target audience as well as barriers to learning. Factors that may hinder the learning process include: lack of time, schedule conflicts, attitudes, or other stressors that create a barrier to learning. The learning process may also be fostered through positive attitudes, community connectedness, and self interest.

Key: ◻ Entry ⍁ Advanced – level information

1.5.2 ⑊ Analyze factors that foster or hinder the learning process

After identification of factors that influence the learning process, health education specialists need to use the information gathered to make program planning decisions. For example, knowing the baseline knowledge level in a target population about a specific health problem or behavior will help health education specialists in developing appropriate learning experiences for the program. Knowing barriers to learning will help health education specialists develop methods that participants can use to overcome barriers and allow learning to occur.

1.5.3 Identify factors that foster or hinder attitudes and beliefs

Pre-existing attitudes or beliefs about a health problem or behavior have a major influence on the success of behavior change programs. Throughout the needs assessment, it is important to observe what attitudes and beliefs a target population has about a particular health problem or behavior, as well as what misconceptions they have.

1.5.4 Analyze factors that foster or hinder attitudes and beliefs

Once attitudes and beliefs are identified, health education specialists can plan behavior change interventions that address negative attitudes and beliefs, and can work to modify them to facilitate behavior change. Health education specialists can also help encourage or build upon positive attitudes and beliefs to facilitate behavior change.

1.5.5 ⑊ Identify factors that foster or hinder skill building

Sometimes people do not engage in health promoting behaviors, because they lack sufficient skills to do so. Health education specialists need to identify specific skills that the target population must have to promote behavior change, and then uncover reasons why some individuals have these skills and others do not.

1.5.6 ⑊ Analyze factors that foster or hinder skill building

Once barriers and facilitators are discovered, they can be analyzed in terms of importance and feasibility, and addressed accordingly in the program planning process. Once important and modifiable factors are identified, they can be emphasized in a program to build skills necessary to elicit behavior change. Please refer to Chapter II for more information on program planning.

Competency 1.6:
Examine Factors that Enhance or Compromise the Process of Health Education

Factors that should be identified during the needs assessment include the following:

- *Predisposing factors:* individual knowledge and affective traits
- *Enabling factors:* factors that make possible a change in behavior
- *Reinforcing factors:* feedback and encouragement resulting from a changed behavior, perhaps from significant or important others

Key: ◻ Entry ⑊ Advanced – level information

These factors may have a direct impact on health-risk factors and how the health education program is planned and implemented (Green & Kreuter, 2005; McKenzie et al., 2009).

1.6.1 Determine the extent of available health education programs, interventions, and policies

Health education specialists need to consider what health education programs, services, or policies already exist in the priority community. The health care system in the United States is diverse, including hospitals, insurance companies, regulating bodies, physicians, therapists, accrediting organizations, and others (Healey & Zimmerman, 2010). The health education specialist can use a community resource guide, contacts from a variety of health organizations, and community members to identify the existence and availability of current health education related services, as well as the lack of existence, accessibility, and effectiveness of local and current programs or resources.

1.6.2 Assess the quality of available health education programs, interventions, and policies

Once existing health education programs, interventions, and policies are identified, health education specialists must determine the effectiveness and quality of such services. Health education specialists can review evaluation reports (if available), interview personnel involved in projects, and have discussions with people from the target population regarding perceptions of existing programs, interventions, and policies. Please refer to Chapter III for information on how to implement effective health education programs and Chapter IV for information on how to evaluate them.

1.6.3 Identify existing and potential partners for the provision of health education services

It is the role of the health education specialist to identify gaps or overlaps in existing programs by communicating with stakeholders in the community. In identifying the provision of health education services, the health education specialist should identify the quality of service, as well as the service used by clients and the service capacities. Additionally, the health education specialist should look at the levels and patterns of services being provided.

At this stage, it is also important to consider potential partnerships with other agencies or organizations that have similar goals in mind. Working with existing partners and forming new partnerships can help agencies share resources as they work toward a common goal. Please refer to Chapter V for more information on the health education specialist's role in developing partnerships.

1.6.4 Assess social, environmental, and political conditions that may impact health education

Forces outside a health education specialist's control can impact the acceptability of a program or the willingness of participants to internalize health information. Social stigma associated with diseases (such as sexually transmitted infections) might make participants unwilling to participate in prevention programs. Conditions of the learning environment, such as uncomfortable accommodations or noise level, can impede the learning process. The actual physical environment, including safety of the physical environment, can also impact opportunities to deliver health education (lack of physical activity resources such as sidewalks or parks, no safe place to walk). The current political climate can also make it difficult to deliver health promotion programs on controversial topics, such as prevention of teen pregnancy.

1.6.5 Analyze the capacity for developing needed health education

Capacity, or asset-based, assessments can also be conducted to complement the needs assessment. These assessments focus on individual and group resources to analyze a community's strengths (Gilmore & Campbell, 2005). Assets and resources are community contributions that may prevent the health problem from occurring or assist in its solution (Issel, 2009). Community empowerment through capacity building helps communities solve their own problems with their own resources (Doyle et al., 2010).

To implement an assets-based assessment to measure the community's capacity to solve its health problems, Beaulieu (2002) recommends the following steps:

1. identify community resources (persons, groups, places), abilities, skills, networks, strengths, talents;
2. create or strengthen the relationships between community members and community organizations;
3. mobilize the community around its strengths/resources;
4. rally the community to develop a healthy vision of the future; and
5. introduce any outside resources to fill gaps.

Logic models can also be used after the needs assessment phase to assess community capacity. In a logic model, program inputs are linked to program activities or events. The outputs of the activities or programming are then linked to the short-, intermediate-, and long-term outcomes or intended program effects (Gilmore & Campbell, 2005). Logic models have the potential to serve as visual roadmaps around which key evaluation/research questions can be generated. Please refer to Chapter IV for additional information on logic models.

1.6.6 Assess the need for resources to foster health education

Health education specialists must analyze all of the data collected from the needs assessment. The goal of the needs assessment is to identify and prioritize the health problems, prioritize strategies to address them, and identify resources to support them (e.g., fiscal and human resources). This process may be formal or informal (McKenzie et al., 2009).

Conducting resource inventories can provide further insight into the data being analyzed. This process allows for a health education specialist to identify the gaps or needs in health education services, the delivery of those services, and the health education efforts being exerted. Using agency records and interviews allows a health education specialist to establish who is providing health education services and the comprehensiveness and continuity of those services. However, the information gathered is only as complete as the records provided and the extent to which the agency cooperates with the process of data gathering (McKenzie, Pinger, & Kotecki, 2008).

Key: ☐ Entry ⦚ Advanced – level information

ASSESS NEEDS, ASSETS, AND CAPACITY FOR HEALTH EDUCATION

Assessment of current fiscal and personnel needs is also important. Health education programs often require funding for equipment, supplies, and sometimes, personnel. At this stage, health education specialists can begin to outline a preliminary budget as well as to search for potential funding opportunities.

Competency 1.7:
Infer Needs for Health Education Based on Assessment Findings

The final step in the needs assessment is validating the needs identified in the assessment. It must be confirmed that the identified needs are the real needs of a population.

1.7.1 Analyze assessment findings
The following steps can be used to infer the need for health education from obtained data:

1. analyze data, primary and secondary;
2. compare data with local, state, national, or historical situation;
3. consider the social, cultural, and political environment;
4. set priorities by:
    • assessing the size or scope of the problem;
    • determining the effectiveness of possible interventions; and
    • determining appropriateness, economics, acceptability, resources, and legality of the possible intervention.
                                        (Doyle et al., 2010; McKenzie et al., 2009)

1.7.2 ▨ Synthesize assessment findings
The assessment findings are assessed by various methods such as survey, interview, observation and focus group. It is important for health education specialists to be able to identify the strengths and limitations of different assessments. Thus, the process of synthesizing across different needs assessment approaches is helpful to health education specialists for making effective and appropriate decisions.

1.7.3 Prioritize health education needs
Once a health problem or problems are selected for program development, health education specialists must decide on the level or levels of prevention on which to focus their effort. Primary prevention efforts are targeted toward healthy individuals to attempt to reduce risk for illness or injury. Secondary prevention efforts often involve screenings to help diagnose existing disease, so that a person can seek treatment. Tertiary prevention efforts focus on rehabilitation after a major health event or diagnosis (McKenzie et al., 2009). The health education specialist must also confirm that health education needs match the program needs. For example, the health education needs must be determined appropriately for the right population. The needs assessment must be able to validate the community needs and to begin the process of assigning value to the various promotion efforts that need to be developed and implemented in the community (Healey & Zimmerman, 2010; Workgroup for Community Health and Development, 2010).

Key: ▢ Entry ▨ Advanced – level information

Health education specialists can prioritize health needs by using the following criteria.

- Assessing the size or scope of the problem
  - Percentage of the population directly affected
  - Seriousness of the problem
  - Urgency/critical nature of the problem
  - Severity of the problem
  - Morbidity/mortality severity, duration, and/or disability associated with the problem
  - Medical costs associated with the problem
  - Potential number who may be affected by the problem
- Determining the effectiveness of possible interventions
  - How effective are health education interventions in addressing the problem? Are they meeting stated goals and objectives?
  - Are the potential interventions accessible to the affected population?
  - How were the needs for the potential programs determined? Are the needs of the population being met? If not, why?
- Determining appropriateness, economics, acceptability, resources, and legality of the possible intervention
  - What health education programs are presently available to the population(s) affected?
  - Are the programs being utilized? If not, why?
  - Given the population, is the intervention appropriate and in accordance with societal/group norms?
  - Are there sufficient resources for implementation?
  - Is the intervention legal?

(Healey & Zimmerman, 2010)

1.7.4 Identify emerging health education needs

Addressing the diverse health needs is difficult and a challenge to health education specialists. How to identify emerging health education needs should be a priority. A simple approach to prioritizing health education needs is to consider only whether an intervention can actually make a change in the health problem and whether the health problem is important or worth addressing. Each of the health problems can be rated with regard to its degree of importance and changeability. Health problems classified as having both high changeability and high importance ought to be addressed first, as shown in Table 1.2 (Issel, 2009).

Table 1.2
Program prioritization based on the importance and changeability of the health problem

	Highly Important	Less Important
High Changeability	High priority	Lower priority
Lesser Changeability	High priority with innovative program	No program

ASSESS NEEDS, ASSETS, AND CAPACITY FOR HEALTH EDUCATION

1.7.5 Report assessment findings

Based on assessment, health education specialists should prepare the report of needs assessment before engaging in intervention program planning and implementation. They should consider who they will be presenting assessment findings to, such as researchers, community members or funding agencies. Strengths and limitations of the findings should also be discussed.

Key: ◻ Entry ⫘ Advanced – level information

CHAPTER II

Area of Responsibility II
Plan Health Education

2.1: Involve priority populations and other stakeholders in the planning process
Sub-competencies:

2.1.1 Incorporate principles of community organization
2.1.2 Identify priority populations and other stakeholders
2.1.3 Communicate need for health education to priority populations and other stakeholders
2.1.4 Develop collaborative efforts among priority populations and other stakeholders
2.1.5 Elicit input from priority populations and other stakeholders
2.1.6 Obtain commitments from priority populations and other stakeholders

2.2: Develop goals and objectives
Sub-competencies:

2.2.1 ▧ Use assessment results to inform the planning process
2.2.2 Identify desired outcomes utilizing the needs assessment results
2.2.3 ◻▧ Select planning model(s) for health education
2.2.4 ▧ Develop goal statements
2.2.5 ▧ Formulate specific, measurable, attainable, realistic, and time-sensitive objectives
2.2.6 Assess resources needed to achieve objectives

2.3: Select or design strategies and interventions
Sub-competencies:

2.3.1 ▧ Assess efficacy of various strategies to ensure consistency with objectives
2.3.2 Design theory-based strategies and interventions to achieve stated objectives
2.3.3 ◻▧ Select a variety of strategies and interventions to achieve stated objectives
2.3.4 Comply with legal and ethical principles in designing strategies and interventions
2.3.5 Apply principles of cultural competence in selecting and designing strategies and interventions
2.3.6 Pilot test strategies and interventions

2.4: Develop a scope and sequence for the delivery of health education
Sub-competencies:

2.4.1 Determine the range of health education needed to achieve goals and objectives
2.4.2 Select resources required to implement health education
2.4.3 Use logic models to guide the planning process
2.4.4 ▧ Organize health education into a logical sequence
2.4.5 ▧ Develop a timeline for the delivery of health education
2.4.6 Analyze the opportunity for integrating health education into other programs
2.4.7 Develop a process for integrating health education into other programs

Key: ◻ Entry ▧ Advanced – level information

2.5: Address factors that affect implementation

Sub-competencies:

2.5.1   Identify factors that foster or hinder implementation

2.5.2   Analyze factors that foster or hinder implementation

2.5.3   Use findings of pilot to refine implementation plans as needed

2.5.4   Develop a conducive learning environment

The Role

Program planning begins with the assessment of existing health needs, problems, and concerns. The extent to which these are directly linked to health behaviors determines the specific changes in behaviors for which the program planning process is set in motion. Relevant people are identified and involved in the project, objectives are established, educational methods are selected, and resources are located. It is within this process that planning for program evaluation begins as well (NCHEC et al., 2010a).

Settings

The following text describes how planning is used in different practice settings (NCHEC et al., 2010a).

Community Setting. In a community setting where a needs assessment has identified a significant health problem, the health education specialist convenes representatives of relevant groups to identify populations in need of health education. The health education specialist also seeks input and promotes involvement from those who will affect and be affected by the program. Health education specialists should rely on the results of the needs assessment and available research to apply principles of community organization to integrate health education within existing health programs. Another key responsibility of health education specialists is to formulate objectives and develop interventions appropriate to meet the needs of target populations. Identifying and assessing community resources and barriers affecting implementation of the program unique to the community setting can help health education specialists achieve this. The selection of program activities and interventions depends on the characteristics of the priority population, its constraints and concerns, the budget and timeframe, and the fit between program schedules and other obligations of the participants.

School (K-12) Setting. The decision to provide health education in schools is usually made by administrators or mandated by policy or law. The school health education specialist organizes an advisory committee (consisting of teachers, administrators, members of the community, representatives from voluntary agencies, parents, youth group leaders, clergy, and students) to select or develop health education curricula and materials. These decisions should be based on research results and best practices and should consider available resources and barriers to implementation, such as time and space. Objectives should be based on the needs of school-aged children and adolescents. Curricula should follow a logical scope and sequence.

Health Care Setting. The health education specialist in the health care setting works with nurses, physicians, nutritionists, physical therapists, and other health care professionals to plan patient and community education programs. The team develops education programs for patients and their families to promote compliance with medical directions and enhance understanding of medical procedures and conditions. The role of the health education specialist in this setting is to assist the team in establishing objectives, identifying staff roles in providing education, selecting teaching methods and strategies, evaluating results, documenting the education effort, designing promotion activities, and training interdisciplinary staff to conduct the program, as appropriate.

Business/Industry Setting. In the workplace, the health education specialist analyzes data from numerous sources (including insurance records, safety records, workers' compensation claims, and employee self-report questionnaires) to provide a basis for a presentation to management outlining the benefits and costs of a health education program. After gaining administrative support, the health education specialist convenes an employee committee with representatives from all levels of the organization to make recommendations concerning program priorities, objectives, scheduling, publicity, incentives, and fees. The health education specialist leads the team in developing data- and theory-based interventions and strategies to meet the needs of employees.

College/University Setting. The health education specialist in a higher education setting analyzes research results, current professional competencies, accreditation standards, and certification requirements and uses the results to design professional preparation programs that will encourage the development of essential health education planning competencies in candidates, regardless of future practice setting.

University Health Services Setting. The health education specialist who practices in student health services works side by side with clinical practitioners. The health education specialist uses the needs assessment to develop program and behavioral objectives and to design interventions that reduce health risks and improve health. The health education specialist works with clinical practitioners and others to integrate health education into other programs, including treatment regimens and campus-wide activities. He or she also evaluates the efficacy of educational methods in achieving objectives.

Key Terms

- **Programs** are defined as a set of planned activities over time designed to achieve specific objectives (Green & Kreuter, 2005).

- **Program planning** is the process of identifying needs, establishing priorities, diagnosing causes of problems, assessing and allocating resources, and determining barriers to achieving objectives (Green & Kreuter, 2005).

- A **mission statement** is a statement of the distinctive purpose of and unique reason for the existence of a program. A mission statement can be a one-sentence statement or a short narrative that broadly defines the program's purpose. Mission statements are enduring over time and identify the scope or focus of the organization or program (Ginter, Swayne, & Duncan, 2002).

- **Goals** are general, long-term statements of desired program outcomes and provide the direction upon which all objectives are based (Rees & Goldsmith, 2009).

Key: ▢ Entry ◣ Advanced – level information

○━▸ **Objectives** are statements that describe, in measurable terms, the changes in behavior, attitude, knowledge, skills, or health status that will occur in the intervention group as a result of the program. Objectives are small, specific steps that enable the goal to be met (Wurzbach, 2004).

○━▸ **Stakeholders** are individuals or agencies that have a vested interest in the health education program (Bartholomew, Parcel, Kok, & Gottlieb, 2006).

○━▸ A **community-based organization** (CBO) is a public or private, nonprofit organization of demonstrated effectiveness that is representative of a community or significant segments of a community and provides educational or related services to individuals in the community (Sherow, Weinberg, Sloan, & Morin, 2002).

○━▸ **Social marketing** is the use of marketing principles to promote a product, idea, or attitude among members of a population (Hastings, 2008). Good social marketing sets behavioral goals, involves consumer research, uses theory wisely, segments and targets populations, among other attributes (Hastings, 2008).

○━▸ **Health communication** is an attempt to share information with, influence, and support a variety of audiences to engage in healthy behaviors or support health-related policies (Schiavo, 2007).

○━▸ **Cultural competence** is the "ability of an individual to understand and respect values, attitudes, beliefs and [morals] that differ across cultures, and to consider and respond appropriately to these differences in planning, implementing, and evaluating health education and promotion programs and interventions" (Joint Committee on Health Education Terminology, 2002, p. 5).

Competency 2.1:
Involve priority populations and other stakeholders in the planning process

Often, planners need to begin the planning process by gaining support from key people to ensure that planning and implementation proceed smoothly and by ensuring necessary resource support. Groups of key people, or **stakeholders**, include those involved in the program operations, those served or affected by the program, and the primary users of the program (McKenzie et al., 2009). When seeking support from stakeholders, the planner should be able to explain to them why the program is necessary (McKenzie et al., 2009).

2.1.1 Incorporate principles of community organization

Well-planned health education programs (a) incorporate collected data about the health issues addressed and/or about other similar programs, and (b) organize at the grassroots level to involve the populations that will be affected.

A health education program will be most successful if the priority population feels it has been instrumental in program development. It is important to provide a sense of ownership and empowerment among those in the population of interest. In general, the community organization process includes community recognition of the issue, entrance of health education specialists into the community to help organize the citizens, community assessment, priority setting, selection and implementation of an intervention, and evaluation and reassessment of the action plan (McKenzie et al., 2008).

2.1.2   Identify priority populations and other stakeholders

The use of needs assessment data is one avenue for identifying a priority population for a health education program (McKenzie et al., 2009). Expressed, actual, perceived, and normative needs should all be addressed in the assessment, as community concerns may not always reflect empirical evidence (Doyle et al., 2010; Issel, 2009). Priority populations may also be identified as a result of a current health crisis, a public figure's "going public" regarding his or her health status, or requests of health officials and/or members of the community (McKenzie et al., 2009).

The priority population consists of the entire population if an intervention is being implemented for the total community. The target audience for an intervention or program includes individuals who are part of the at-risk population. Participants are individuals who receive the intervention or participate in the program. The participants' role is important, because it affects program evaluation (Issel, 2009).

2.1.3   Communicate need for health education to priority populations and other stakeholders

Expressing the need for a program, especially to those who will be involved, is a necessity (McKenzie et al., 2008). Communication methods may range from simple to very complex and include basic information, yet still state the need for health education efforts. This also provides an opportunity for health education specialists to reach a wide range of participants, as well as convey program goals and objectives (McKenzie et al., 2008). Communication methods may include announcements in newsletters, communication at public meetings, as well as media messages.

Communication channels are a method for message dissemination to the population. According to McKenzie et al. (2008), the four primary communication channels include:

- intrapersonal;
- interpersonal;
- organization and community; and
- mass media.

Please see Chapter VII for more information about health communication techniques.

2.1.4   Develop collaborative efforts among priority populations and other stakeholders

Community groups and collaborative efforts are often referred to as coalitions (Butterfoss, 2007). Collaborative efforts provide the opportunity for program planners to bring together representatives from diverse organizations, segments, or constituencies within the community to work toward a common goal. Additionally, they bring together a combination of resources and expertise (McKenzie et al., 2009).

Key: ◻ Entry   \\\ Advanced – level information

No two coalitions or community efforts are formed or operate in the same way. It is important that community efforts structure themselves to fit the goals and objectives of the program. Butterfoss (2009) identified the following as steps for an effective coalition:

1. analyze the issue or problem on which the coalition will focus;
2. create awareness of the issue;
3. conduct initial coalition planning and recruitment;
4. develop resources and funding for the coalition;
5. create coalition infrastructure;
6. elect coalition leadership; and
7. create an action plan.

Ideally, the efforts and participation of a coalition will continue throughout the program and sustain community action. The health education specialist develops a plan to encourage the coalition's participation in the entire programming process, from goal creation and resource allocation to project implementation and evaluation (Doyle et al., 2010).

Building a coalition or community-wide effort can be a complex and sometimes challenging task. A simple partnership, in which your organization pairs with just one community organization, may be a quicker, easier strategy to enhance health education efforts. To promote this type of collaborative effort, the health education specialist researches the partner organization's mission; establishes clear goals, tasks, and communication methods; and continually monitors effectiveness (Doyle et al., 2010). The drawback of this approach is that resources are limited in comparison with a coalition approach.

2.1.5 Elicit input from priority populations and other stakeholders

The following people may be interested in being part of the program planning process:

- •individuals who represent various groups within the priority population;
- •representatives of other stakeholders not represented in the priority population; and
- •individuals who have key roles within the organization sponsoring the program.

(McKenzie et al., 2009)

Obstacles to obtaining input from these individuals (lack of time, lack of awareness, lack of transportation or communication capabilities, lack of interest) need to be removed. To remove these obstacles, make personal contact with key representatives, provide incentives for participation, choose easily accessible meeting locations, and conduct training programs for them (Issel, 2009).

Key: ◻ Entry ⫿ Advanced – level information

2.1.6 Obtain commitments from priority populations and other stakeholders

It is essential for health education specialists to gain support from the community surrounding the priority population. It is most important to have support from community leaders and groups, including:

- local elected officials;
- clergy;
- influential members of the community;
- community-based organizations;
- local departments of health or related agencies; and
- print journalists and broadcast media representatives.

Decision-makers in the community are able to provide financial, organizational, and/or administrative support to the program planning process.

A comprehensive plan also includes identifying individuals in the community to be part of the planning committee. A planning committee may consist of the following:

- representatives from all segments of the priority population;
- active community members;
- influential members of the community;
- representatives of the sponsoring agency;
- stakeholders; and
- effective leaders.

(McKenzie et al., 2009)

It is important to understand group dynamics and focus on team building to develop the support necessary for successful program planning (Johnson & Johnson, 2005). Planning groups, such as consortia and planning boards, help to increase community and stakeholder involvement to enhance the strategic plan. A group leader can be selected or appointed or may emerge naturally; therefore, a standardized process for leadership selection should be stated at the beginning of formation of the planning committee or team. The person in the leadership position may change as the task or stage changes (Issel, 2009).

Competency 2.2:
Develop goals and objectives

All successful health education programs begin with the development of appropriate goals and objectives. Goals help to measure a program's processes and outcomes. Processes might include program components, activities, delivery, and time frame, while the outcomes could include short-term changes (knowledge, attitudes, skills, behaviors) or long-term changes (behavior adherence, health status).

Key: ▢ Entry ⩘ Advanced – level information

AREA OF RESPONSIBILITY II

2.2.1 ◣◣ Use assessment results to inform the planning process

Needs assessment data for the priority population and its health issue(s)/concern(s) should be carefully considered and used in planning a corresponding health education program. These data will not only justify the program to stakeholders (including potential funders), they will help "sell" the importance of the program to the population of interest. The use of needs assessment research will also help ensure the development of a program that will avoid pitfalls experienced by others and one that will prevent health education specialists from having to "reinvent the wheel" (McKenzie et al., 2009).

Data assists the health education specialist in understanding the breadth and depth of the health issues in a community. Existing data, such as archived, published literature or publicly accessible databases, can be used in a secondary analysis. Primary data, collected by means of interviews, surveys, emails, letters, or forums provides information regarding community perceptions and attitudes about the health issues. Population-based data can be analyzed with computerized statistical tests and epidemiological techniques. Data derived from this analysis will be used to develop a profile of the community. The profile provides an easy-to-understand statement of what has been found (Issel, 2009).

2.2.2 Identify desired outcomes utilizing the needs assessment results

Data collection should not be conducted in a vacuum or with no end goal in mind. Prior to the data collection activity, researchers and practitioners must determine the outcomes to be achieved. These may include changing behavioral risks, modifying environmental characteristics, influencing public policies, and raising awareness among the media. Data collection without a defined goal for its use wastes both financial and human resources.

2.2.3 ◻◣◣ Select planning model(s) for health education

Advanced-level health education specialists are typically responsible for selecting planning models to be used in health education interventions and programs. Entry-level health education specialists should have knowledge of planning models that are commonly used in health education. Although health education specialists address goals and objectives in program planning, other components should not be ignored. Important components of program planning include:

- understanding and engaging the priority population;
- conducting a needs assessment;
- developing goals and objectives;
- creating an intervention;
- implementing the intervention; and
- conducting program evaluation.

(McKenzie et al., 2009)

Program planning includes designing an appropriate intervention. It is important to select the level of prevention (primary, secondary, or tertiary) and the level of influence (intrapersonal, interpersonal, institutional, organizational, community, or policy) on which the program will focus. Programs should be based on sound and appropriate learning and educational theories, and tailored to meet the needs of the participants (McKenzie et al., 2009).

Key: ◻ Entry ◣◣ Advanced – level information

PLAN HEALTH EDUCATION

Individuals often confuse theories with planning models. Planning models are those that help lay out the program planning steps to ensure that a health education specialist has anticipated potential problems in a program and has developed solutions. The planning models discussed in this chapter are ones that have been commonly used by health education specialists when planning programs for individuals and communities (Cottrell et al., 2009). Health education specialists use models early in the planning process to help create an "ideal" or "real world" strategy for future implementation of their program (Goodson, 2010).

Other items to consider in intervention design include:

- available resources;
- previously used effective strategies; and
- single or multiple strategies.

(McKenzie et al., 2009)

The PRECEDE-PROCEED Model

The PRECEDE-PROCEED model (Green & Kreuter, 2005) is currently the most used formal planning model in health education. This model, developed as PRECEDE in the 1970s, was expanded in the 1980s to incorporate PROCEED. The model has eight phases:

PRECEDE

Phase 1: *Social assessment* – define the quality of life of the priority population.
Phase 2: *Epidemiological assessment* – identify the health problems of the priority population, and determine and prioritize behavior (individual) and environmental (external) risk factors associated with the health problem.
Phase 3: *Educational and ecological assessment* – determine predisposing (individual knowledge and affective traits), enabling (those that make possible a change in behavior, such as skills), and reinforcing (feedback and encouragement for a changed behavior, perhaps from significant or important others) factors.

PROCEED

Phase 4: *Administrative and policy assessment* – determine the resources (funding, staff, other) available for the program.
Phase 5: *Implementation* – select strategies and activities; begin program.
Phase 6: *Process evaluation* – document program feasibility.
Phase 7: *Impact evaluation* – assess the immediate effect of an intervention.
Phase 8: *Outcome evaluation* – determines whether long-term program goals were met.

(Green & Kreuter, 2005)

Key: ◻ Entry ⋀ Advanced – level information

MATCH: Multilevel Approach to Community Health

MATCH, a multi-level community planning model, consists of five phases with several steps within each stage (Simons-Morton, D.G., Simons-Morton, Parcel, & Bunker, 1988). The phases include:

- goals selection;
- intervention planning;
- program development;
- implementation preparations; and
- evaluation.

The model recognizes that intervention planning should be aimed at multiple objectives and a variety of individuals. MATCH can be used in a variety of settings (Simons-Morton, Greene, & Gottlieb, 1995).

Social Marketing for Community-Level Planning

Social marketing is a program planning process designed to influence the voluntary behavior of a specific audience to achieve a social, rather than financial, objective (McKenzie et al., 2009). The process uses the basic principles of marketing and includes the "marketing mix." The marketing mix encompasses price, place, promotion, and product (Goldman, 2009).

Health Communication for Community-Level Planning

Health communication is the process of informing a priority population about a health issue. It includes many methods to reach the priority population, including media advocacy, written materials, and other forms of interactive communication. To reach populations about behavior change, health communication uses interpersonal, small group, organizational, community, and mass media channels (McKenzie et al., 2009). One example of health communication put into action is the CDCynergy model (CDC, 2003a).

CDCynergy

This community-level model has six phases of program planning:

1. define and describe the problem;
2. analyze the problem;
3. identify and profile the audience;
4. develop communication strategies;
5. develop evaluation plan; and
6. launch the plan and obtain feedback.

These interrelated phases help the health education specialist to understand the priority population and what communication strategies will best help those in the priority population to change their behaviors (CDC, 2003a).

Key: ◻ Entry ⋀ Advanced – level information

2.2.4 ∥∖ Develop goal statements

One of the first items to consider when designing a health promotion intervention is whether the strategies address goals and objectives set by the program planners. In the program planning stages, it is important to develop and express a mission statement and goals and objectives to provide program direction and a foundation for the program evaluation (McKenzie et al., 2009).

A mission statement encompasses the distinctive purpose and unique "reason for being" of a program. A mission statement can be a one-sentence statement or a short narrative that broadly defines the purpose. Mission statements are enduring over time and identify the scope or focus of the organization or program (Ginter et al., 2002).

Examples:

- *The mission of the South County Senior Services is to provide easy access to health information and health care resources to senior citizens in South County.*
- *The mission of XYZ's employee wellness program is to improve the health status of our employees.*

Goals are general, long-term statements of desired program outcomes and provide the direction upon which all objectives are based (Rees & Goldsmith, 2009).

Examples:
The goal of the program is to:

- *Reduce the number of osteoporosis-related fractures among elderly men and women who live in the area served by the health department.*
- *Reduce the number of obesity-related type 2 diabetes cases in Caucasian men.*

2.2.5 ∥∖ Formulate specific, measurable, attainable, realistic, and time-sensitive objectives

Objectives are statements that describe, in measurable terms, changes in health status, behavior, attitude, or knowledge that will occur in the intervention group as a result of the program. These are the small, specific factors that enable the goal to be met. Objectives are usually written to include *"**Who** will do **How** Much of **What** by **When?**"* (Deeds, 1992, p. 36).

A program should have objectives relevant to the program goal. There are many types of objectives, including program or outcome objectives, behavioral and environmental objectives, learning objectives, and administrative objectives. Table 2.1 outlines the different types of objectives.

Program or outcome objectives are related to the goal(s), but are specific, measurable statements of what the educator wants to accomplish at a given time. They represent the change in health status that is the desired result of the program or intervention. These are the ends rather than the means. Program or outcome objectives include items such as changes in morbidity, mortality, or quality of life (Deeds, 1992; McKenzie et al., 2009; Simons-Morton et al., 1995).

Examples:

- *Within three years, osteoporosis-related fractures will decrease by 25 percent in the residents of South County.*

Behavioral objectives describe the behaviors or actions that the population will engage in to resolve the problem and lead to attainment of the program goal. They are statements of desired outcomes that indicate who is to demonstrate how much of what action and by when (Green & Kreuter, 2005).

Examples:

- *Among those attending the program, weight-bearing activity will increase by 50 percent over the following six months.*
- *Fast food consumption will be eliminated from the diet of all program participants after the second week of program implementation.*

Learning or instructional objectives are short-term, specific descriptions of behavioral (cognitive, affective, and skill dimensions) results sought in relation to the content being taught. Health education specialists should formulate and state objectives with precision. Meaningful objectives should include implied or stated evaluation standards (Fodor, Dalis, & Giarratano-Russel, 2002).

Examples:

- *The participants will be able to correctly identify three forms of weight-bearing activity after the first session.*
- *After the completion of the program, the participants will be able to state the importance of calorie control for weight loss.*

Behavioral and learning objectives may also be referred to as impact objectives: short-term/intermediate, measurable, and realistic guidelines to help accomplish the health goal (Doyle et al., 2010).

Administrative objectives detail the tasks program facilitators must accomplish for the program to succeed. They are the daily tasks and work plans that lead to the accomplishment of all other planned objectives (McKenzie et al., 2008). Administrative objectives are also referred to as process objectives (McKenzie et al., 2008).

Examples:

- *Before the start of the program, physical-activity resources will be placed in each of the communities served by the health department by the planning committee members.*
- *Prior to the start of the program, planners will contact ten OB/GYN physicians to gather support for the program.*

Environmental objectives refer to environmental, or nonbehavioral, influences on a health problem. These factors include social, physical, and psychological environments (McKenzie et al., 2008).

Key: ☐ Entry ░ Advanced – level information

Examples:

•*By 2010, the number of high air pollution alert days in the city will decrease by 10 percent.*

The following is a guide to determine the appropriateness of objectives:

Objectives should:

•be clear statements;
•include just one indicator;
•state reasonable time frames;
•be stated in terms of performance, not effort;
•be realistic and within the control of those responsible; and
•be relevant, logical, feasible, observable, and measurable.

Writing measurable objectives
To ensure that objectives are measurable, criteria for measurement must be added. This can be accomplished by using verbs that show action – using verbs that describe the expected behavior or performance. These action verbs make objectives more precise, less likely to be misinterpreted, and easier to evaluate.

Table 2.1
Types of Objectives

Objective	Result	Evaluation
Program objective	Changes in morbidity, mortality, quality of life	What is the outcome? Is there a change in health status and is it attributed to the program?
Environmental objective	Changes in environment	How has the environment changed to improve behavior and health?
Behavioral objective	Changes in behavior, behavioral adaptation	What is the impact? Is there adoption of a new healthier behavior and can it be attributed to the program?
Learning objective	Changes in knowledge, attitude, practices, etc.	Is there the requisite change in knowledge, attitudes, habits, and skills needed for behavior change?
Administrative objective	Adherence to time line tasks, completion of activities, efficient use of resources	Is the program working? Are people attending? Are the methods appropriate?

Note. Adapted from (Deeds,1992; Cleary & Neiger, 1998; McKenzie et al., 2009).

Key: ◘ Entry ⫽ Advanced – level information

2.2.6 Assess resources needed to achieve objectives

Both researchers and practitioners need to give careful attention to the resources needed to achieve the desired objectives. These may include human resources who have varying skills in finance and budgeting, statistics, social and behavioral theory, communications, or administration. In addition, tangible resources such as computers, paper, writing implements, office space, and transportation, among others, require thoughtful planning.

Competency 2.3:
Select or design strategies and interventions

Designing effective health education programs requires careful planning regarding the content, process, and amount of time needed to deliver an intervention. Health education specialists need to consider their priority population's needs and interests, as well as evidence-based strategies when planning a program.

2.3.1 ▨ Assess efficacy of various strategies to ensure consistency with objectives

It is essential to ensure that interventions or strategies selected yield the desired outcomes, whether these are individual behavioral change, environmental modifications, or policy shifts. For example, to stop the prevailing trend of obesity among children, educating youth on healthy food choices will be useless unless their school, home, and community environments make healthier options (for example, fruits, vegetables, and grains) available to them. In addition, enactment and enforcement of policies within the school (such as removal of soda and candy machines) or social environment (for example, tax on sugary snacks, funding for recreational areas) will help facilitate the desired outcome of obesity prevention or mitigation.

2.3.2 Design theory-based strategies and interventions to achieve stated objectives

In the absence of a theoretical perspective underpinning health interventions, researchers and practitioners will be hampered in their efforts to understand what worked, what did not, and possible reasons for success and failure. However, without a theoretical framework, health education specialists will not be able to tweak a program's design or delivery in order to better achieve desirable outcomes in the target population. Please refer to Chapter III for a description of behavior change theories.

2.3.3 ▨ ▢ Select a variety of strategies and interventions to achieve stated objectives

Once goals have been set and objectives determined, the most effective strategies to meet the goals and objectives are selected. The most appropriate interventions should be based on theory, available resources, and reasonable fit. A variety of strategies can be used to meet the objectives of a program. These include educational, health engineering, community mobilization, health communication, health policy and enforcement, and health-related community service strategies. A more detailed discussion of each strategy follows.

Key: ▢ Entry ▨ Advanced – level information

PLAN HEALTH EDUCATION

Educational strategies are activities usually associated with classroom-based courses, workshops, distance learning courses or seminars. Some examples of educational strategies are:

- audiovisual materials;
- printed materials;
- e-learning courses;
- social networking such as Twitter, Facebook, and MySpace;
- classroom techniques;
- brainstorming;
- case studies;
- lectures;
- panel discussions;
- role playing;
- simulations;
- outside classroom techniques;
- health fairs; and
- field trips.

(Gilbert, Sawyer, & McNeill, 2011)

Health engineering strategies change the social or physical environment in which people live or work. They usually affect a large number of people and may change behavior by influencing awareness, attitudes, and knowledge or through guided choice. An example of a health engineering strategy includes modification of offerings (inclusion of only healthy foods or beverages) in vending machines (Butterfoss, 2007).

Community mobilization strategies directly involve participants in the change process. These strategies include initiatives such as coalition building and lobbying. Other examples of community mobilization strategies are community organization, community building, and community advocacy (McKenzie et al., 2009).

Health communication strategies use all types of communication channels (for example, print media, radio, television, billboards, newsletters, flyers, direct mail, E-mail, and self-help materials) to change behavior. These activities can impact knowledge, awareness, or attitudes. Communication may also provide cues for action and provide reinforcement of behaviors (McKenzie et al., 2009).

Health policy and enforcement strategies mandate actions through laws, regulations, policies, or rules. Such actions are justified on the basis of "the common good;" that is, they are actions implemented to protect the public's health (McKenzie et al., 2009).

Health-related community service strategies include services, tests, or treatments to improve the health of the priority population (McKenzie et al., 2009) Examples include activities that enable individuals to evaluate their personal level of health through the use of health-risk appraisals, screenings, (such as blood pressure screenings) and self-examination (such as breast self-examination).

Key: ☐ Entry ⑧ Advanced – level information

2.3.4   Comply with legal and ethical principles in designing strategies and interventions

Health education specialists are expected to abide by a Code of Ethics for the Health Education Profession (Coalition of National Health Education Organizations [CNHEO], 1999) as well as applicable laws (such as HIPAA, further described in Chapter IV). The Code of Ethics helps to ensure that the integrity and ethics of the profession are upheld as difficult ethical challenges emerge. Health education specialists must use their knowledge and experience to fulfill their responsibilities to the public, profession, employers, in the delivery of health education, in research and evaluation, and in professional preparation.

2.3.5   Apply principles of cultural competence in selecting and designing strategies and interventions

Regardless of the type of strategy used, the method must "fit," or meet the needs of, the priority population in order for a program to be effective. The characteristics of the priority population will dictate how the intervention is received. Cultural competence is the "ability of an individual to understand and respect values, attitudes, beliefs and [morals] that differ across cultures, and to consider and respond appropriately to these differences in planning, implementing, and evaluating health education and promotion programs and interventions" (Joint Committee on Health Education Terminology, 2002, p. 5). It is important for health education specialists to identify how the characteristics of a chosen strategy fit the population's culture and are relevant to the priority population (McKenzie et al., 2009).

2.3.6   Pilot test strategies and interventions

Using formative evaluation techniques to pilot test strategies and interventions is essential to program planning. Pilot testing can help ensure that messages and images are clear and consistent, culturally relevant, and motivational. Focus groups and self-reported knowledge, attitudes, and behavior surveys can help to reveal what the target audience understands and what barriers and facilitators to behavioral change exist. Data and information gathered from a pilot test can help refine a program to increase likelihood of success.

Competency 2.4:
Develop a scope and sequence plan for the delivery of health education

A successful health education program is one that is well planned. Each program should be based on findings from a thorough needs assessment and should incorporate feedback from stakeholders. Quality health education program plans are based in theory and use a planning model during development, implementation, and evaluation. A successful health education program incorporates goals and measurable objectives that help to reach intended outcomes and has evaluation as a planned component (Cottrell et al., 2009). Using all of this knowledge, a health education specialist can begin to create a timeline for delivery of the program. In creating this timeline, health education specialists need to consider the length of time necessary to deliver an effective intervention while also considering resources. Difficult decisions regarding the possible content that can be covered in the timeframe, as well as the logical sequence of it, will have to be made so that the learning modules can be developed.

Key: ◻ Entry   〽 Advanced – level information

2.4.1 Determine the range of health education needed to achieve goals and objectives

The health education specialist is responsible for deciding what and how much information will be discussed regarding a specific health topic during a health education program. This is determined by considering:

- needs assessment data;
- culture of the priority population;
- literacy level of the priority population;
- the priority population's previous experience regarding the health issue;
- budget constraints;
- time restrictions of program participants; and
- availability of space to conduct programs.

Regardless of the health education setting, the health education specialist should plan instruction for optimal educational effectiveness. The plan for action should sequence the units or modules (including objectives, health topic content, and teaching strategies) for the specific health education course or workshop being facilitated. The plan of instruction should focus on continuity, sequence, and integration (Fodor et al., 2002). The instruction plan should provide the scope and sequence or "bigger picture" for what the program will look like.

Learning Principles

It is difficult to teach people who do not want to learn. To facilitate the learning process, the health education specialist should focus on increasing participants' motivation to learn. Using the following ten principles may help (Minelli & Breckon, 2009).

1. *Use several senses*. People retain:
   - 10 percent of what is read;
   - 20 percent of what is heard;
   - 30 percent of what they see;
   - 50 percent of what they hear and see;
   - 70 percent of what they say; and
   - 90 percent of what they do and say.

2. *Actively involve participants*. Use methods that enable them to be active, rather than passive, participants. For example, use discussion rather than lecture.

3. *Provide an appropriate learning environment*. Keep extraneous interference and distractions to a minimum and ensure comfortable accommodations.

4. *Assess learner readiness*. People learn only when they are physically and emotionally ready.

Key: ◘ Entry ◣◣ Advanced – level information

5. *Establish the relevance of the information.* People tend to learn what they perceive is important to them. Knowing what is important to participants can help you make the information meet their needs.

6. *Use repetition.* Learning is enhanced if information is repeated several times in a variety of ways.

7.*Strive for a pleasant learning experience.* Encouragement through frequent, positive feedback and recognizable progress contribute to a positive experience.

8. *Start with the known and move toward the unknown.* Present information that builds from the simple to the complex in an organized manner.

9. *Generalize the information.* Learning is more likely to occur if the information is applied to more than one setting or situation.

10. *Appropriately pace delivery of the information.* Adjust the rate at which information is covered to meet the needs of the participants.

2.4.2   Select resources required to implement health education

It is important that information and resources used in any health education program be developmentally and culturally appropriate for the priority population. During the planning process, the health education specialist will need to assess whether appropriate materials are available and how to attain them. If they are not available, materials will need to be developed to meet program objectives. Information and resources should be researched early in program planning to ensure that there is time to develop adequate materials if needed (Plomer & Bensley, 2009).

2.4.3   Use logic models to guide the planning process

In its most fundamental form, a logic model depicts programmatic milestones in a flowchart that leads to program results (Healy & Zimmerman, 2010). Logic models include inputs, activities, outputs, outcomes, and impact. Programmatic effectiveness (success in achieving outcomes) and efficiency (success in using resources, both human and financial) can be easily measured through logic models. Please refer to Chapter IV for more information on logic models.

2.4.4 ⫼   Organize health education into a logical sequence

Health education programs must be carefully planned, implemented, and evaluated. Templates used in basic logic models allow evaluators to move freely back and forth among the elements of a flowchart to determine reasons for success and failure of a program (Healy & Zimmerman, 2010). Through examination of the logical sequence of inputs, activities, outputs, outcomes, and impact, health education specialists are armed with the necessary information to make recommended changes to improve programmatic effectiveness and efficiency.

Key: ⬛ Entry ⫼ Advanced – level information

2.4.5 ◗◗ Develop a timeline for the delivery of health education

Every project or program conducted by health education specialists requires an orderly sequence of milestones and deliverables. It is essential that these be determined in advance, so that all parties involved can anticipate what to expect when. This is particularly important for funded projects in which payment is "triggered" by the delivery of products and services such as interim progress and final reports. By scheduling tasks and responsible parties a priority, adjustments can be made to achieve desired outcomes.

2.4.6 Analyze the opportunity for integrating health education into other programs

Whenever there is an opportunity to present health education as a prevention option within a health program, the health education specialist should be prepared to do so. This may develop an avenue to market health education. In addition, this allows for the coordination of community resources that would be used within the health education component of an existing program.

2.4.7 Develop a process for integrating health education into other programs

The most effective health education programs will be planned with the aid of a planning model and will incorporate theory when the intervention is created. These steps, however, will not be enough to ensure the program is meeting the priority population's needs. Several extensive, well-researched documents have been published to keep health education programs moving in a direction to positively affect individual and community behavior change. The following documents can be consulted when planning for program development: *Healthy People 2020* (Office of Disease Prevention and Health Promotion, 2009), national and state standards and benchmarks for school health education, and agency/organization mission statements. After researching standards, benchmarks, and mission statements, health education specialists can contact agencies already working with the priority population to see if they can integrate health education efforts into programs that are ongoing.

Competency 2.5:
Address factors that affect implementation

All strategies that make up an intervention require resources for implementation. In addition, there are a number of other logistical activities that must be carried out. A health education specialist must be able to assess what is needed for program creation and delivery prior to implementation.

2.5.1 Identify factors that foster or hinder implementation

There are many potential barriers to the implementation of health education programs, which should be anticipated early in the planning process. Barriers might include lack of community support, agency administration support, or funding. Other barriers might be over-extended health education specialists with limited time for program planning, a lack of coordination of resources within the community, or territorial issues among local agencies. A skillful planner is familiar with, or becomes familiar with, the community and its potential issues and will have a plan to overcome challenges that may lie ahead. A positive attitude, sense of

Key: ◗ Entry ◗◗ Advanced – level information

humor, and willingness to accept the community process will aid in the successful implementation of health education programs (Roe, K.M., Roe, & Strona, 2009).

2.5.2 Analyze factors that foster or hinder implementation

Although a program may be fully funded and perfectly designed, there may be factors that affect implementation, either negatively or positively. For example, a target audience may be reluctant to participate in a program, such as families who refuse to allow fire fighters to enter their home to conduct a home safety check or install free smoke alarms. These families may fear scrutiny of their living situation by authority figures. In addition, there may not be enough time for health education specialists to carry out a program in its entirety due to schedule changes of personnel or budget cuts due to an eroding tax base in a declining economy. In other instances, the target audience may be highly receptive to the program, such as parents who voluntarily attend a car seat checkup event shortly after the birth of their child. Health education specialists need to seize this "teachable moment" to recognize and take advantage of the educational opportunity, in this case, to ensure that parents appropriately restrain their infant.

2.5.3 Use findings of pilot to refine implementation plans as needed

Pilot studies can provide enormous benefit in ensuring that program design and implementation are sound. Oftentimes, however, real-world experience indicates that the program needs to be refined to truly be effective. In a pilot study, it might be found that content could not be delivered in the specified time period, the audience could not understand certain concepts, or the method of instruction was not the most preferred method for participants. Health education specialists should take information from the pilot study to modify content or delivery method for full implementation of the program.

2.5.4 Develop a conducive learning environment

Environments conducive to learning have both psychological and physical characteristics. Psychologically, students must feel comfortable with the pace of teaching, mix of didactic and experiential instruction, and methods of examination. Other factors affecting the learning environment include meaningfulness, open community, learning aids and consistency. Physically, the learning environment must be clean, safe, lighted, well-equipped with furniture in good repair and adequate audiovisual equipment, and heated or cooled to the right temperature. Clients or participants of a health education program may associate comfort with what is learned. Health education specialists should strive to ensure that their students are instructed in a conducive learning environment and should make learning satisfying.

Key: ☐ Entry ⋈ Advanced – level information

CHAPTER III

Area of Responsibility III
Implement Health Education

3.1: Implement a plan of action
Sub-competencies:

3.1.1   Assess readiness for implementation

3.1.2   Collect baseline data

3.1.3   Use strategies to ensure cultural competence in implementing health education plans

3.1.4   Use a variety of strategies to deliver a plan of action

3.1.5   Promote plan of action

3.1.6   Apply theories and models of implementation

3.1.7   Launch plan of action

3.2: Monitor implementation of health education
Sub-competencies:

3.2.1   Monitor progress in accordance with timeline

3.2.2   Assess progress in achieving objectives

3.2.3   Modify plan of action as needed

3.2.4   Monitor use of resources

3.2.5   Monitor compliance with legal and ethical principles

3.3: Train individuals involved in implementation of health education
Sub-competencies:

3.3.1   Select training participants needed for implementation

3.3.2   ⚊ Identify training needs

3.3.3   ⚊ Develop training objectives

3.3.4   ⚊ Create training using best practices

3.3.5   Demonstrate a wide range of training strategies

3.3.6   Deliver training

3.3.7   ⚊ Evaluate training

3.3.8   ⚊ Use evaluation findings to plan future training

The Role

Health education specialists educate and motivate people in their pursuit of healthful behaviors. Regardless of the setting in which they work, health education specialists must be able to infer objectives suitable to the program, select media and methods appropriate to the intended audience, conduct programs as planned, make revisions to programs and objectives, and train those involved in implementation of the program, all consistent with results from having monitored their programs in action (NCHEC et al., 2010a).

Key: ▢ Entry ⚊ Advanced – level information

Settings

The following text describes how implementation is used in different practice settings (NCHEC et al., 2010a).

Community Setting. Health education specialists working for behavior change in the community face dual challenges of motivating a diverse population to pursue healthy behaviors. Health education specialists may also desire to change community environment, norms or capacity. Therefore, health education specialists working in the community setting must use a variety of coordinated approaches to reach program objectives. A health education specialist attempting to improve families' dietary choices, for example, might form an advisory group or community coalition to ensure community needs, interests, and cultures are incorporated into the program. He or she would identify a wide range of intervention strategies to be carried out in a number of locations in order to engage subgroups of the population. Examples of such intervention strategies include increasing awareness of dietary choices through local media, coordinating with local grocery chains to provide educational materials and stock healthier items, arranging for a cooking demonstration at a community center or other place of gathering for the intended audiences, collaborating with community planners to make a community vegetable garden or farmer's market available, or working with schools to change vending machine policies.

School (K-12) Setting. In the school setting, health education specialists work to increase students' knowledge and to promote positive attitudes and behaviors with respect to health. Typically provided with a curriculum by the school administration, a school-based health education specialist infers objectives appropriate to students' learning potential and abilities and decides on appropriate teaching techniques. Lesson plans are informed by the health education specialist's awareness of the students' learning needs, degree of parental support, and related factors. Student learning is assessed and monitored to facilitate revisions in the curriculum and instructional methods. The health education specialist also works with administrative staff, faculty, parent groups and community groups to encourage school policies that support healthy behaviors.

Health Care Setting. Health education specialists employed in health care settings function as independent participants, as well as liaisons between patients and providers. A health education specialist in this setting might conduct a program to support patients' weight loss efforts. He or she might offer classes, supported by presentations from the health care providers, and make use of educational materials consistent with the patients' needs. The health education specialist might arrange for opportunities to apply the information learned through cooking classes or a grocery store tour to improve ability to read food labels. He or she would monitor participant outcomes and providers' reactions, the process of delivering such activities, and would make changes to the program and objectives as warranted.

Business/Industry Setting. In the workplace, health education specialists work with employers to offer educational programs that respond to employees' health needs (such as programs to improve diet) in a manner conducive to employee participation. The health education specialist would need to understand the needs and interests of employees, as well as the workplace culture and ways of doing business that might affect healthy behaviors. Employees might be offered healthful food choices in the company cafeteria, exercise classes, stress reduction counseling, and smoking cessation therapy, all supplemented by educational materials.

Key: ◻ Entry ⫣ Advanced – level information

IMPLEMENT HEALTH EDUCATION

College/University Setting. A health education specialist working in a higher education setting might conduct an introductory-level health class in which he or she guides each student through a personal change project tailored to the student's interests, preparedness for the course, and learning style. Objectives of the project would be determined and modified as needed to fit the needs of the student and the class. PowerPoint presentations, use of technology, and role-playing are among the instructional methods that might be used. Student feedback and instructor observations can be used to refine future programs to more effectively achieve goals within a course's curriculum.

University Health Services Setting. In conjunction with health care providers, health education specialists in a university health services setting work with the entire university community. Programs are constructed in response to established needs of faculty, staff, and students. For example, with the support of appropriate university personnel, the health education specialist might work with residence hall officials to offer educational sessions in student dormitories on the topic of contraception, alcohol use or dating violence. Program availability would match student needs and be supported by media intended to appeal to the college student. Incentives could be offered to encourage attendance. The health education specialist would monitor students' interest and attendance and request feedback from students and instructors to improve future programs.

Key Terms

○━ **Culture** involves ideas, beliefs, values, customs, and norms that are learned from family and community, and are passed down from generation to generation (Doyle et al., 2010).

○━ **Cultural competence** is the ability of health organizations and practitioners to recognize the cultural beliefs, values, attitudes, traditions, language preferences, and health practices of diverse populations and to apply that knowledge to produce a positive health outcome (United States Department of Health and Human Services [USDHHS], 2001).

○━ **Health literacy** is the degree to which individuals have the capacity to obtain, process, and understand basic health information and services needed to make appropriate health decisions (Institute of Medicine, 2004).

○━ **Implementation** is the process of putting a project, service, or program into effect. In implementation, one seeks to accomplish the setting up, management and execution of the project, service or program (Timmreck, 2003).

○━ An **intervention**, or program, is a set of learning activities, delivery plan, and evaluation activities designed to achieve the desired outcomes of the program. Interventions or programs may use single or multiple strategies to accomplish objectives. An intervention is a specific component of a more comprehensive program (Green & Kreuter, 2005).

○━ An **intervention strategy** is a specific technique or approach used in an intervention to get the desired outcome (Bartholomew et al., 2006).

Key: ▢ Entry ⫾⫾ Advanced – level information

- **Learning activities** are the means used to carry out the program. These are the instructional sessions that will address the learning objectives (Simons-Morton et al., 1995). In this chapter, the phrase learning activities is used interchangeably with program activities.

- **Plain language** is a strategy for making written and oral information easier to understand. It is one important tool for improving health literacy (Plain Language Action and Information Network, n.d.).

- **Program** refers to the full range of components required to bring about the intended changes in health and social outcomes (Green & Kreuter, 2005).

- A **tailored message** is any combination of information and behavior change strategies intended to reach one specific person or group, based on characteristics unique to that person, related to the outcome of interest, and derived from an individual assessment (Krueter, Farrell, Olevitch, & Brennan, 2000).

- A **targeted message** is intended to reach some specific subgroup of the general population, usually based on a set of demographic characteristics shared by its members (Krueter et al., 2000).

Competency 3.1:
Implement a plan of action

An action plan for program implementation describes how goals and objectives will be achieved, identifies resources needed and how responsibilities will be assigned (Brownson, Baker, Leet & Gillespie, 2003). Building on the assessment and planning activities related to a particular health issue or problem, a plan of action is developed in conjunction with members of the intended audience and those who can hinder or help implementation of the program.

The following are five generic phases of the implementation process in health education:

Phase 1: Engagement of individuals or organizations that make a decision to adopt an intervention or a program. Acceptance of the **intervention** or **program** by the priority population and by individuals or organizations delivering the intervention is critical to implementation. If needs assessment and planning processes included these individuals or groups, Phase 1 may have been accomplished at that time.

Phase 2: Specify tasks and estimate resources. During Phase 2 the health education specialist develops a detailed list of all program activities and identifies the relationships between and among them. Especially important are aspects of the program that are necessary for other components to take place. Resources needed may include personnel, space, supplies, equipment, marketing, communication, and direct educational needs.

Phase 3: Establish a system for program management. Once all of the activities, corresponding tasks, and resources have been identified, a system or schedule should be developed to ensure that the program progresses as planned. Typically, personnel and financial resources need to be managed.

Phase 4: Put the plans into action. This phase can be accomplished through pilot testing, phasing-in, or total implementation (McKenzie et al., 2009).

- *Piloting, pilot testing, or field testing* allows for a trial run of the program on a small scale. For piloting to have maximum utility, interventions should be conducted with individuals of the priority population in the same setting and delivered by individuals as intended for full implementation.
- *Phasing-in* differs from piloting in that the program is offered in increments rather than all at once. Phasing in is not considered a trial run. The program can be phased in by limiting the number of participants, locations, or interventions offered.
- *Total implementation* is when the entire program begins at the same time. This may be easier to accomplish when the number of interventions and intervention strategies are limited and focused on one audience.

Phase 5: Ending or sustaining a program or intervention. The final phase of the implementation process includes determining how long a program or intervention should run. To best determine the fate of the program or intervention, health education specialists need to consider the program outcomes, type of resources needed, and support from community partners.

3.1.1 Assess readiness for implementation

Health education specialists should consider readiness for implementation at organizational and individual levels. He or she should compare program goals and objectives with the characteristics of groups, communities, or organizations that might have experience in delivering the intervention strategies. Identifying and contacting individuals whose professional background and experience would bring skills and abilities to help groups, communities, or organizations will increase readiness to implement health education programs. Where and when necessary, the health education specialist should help facilitate capacity-building among key stakeholders to increase readiness to move health education programs forward. Several methods for determining capacity exist, some using outside experts and others using only local individuals and organizations (Beaulieu, 2002).

3.1.2 Collect baseline data

Prior to program implementation, the health education specialist should review available quantitative and qualitative data from national, state and local resources to assess health knowledge, beliefs, attitudes and values of the intended audiences related to the health topic, and their psychomotor capabilities or skills related to outcomes. Please refer to Chapter IV for more information on quantitative and qualitative data collection. Many times primary data collection is required, especially if the health education specialist wants to understand the local impact of a health issue.

It may not be necessary to collect new information for each intervention. Secondary data sources (data collected for another purpose) might also provide information needed for a program. Some common secondary data sources include the U.S. Census (www.census.gov) and the Behavioral Risk Factor Surveillance System

(BRFSS) (www.cdc.gov/brfss/). The type of data needed might also be available through other sources in the community, such as local organizations with an interest in the same population. Baseline data are important because they provide the beginning measure for evaluating changes in behavior, practices or skills associated with the program goals. Please refer to Chapter I for more information on primary and secondary data.

3.1.3 Use strategies to ensure cultural competence in implementing health education plans

Culturally and linguistically competent health education specialists value diversity, develop the capacity for self-assessment, raise awareness of dynamics inherent when cultures interact, use organizational processes to institutionalize cultural knowledge, and strive to develop individual and organization adaptations to diversity (Institute of Medicine, 2002). A sign of **cultural competence** is the integration and transformation of knowledge about individuals and groups of people into specific standards, policies, practices, and attitudes used to increase the quality of services, and improve outcomes. Delivering programs in a culturally sensitive manner requires conscientious attention by the program planners. This may mean providing an environment in which people from diverse backgrounds feel comfortable discussing culturally derived health beliefs and sharing cultural practices.

Low health literacy skills or Limited English Proficiency (LEP) in an audience affects the way an intervention is delivered. **Health literacy** differs from general literacy in that it takes into account the setting or situation in which the reading and writing occur (Schwartzberg, VanGeest & Wang, 2005). Types of literacy include quantitative literacy, document literacy, computer literacy, health literacy, media literacy, and prose literacy. Poor health literacy is linked to poor health outcomes (Williams et al., 1995; Gazmararian, et al., 1999; Berkman et al., 2004).

Literacy level, preferred language, and preferred media sources should be considered when delivering health messages. For example, a lower percentage of adults with Below Basic literacy level get health information from written sources. A higher percentage of adults in the Below Basic and Basic levels of literacy get health information from television and radio (Institute of Educational Services [IES], 2006). In addition when an audience is culturally diverse, matching the message source as closely to the audience in key demographics is important to message credibility. Where languages other than English are spoken, care must be taken to ensure accurate translations or better yet, develop health messages with that culture in mind to accurately put the behavior into the proper cultural context. Tenets of LEP are useful when an audience's first language is not English.

Health information for people with LEP needs to be communicated plainly in their primary language, using words and examples that make the information understandable (USDHHS, 2009). Interventions not offered in other languages should use design techniques for low-literate audiences to improve reception of the instruction, including oral delivery (Plain Language Action and Information Network, n.d.; Doak, C.C, Doak & Root, 1996).

Key: ☐ Entry \\\ Advanced – level information

3.1.4 Use a variety of strategies to deliver a plan of action

The scope and sequence of a program may contain many intervention strategies. An intervention may include single or multiple strategies and methods through which program goals and objectives are achieved. The implementation of an intervention requires a variety of skills and knowledge by the health education specialist, including the capability to use technology, create appropriate timelines, manage program resources, and carry out an evaluation.

Behavior is multifaceted; therefore, multiple strategies are often needed to change behavior. Interventions or programs designed to motivate behavior change include planned strategies or activities for groups or individuals. Other strategies may include interventions focused on organizational, community, environmental or policy change levels. A program could include a mix of strategies such as those that are client-centered, provider-centered, or systems-centered to achieve its goals. When selecting individual strategies or activities, make sure that each one has evidence of efficacy. Even though the strategy may be shown to work, not all interventions using that strategy may achieve the desired outcomes. The health education specialist should look for evaluation results in the literature, program reports, or through communication with program administrators.

New communication technologies such as Web 2.0, text message or short-message service (SMS), and other technologies offer methods for delivering health education strategies, interventions, and programs. Web 2.0 refers to a new generation of tools. Examples of Web 2.0 tools include blogs, mashups, podcasts, feeds, social networking sites, video sharing, and wikis (Bennett & Glasgow, 2009; Giustini, 2006). SMS has been used in clinical care and preventive health behavior interventions (Fjeldsoe, Marshall, & Miller, 2009). Other technologies such as personal digital assistants (PDAs) are being used by healthcare personnel and students in health education programming (Lindquist, Johansson, Petersson, Saveman, & Nilsson, 2008). The health education specialist must determine the audience preference for receiving health information before deciding which technology, if any, to use. Further, they must stay abreast of changes and advances in technology, as they are continuously changing.

3.1.5 Promote plan of action

A one-size-fits-all approach to promoting programs has been replaced by tailored and targeted promotion campaigns based on the ethnic and demographic characteristics and behaviors of the population being served. Health messages need to appeal to the audience's needs, preferences, and health concerns. **Tailored messages** are individually focused messages that appeal to a specific sub-population, typically using information obtained from the individuals themselves. Today, computer tailoring of messages and materials can enable a program to reach a larger audience (Gilbert, Sawyer, & McNeill, 2011). By contrast, targeting messages focuses on subgroups, such as demographic variables, of an audience and typically uses techniques of market segmentation.

3.1.6 Apply theories and models of implementation

Theories are the backbone of every well-planned intervention. Although abstract in nature, they provide a guide as to what to expect about human behavior. According to Kerlinger (1986), "a theory is a set of interrelated concepts, definitions and propositions that present a systematic view of events or situations by specifying relations among variables, in order to explain and predict the events or situations" (as cited in Glanz et al., 2008b, p. 26). Models draw on a number of theories to help understand a specific problem in a particular setting or context.

Theories and models used in designing interventions allow health education specialists to select strategies for implementation based on what is known about influences on human behavior. Additionally, most theories and models are laid out in a way that helps the health education specialist measure change.

It is the responsibility of the health education specialist to select the theory or model that will be used to guide program implementation, based on the concepts and constructs of a theory and the program goals and objectives. Currently, there are six popular textbooks that outline the most commonly used theories of health behavior and health promotion. They are:

- Health Behavior and Health Education: Theory, Research, and Practice. 4th edition (Glanz et al., 2008a);
- Emerging Theories in Health Promotion Practice and Research: Strategies for Improving Public Health (DiClemente, Crosby, & Kegler 2002);
- Social and Behavioral Theory in Public Health (Edberg, 2007);
- Theoretical Foundations of Health Education and Health Promotion (Sharma, M. & Romas, J.A., 2008);
- Introduction to Health Behavior Theory (Hayden, J., 2008); and
- Theory in Health Promotion Research and Practice: Thinking Outside the Box (Goodson, 2010).

Some common theories and models used in health education are briefly described below.

Social Cognitive Theory
Social Cognitive Theory states that learning is an interaction between a person and his or her environment, cognitive processes, and behavior (Bandura, 1986). In this theory, this interaction is referred to as reciprocal determinism. Although different sources will discuss the components in different ways, there are several major constructs associated with this theory: behavioral capability, expectations, expectancies, self-control, emotional coping responses, reciprocal determinism, and self-efficacy. Social Cognitive Theory constructs have been adopted by other models as an underpinning for behavior change. More specifically, self-efficacy, a person's confidence in performing a behavior and overcoming possible barriers to that behavior, has been adopted by several other models.

Transtheoretical Model
The Transtheoretical Model (Prochaska, 2005), often called the Stages of Change Model, incorporates components of many theories (thus the term "transtheoretical"). It is particularly useful in that planned interventions can target people where they are in their motivation for a particular behavior. This model has several major constructs: stages of change, processes of change, decisional balance, and self-efficacy. The stages of change construct received considerable attention, due to its use in determining readiness to change. For example, in a smoking cessation program, there could be several intervention materials and strategies; however, the use of the appropriate materials and strategies for individuals would depend on each person's readiness to change his or her smoking behavior.

IMPLEMENT HEALTH EDUCATION

This model proposes that change is a process, not an event, and that change occurs as people move through a series of stages to adopt a new behavior. The stages are as follows:

- *Precontemplation:* person is not intending to take action in the next six months; some people may be unaware of or in denial about the problem.
- *Contemplation:* person is aware there is a problem and is intending to take action in the next six months.
- *Preparation:* person is intending to take action in the immediate future, usually in the next month.
- *Action:* person has taken action (changed behavior) within the past six months.
- *Maintenance:* person has changed his or her behavior and has maintained the change for more than six months.
- *Termination:* person has no temptation to return to the old behavior and has 100 percent self-efficacy.

(Prochaska, J., Redding, C. & Evers, 2008)

A person can be in any stage with any behavior and move back and forth through the stages, depending on external factors affecting the individual. When using this model, health education specialists can develop materials and interventions for each stage to match individual needs for behavior change.

Health Belief Model

The Health Belief Model (Hochbaum, 1958; Rosenstock, Strecher, & Becker, 1988) is a popular behavior change model that has been extensively used and researched over the years. It is an individual-level model first developed by social psychologists in the U.S. Public Health Service to understand why individuals did not act on information about prevention or disease detection. Generally in this model, there are six major constructs thought to affect behavior change: perceived susceptibility, perceived severity, perceived benefits, perceived barriers, cues to action, and self-efficacy.

Theory of Reasoned Action and Theory of Planned Behavior

The Theory of Planned Behavior builds upon the Theory of Reasoned Action (Ajzen, 1988). Both theories recognize behavioral intention as key in determining behavior (Montano & Kasprzyk, 2008), and assume that behavior change is influenced by a person's attitude toward the outcome and the social or subjective norms of people important in the person's life. The Theory of Planned Behavior adds the construct of behavioral control. When using these theories, health education specialists examine the individual's motivation to perform the behavior, determine what the individual's peers think of the behavior, and assess the difficulty the individual will have in performing the behavior.

Diffusion of Innovations Theory

The Diffusion of Innovations Theory (Rogers, 2003) is a community-level theory that describes the rate at which a new program or activity will spread throughout a group of people. According to this theory, the characteristics of those accepting the new program help to explain community readiness to change.

- *Innovators* are the first to adopt the new idea or program.
- *Early Adopters* wait until after the innovators adopt.
- *Early Majority* adopts once the opinion leaders have done so.
- *Late Majority* adopts once the new idea or program becomes the norm.
- *Laggards* are the last to adopt or they may never adopt.

Key: ◻ Entry ◼ Advanced – level information

Health education specialists motivate groups of people to adopt the new idea or program by demonstrating how much better it is than the status quo. The theory also incorporates constructs related to the innovation: relative advantage, compatibility, complexity, observability, and trialability. Using the Diffusion of Innovations Theory, communication channels are used to integrate the idea into something already accepted in the community.

Ecological Models

Ecological models focus attention on the interaction of the individual and environment, which requires the health education specialist be familiar with individual behavior change strategies as well as strategies for policy and environmental change. Several ecological models have been proposed, each with a unique way to frame this interaction. Sallis, Owen, and Fisher (2008) propose five levels of health promotion strategies: individual, interpersonal, organizational, community, and public policy.

3.1.7 Launch plan of action

The implementation of a program requires a variety of skills and knowledge, including the ability to use technology, carry-out appropriate timelines, manage program resources, and conduct an evaluation.

Health education specialists seldom have unlimited resources available to them. Most successful programs are the result of efforts and resources of a number of different people and organizations. Thus, health education specialists need to have skills to work with others who have similar interests and a stake in the outcomes of successful health education programs. Skills in communication, group dynamics, community organizing, and community building are essential (McKenzie et al., 2009). It is the responsibility of health education specialists to guide groups as they go through the evolutionary stages of group dynamics, while not leading or becoming part of the group (Goldman & Schmaltz, 2005).

The group facilitator aims to enhance group cohesion and cooperation by working with the group to help plan effective meetings, create meeting agendas with action items, distribute meeting minutes, and attend to meeting details. Facilitators model effective group leadership by believing in group processes, caring about group members, actively listening, and communicating openly and respectfully (Roe et al., 2009). Further, having conflict management and resolution skills, decision-making skills, and meeting management skills allows health education specialists to facilitate actions that will eventually improve health status rather than have them derailed by interpersonal dynamics.

Relationships between organizations or groups can fall into one of four levels: networking, coordinating, cooperating, or collaborating. Understanding when each type is appropriate will help the health education specialist plan and allocate time and resources. Below are definitions for the levels of interaction between groups as outlined by Himmelman (2002). In Table 3.1, the four strategies for working relationships are defined. It is important to note that each strategy can be appropriate for a coalition depending on what is to be achieved by the relationship.

Table 3.1.
Four Strategies used by Coalitions

Strategy	Definition
Networking	Exchanging information for mutual benefit
Coordinating	Exchanging information and altering activities for mutual benefit and to achieve a common purpose
Cooperating	Exchanging information, altering activities, and sharing resources for mutual benefit and to achieve a common purpose
Collaborating	Exchanging information, altering activities, sharing resources, and enhancing the capacity of another for mutual benefit and to achieve a common purpose

Competency 3.2:
Monitor implementation of health education

When implementing programs, health education specialists must monitor all aspects of the program, including content delivery, adherence to timelines, progress toward objectives, and use of financial resources. Data collection and maintenance of records are important tasks that health education specialists must perform in order to ensure proper delivery of the program.

3.2.1 Monitor progress in accordance with timeline
Health education specialists should produce a timeline with major activities and outputs identified, and monitor program implementation progress. Several methods for doing this exist, such as a Gantt method, a Program Evaluation and Review Technique (PERT), and a Critical Path Method (CPM). These methods create an illustration to help schedule and depict a project timeline and/or project management plan. Tools and resources are available online and through software packages to assist health education specialists in developing the chart or model. Each of these methods allows a health education specialist to visually identify the progress of project implementations. Identifying to whom and how frequently to report progress, as well as useful methods preferred for reporting, are also key aspects of monitoring the health education specialist should address.

3.2.2 Assess progress in achieving objectives
Logic models display the sequence of actions that describe what the program is and will do to achieve outcomes. Logic models are commonly used in program development and evaluation, and are required by some funding agencies. A logic model has five core components.

1. Inputs, which are the resources, contribution, and investments that go into the program.
2. Outputs, which are the activities, services, events and products that reach people who participate or who are targeted by the program.
3. Outcomes, which are the results or changes in individuals, groups, communities, organizations, or systems.
4. Assumptions, or the beliefs we have about the program, the people involved, the context of the program, and the way we think the program will work.
5. External factors are the variety of factors that interact with and influence the program action.

(University of Wisconsin, Cooperative Extension, 2008).

The outputs listed in a logic model are helpful in tracking the program's progress towards the objectives. By tracking this progress, the health education specialist may better understand why an intervention might have gone well or poorly. The logic model, which includes process evaluation, helps to identify where and when something occurred that differed from what was planned. Please refer to Chapter IV for more information on logic models.

3.2.3   Modify plan of action as needed

Seldom is the perfect intervention already designed and ready to use. Typically a health education specialist must select an intervention that is reasonable, given the audience, desired outcome and resources available for implementation. The health education specialist must have a plan of action which is flexible, know who to involve when modifying the plan of action, and know when approvals are needed and from whom they are needed when modifying the plan.

Modifying the plan does not always mean the intervention is modified. But when the intervention is modified, primary attention should be focused on maintaining fidelity to the original intervention. Some modifications have been found to affect the efficacy of the intervention in the field. Conversely, adapting an intervention is a fundamental activity in implementation, coming to a common ground between the delivery of the intervention and the characteristics of the group using it. If adaptation to an intervention results in a form that is far from the original, tested form, it is prudent to evaluate the adapted intervention for the desired outcome.

3.2.4   Monitor use of resources

The health education specialist should realize the importance of monitoring resources used in an intervention and program as a whole. Resources include a variety of items, including personnel, time, money, space, goodwill, and materials. Careful recordkeeping of expenses is necessary, particularly if the program is funded by a grant. Funding agencies often require progress reports that describe expenses and revenues. Please refer to Chapter V for more details regarding managing fiscal resources.

3.2.5   Monitor compliance with legal and ethical principles

In a profession such as health education, which addresses many controversial issues and topics, health education specialists have ethical obligations to colleagues, students, employers, and the public. Examination of beliefs and principles, as well as discussion of ethics, is encouraged to determine whether decisions are fair and practical and will ensure the greatest good (Minelli & Breckon, 2009).

Key: ◻ Entry \\\ Advanced – level information

IMPLEMENT HEALTH EDUCATION

Health education professionals are expected to behave ethically and according to the Unified Code of Ethics, as approved by the Coalition of National Health Education Organizations (CNHEO) (See Appendix A). Ethical dilemmas — issues with two sides and involving a judgment of right or wrong — face the health education specialist every day. The CNHEO Code of Ethics not only sets the standard for the health education specialist, but also tells the public what it should expect from the practitioner (Cottrell et al., 2009).

Ethics permeate all aspects of the health education specialist's roles. Practicing within the boundaries of the profession's ethical standards is imperative. Because health education specialists are an important factor in behavioral development, it is expected for professionals to stay current in their knowledge and health-related content, as well as effective interventions and strategies (Bensley, 2009).

Negligence is the failure to act in a careful or reasonable manner. Negligence may result from omission (not doing something you should have done) or commission (doing something you should not have done). To reduce the likelihood of legal improprieties:

- be aware of legal liabilities;
- use only professionals or experts in the area being presented (when appropriate, they should be licensed, certified, or in other ways credentialed);
- when appropriate, require medical clearance for participation;
- instruct staff not to practice outside their area of expertise; and
- follow building codes and regulations.

(Anspaugh, D.J., Dignan, & Anspaugh, 2000)

Human subjects protection establishes a standard for ethics, and details can be found in the Belmont Report (National Commission for the Protection of Human Subjects of Biomedical and Behavioral Research, 1979). This report summarizes the basic ethical principles and guidelines for the protection of human subjects of research. Not every health education specialist will conduct research, but everyone should recognize the fundamental concepts for human subjects' protection: respect for persons, beneficence and justice.

Health education specialists conducting research will be required to develop statements of informed consent that allow the person to choose what will or will not happen to them, and are signed by participants indicating their choice. Informed consent includes the following information:

- nature and purpose of the program;
- any inherent risks or dangers associated with participation in the program;
- any possible discomfort that may be experienced from participation in the program;
- expected benefits of participation;
- alternative programs or procedures that would accomplish the same results; and the
- option of discontinuing participation at any time.

(National Commission for the Protection of Human Subjects of Biomedical and Behavioral Research, 1979)

Using **plain language** to create an informed consent document is especially helpful in assuring comprehension.

Key: ◻ Entry ◪ Advanced – level information

Competency 3.3:
Train Individuals Involved in Implementation of Health Education

Depending on the magnitude of the program, health education specialists may be responsible for conducting training programs for professionals, volunteers or stakeholders who will be involved in delivering health education programs. The goals of training sessions should be clearly outlined, and evidence-based strategies to deliver content should be employed. Evaluation of training sessions provides feedback to help improve training sessions for future program personnel.

3.3.1   Select training participants needed for implementation

The health education specialist should think about three aspects of training when selecting individuals to deliver the intervention. First, the characteristics of the individual(s) who will conduct the training are critical to its success. Personal characteristics to look for in instructors include: a desire to teach, the ability to communicate, skill at getting people to participate and being "learner-oriented" (Kirkpatrick, D.L., & Kirkpatrick, 2009).

Second, participants for training sessions are future intervention deliverers. By considering what the intervention requires for successful delivery, some intervention-specific characteristics of participants can be identified. Examples of questions that can be asked follow.

- Are specialized technology skills needed, such as working knowledge of webinars or blogs? Are other skills required?
- Does the intervention require multiple sessions? What does that mean about the availability of the person delivering it? Are multiple persons acceptable or should one facilitator be used throughout?
- Does the audience require a person fluent in their language?
- Would the **intervention strategy** benefit from a particular sort of experience helpful in using the intervention, such as experience in peer-leading?

The health education specialist must take care to select individuals with a match of skills for the intervention.

Third, the health education specialist should understand the organizational context where the intervention is to be delivered. An intervention not supported or poorly supported by an organization may not be delivered properly or at all, thereby making it useless regardless of its proven efficacy.

- Will the individual delivering the intervention have the support of management or decision-makers?
- Has the organization had any experience using the particular intervention strategy?
- Is the strategy in line with the philosophy and mission of the organization? For example, if an organization does not favor drug use, a clean needles intervention would not match their philosophy and would likely not be supported.
- Does the organizational site(s) have the prerequisites for using the strategy? A prerequisite is the absolutely essential characteristics needed in a delivery site, such as sufficient personnel, bilingual or

bicultural staff, access to meeting space, proven relationship with the intended audience, or proven fiscal responsibility. These will vary by intervention. The health education specialist can determine these from the intervention strategy, audience targeted, and setting of the intervention.

These questions about implementation not only assist the health education specialist in selecting individuals to train, but also in setting the stage for successful delivery and later maintenance of the intervention (Livet, Courser, & Wandersman, 2008). Please refer the Chapter VI for more information on training.

3.3.2 ◖◗ Identify training needs

In determining training needs, the health education specialist must consider: intervention characteristics and requirements; the skills, knowledge, and experience of the selected training participants; and the setting for the training. As stated earlier, the health education specialist should understand the critical knowledge and skills necessary for implementing an intervention successfully. The logistics for training should not be overlooked by the health education specialist when identifying training needs. What type of space does the training require? A cooking demonstration, for example, needs a space with a working kitchen. The training might be suited to being delivered in an alternative location such as a home, church, community center, or other gathering place. If a location conducive to skill building is not available, a decision must be made about how or whether to adapt the intervention without compromising effectiveness.

3.3.3 ◖◗ Develop training objectives

Training objectives relate both to the participant and the training opportunity. Objectives for participants are worded in such a way that a participant will have particular knowledge or be able to perform a particular task at an acceptable level at the end of the training. Objectives for the training might include offering an opportunity for a particular learning technique (e.g., role-play), providing a nonjudgmental and respectful atmosphere to encourage dialogue, or allowing time for sharing with colleagues. As always, objectives should be Specific, Measurable, Achievable, Realistic, and Timely (SMART) (Issel, 2009).

3.3.4 ◖◗ Create training using best practices

Health education specialists work with a wide age-range of clients and participants. Training initiatives typically occur with adults. Literature is very clear that adults learn differently than children. Friere (2000), Knowles, Holten and Swanson (2005) pioneered this relatively new field of study. Adult learning (andragogy) differs from children's learning (pedagogy) in several ways (Knowles et al., 2005). Adults need to be involved in planning and evaluation of their instruction. Experience, including mistakes, provides the basis for **learning activities**. Adults are most interested in learning subjects that have immediate relevance to their job or personal life. Adult learning is problem-centered rather than content-oriented. These principles are the foundation for successful trainings with adults. Health education specialists working outside a school setting are encouraged to incorporate these principles into their training skill set. Health education specialists are also encouraged to search the literature for proven methods of training.

Agencies and organizations, such as the CDC, publicize programs and interventions that utilize best practices that may be utilized in training efforts. Where no list can be considered comprehensive or exhaustive, they provide a starting point for health education specialists to consider. Recognized programs are considered grounded in a variety of Areas of Responsibility for health education specialists.

3.3.5 Demonstrate a wide range of training strategies

The health education specialist should be media literate. It is helpful to have a basic knowledge about publication layout and design; the creation, processing, and editing of images whether printed or video; and Web site design to be able to create Web sites and evaluate the quality of health-related Web sites. These are especially important when reaching LEP audiences or low health literate audiences (United States Department of Justice [USDOJ], 2010; Plain Language Action and Information Network, n.d.).

Instructional technology is a vital tool for reaching the target audience and achieving program objectives. For example, the computer can be used to prepare visual aids, access the Internet for instructional resources, or conduct a virtual meeting. CDs and DVDs can be used in interactive presentations. Teleconferencing technology allows participants in different locations to attend discussions and lectures. Scanners and digital cameras can be used in the creation of print media and multimedia presentations (Fodor, Dalis, & Giarratano-Russell, 2002).

3.3.6 Deliver training

Health education specialists must consider the best way to instruct an intended audience while also considering available funds and level of expertise of individuals providing the training. Depending on cost, content and instructional expertise required, a variety of methods should be used, such as on-the-job training, one-on-one training, in-person group work, and distance learning techniques (e.g., video conferences, computer-based training, Internet, or conference calls).

3.3.7 ◼ Evaluate training

To acquire the best results from training provided to individuals, the content and process of training should be evaluated. In most skills-based or competency-based training, there is an associated need for enhancement of knowledge related to the skills being developed. One way to evaluate knowledge gains is through the administration of pre- and post-tests. These may include true/false, multiple choice questions, case-based scenarios, written essays, oral review (e.g., tell what you know), self-assessment of knowledge, or direct observations. It may be useful to do a before and after self-assessment rating by participants to address their perceived competency in performing the skills described in the behavioral objectives of the course. Skills evaluation may take place through direct observation by an expert observer or by written self-assessment.

Participant evaluations at the end of a workshop can be detailed and comprehensive, covering individual sessions and daily activities, and indicating satisfaction with the training. Participants' feedback on each session should be simple and should vary in format to address the main points covered in the course. Sample questions may include:

- What will you do differently as a result of this training?
- What was the most or least useful aspect of the session?
- Were trainee's opinions valued and how?
- What went well or did not go well in the session?

Such questions should be standardized so aggregation of results from multiple offerings can provide more reliable direction for training refinement.

Participants, as well as the individual trainer or facilitator, evaluate the following course components: venue, organization, quality of presentation, and quality of participants' participation. Elements such as meeting stated objectives, clarity of presentation, interest in presentation, and responsiveness to participant's questions and concerns are used in evaluating the training presentations.

3.3.8 ◤◤ Use evaluation findings to plan future training

Qualitative and quantitative evaluation can help to make appropriate revisions in the training. As the training is revised, the health education specialist should keep in mind the stated goals and objectives of the program and specific intervention featured in the training. For complex programs, utilizing an outside expert as a consultant may be useful. Please see Chapter IV for more information regarding evaluation procedures and interpretation of results.

Key: ☐ Entry ◤◤ Advanced – level information

CHAPTER IV

Area of Responsibility IV
Conduct Evaluation and Research Related to Health Education

4.1: Develop evaluation/research plan

Sub-competencies:

4.1.1   ∥ Create purpose statement
4.1.2   ∥ Develop evaluation/research questions
4.1.3   Assess feasibility of conducting evaluation/research
4.1.4   Critique evaluation and research methods and findings found in the related literature
4.1.5   Synthesize information found in the literature
4.1.6   Assess the merits and limitations of qualitative and quantitative data collection for evaluation
4.1.7   ∥ Assess the merits and limitations of qualitative and quantitative data collection for research
4.1.8   Identify existing data collection instruments
4.1.9   Critique existing data collection instruments for evaluation
4.1.10 ∥ Critique existing data collection instruments for research
4.1.11 ∥ Create a logic model to guide the evaluation process
4.1.12 Develop data analysis plan for evaluation
4.1.13 ∥ Develop data analysis plan for research
4.1.14 Apply ethical standards in developing the evaluation/research plan

4.2: Design instruments to collect evaluation/research data

Sub-competencies:

4.2.1   Identify useable questions from existing instruments
4.2.2   Write new items to be used in data collection for evaluation
4.2.3   ∥ Write new items to be used in data collection for research
4.2.4   Establish validity of data collection instruments
4.2.5   Establish reliability of data collection instruments

4.3: Collect and analyze evaluation/research data

Sub-competencies:

4.3.1   Collect data based on the evaluation/research plan
4.3.2   Monitor data collection and management
4.3.3   Analyze data using descriptive statistics
4.3.4   Analyze data using inferential and/or other advanced statistical methods
4.3.5   Analyze data using qualitative methods
4.3.6   Apply ethical standards in collecting and analyzing data

Key: ◻ Entry ∥ Advanced – level information

4.4: Interpret results of the evaluation/research

Sub-competencies:

4.4.1   Compare results to evaluation/research questions
4.4.2   Compare results to other findings
4.4.3   Propose possible explanations of findings
4.4.4   Identify possible limitations of findings
4.4.5   Develop recommendations based on results

4.5: Apply findings from evaluation/research

Sub-competencies:

4.5.1   Communicate findings to stakeholders
4.5.2   ▲▲ Evaluate feasibility of implementing recommendations from evaluation
4.5.3   Apply evaluation findings in policy analysis and program development
4.5.4   ▲▲ Disseminate research findings through professional conference presentations

The Role

Health education specialists at all levels are expected to be able to conduct a thorough review of the literature and to apply research findings from basic and evaluative research. They may also be expected to conduct evaluations of policy, projects, and programs. The ability to aggregate data from one or more programs for the purpose of establishing a point of reference and making comparisons is also important. As the health education specialist progresses within the profession, the required level of skill in conducting research and evaluation becomes more advanced. Health education specialists may be expected to write applications for funding, including research proposals. The ability to evaluate a policy or a program's effectiveness is essential to maintaining its support and funding in an increasingly competitive environment.

Advanced-level health education specialists should be able to: draw on various measures to establish the economic impacts of health education and health promotion programs; help identify other professionals needed for collaborative approaches; and provide information to governments, employers, and program funding sources. They should be able to translate research findings into lay language, making health communications more credible (NCHEC et al., 2010a).

Settings

The following text describes how evaluation is used in different practice settings (NCHEC et al., 2010a).

Community Setting. The health education specialist may use epidemiological principles to explain disease outbreaks or define high-risk neighborhoods within communities that require special program emphasis. The discussion of any topic important to the community, such as unintentional injuries, an outbreak of measles or food poisoning, or sexually transmitted diseases requires mastery of research principles and language. Evaluations may provide necessary information to support programs when reviewed by local or state governments. Competitive proposals not only help secure funding, but also may further encourage collaborative projects within a community.

School (K-12) Setting. Health education specialists practicing in the school setting may be called upon to assist in the documentation of student health knowledge, attitudes and behaviors. Data gained from a review of the literature and from qualitative and quantitative research are provided by health education specialists to school boards and parents in order to help them understand students' needs and interests. Careful use of research approaches may also help dispel intolerance relating to attitudes and behaviors maintained by a small, but vocal population. Evaluation of curriculum goals, objectives, and learning activities is critical to identifying, selecting, and implementing effective curricula. As accountability increases, both qualitative and quantitative research methods are increasingly being emphasized in school settings.

Health Care Setting. A health education specialist practicing in a health care setting must be able to understand and interpret research findings for patients and their families, and may be asked to participate as a member of a research team that investigates behavioral components of adherence to clinical regimens. As medical technologies and treatments are advanced through the conduct of clinical trials, evaluative research becomes increasingly important in addressing chronic disease conditions and the reduction of health-risk behaviors for primary prevention.

Business/Industry Setting. Adults spend the majority of their time in the workplace. Health education specialists in this setting need qualitative and quantitative research skills to demonstrate the efficacy of worksite health promotion programs and the contributions of such programs to productivity and organizational goals. Health education specialists may also be asked to assist in monitoring the work environment for safety compliance and injury reduction. Additionally, using evaluative research, health education specialists may be able to help determine quality and cost-effectiveness of competing health plans to benefit employers and employees.

College/University Setting. Health education specialists are expected to engage in scholarly endeavors that include research, grant writing, and dissemination of research findings. In addition to instructional and administrative responsibilities, university health education specialists frequently collaborate with others within and outside of their respective institutions. These efforts contribute to the scientific body of knowledge encompassing health behavior, disease prevention, and risk reduction strategies and to the discipline of health education.

University Health Services Setting. Health education specialists working in the university health services setting face many of the same issues as those in the business/industry and health care settings. These health education specialists need skills in all facets of research including qualitative and quantitative research. Skills in evaluative research are necessary to determine the efficacy and cost-effectiveness of programs for university faculty, staff, and students.

Key: ☐ Entry ＼＼ Advanced – level information

Key Terms

○━ **Evaluation** assesses a process or program to provide evidence and feedback for the program (Neutens & Rubinson, 2010; Simons-Morton, Greene, & Gottlieb, 1995).

○━ **Research** is an organized process using the scientific method for investigating problems. It involves systematic progression through a series of necessary steps (Baumgartner & Hensley, 2006).

○━ **Reliability** refers to the consistency, dependability, and stability of the measurement process (McDermott & Sarvela, 1999; McKenzie et al., 2009).

○━ **Validity** is the degree to which a test or assessment measures what it is intended to measure. Using a valid instrument increases the chance of measuring what was intended (McKenzie et al., 2009).

○━ **Variables** are operational forms of a construct. They designate how the construct will be measured in designated scenarios (McKenzie et al., 2009).

Competency 4.1:
Develop Plans for Evaluation and Research

Evaluation of health education programs can be complex, and there are many different types of evaluation approaches available (McDermott & Sarvela, 1999).

- Formative evaluation looks at an ongoing process of evaluation from planning through implementation (McKenzie et al., 2009).
- Process evaluation is any combination of measures that occur as a program is implemented to assure or improve the quality of performance or delivery.
- Summative evaluation is often associated with measures or judgments that enable the investigator to draw conclusions (McKenzie et al., 2009). It is also commonly associated with impact and outcome evaluations (McDermott & Sarvela, 1999).
- Impact evaluation focuses on immediate and observable effects of a program leading to the desired outcomes.
- Outcome evaluation is focused on the ultimate goal, product or policy. It is often measured in terms of morbidity and mortality.

Employing evaluation procedures that are explicit, formal, and justifiable is desirable for program improvement (McKenzie et al., 2009).

4.1.1 ▚ Create purpose statement

There are a multitude of reasons to conduct evaluation or **research**. Health education specialists serving as an evaluator or researcher may need to: determine achievement of objectives related to improved health status, improve program implementation, provide accountability to stakeholders, increase community support, contribute to the scientific base for community health initiatives, and inform policy decisions or any combination of these. As health education specialists attempt to explore, explain or describe ideas about some phenomena, program or policy, they will find it necessary to develop an appropriate rationale in order to focus the evaluation and/or research (Brownson, Baker, Leet, & Gillespie, 2003) and to craft a meaningful purpose statement. A purpose statement (also referred to as statement of purpose) identifies in detail what the health education specialist wants to learn over the course of an evaluation or research project. It is usually a sentence or two written with specificity and detail. The purpose statement helps to focus and guide efforts involved with data collection and analysis.

4.1.2 \\ Develop evaluation/research questions

Where program evaluation is concerned, health education specialists serve as evaluators striving to solicit answers to very specific questions that carefully align with the statement of purpose and objectives of a program. These questions follow an understanding of program operations, intentions, and end users (Patton, 2008). These specially developed questions are called evaluation questions.

Evaluation questions help to establish boundaries for the evaluation by stating what aspects of the program will be addressed (Patton, 2008; Weiss, 1998). Creating evaluation questions encourages stakeholders to reveal what they believe the evaluation should answer. Negotiating and prioritizing questions among stakeholders further refines a viable focus. The question-development phase also might expose differing stakeholder opinions regarding the best unit of analysis. Clear decisions regarding the questions and corresponding units of analysis are needed in subsequent steps of the evaluation to guide method selection and evidence gathering. Health education specialists use evaluation questions to monitor and measure processes, activities, outputs and expected outcomes. Process questions help the evaluator understand phenomena such as internal and external forces that affect program activities. Answers to output and short-term outcome questions help evaluators clearly understand how program activities, products or associated services relate to or affect changes in behavior, attitudes, knowledge, skills or the intentions of the participants of a program. Longer-term evaluation questions provide vital links between intervention activities, products and services rendered, and changes in risk factors, morbidity or mortality. Well-developed evaluation questions provide a guide for selecting appropriate data sources, which in turn help to guide an effective analysis plan (CDC, 1999). As with evaluation questions, research questions are carefully developed to align with the purpose of the investigation. Research conducted by health education specialists may ask rhetorical questions that may require value judgments or critical statements, historical questions that require describing the phenomena or scientific questions that may involve generalization beyond the observed phenomena. Stated clearly and unambiguously, a scientific research question implies possibilities of empirical testing. Solutions to the questions will contribute to the body of organized knowledge and/or will lead to new problems and further research (Baumgartner et al., 2005).

4.1.3 Assess feasibility of conducting evaluation/research

The feasibility of evaluation or research depends on resources, time, and politics. Evaluations conducted with sufficient time and strong stakeholder support provide feedback on the processes and program outcomes. The identification of program outcomes along the course of a health education project or intervention will provide health education specialists with important programmatic insights that can help improve programming and ensure optimal results and outcomes. Health education specialists considering evaluation should strive for the most rigorous evaluation design that is adequate in terms of utility, accuracy, and costs in time and resources. Evaluation plans that employ research designs such as randomized control trials, cohort studies and case control/comparison studies provide a higher-level confidence to the evaluator and stakeholders about the **validity** of the investigation. Moreover, these designs provide measurable estimates of the probability that effects are due to phenomena that should or should not be attributed to the program. However, evaluation designs vary in cost, dedicated time, and outcomes, and are not always feasible. Unavoidable compromises in design are often made that jeopardize the validity, accuracy and utility of the evaluation (CDC, 1999), but are still adequate to answer evaluation questions. At times, cross-sectional, observational and anecdotal inquiries are more feasible than more rigorous designs, and can provide less expensive, yet useful information. The same factors affect decisions about study designs for research.

4.1.4 Critique evaluation and research methods and findings found in the related literature

Health education specialists should be familiar with appropriate and adequate literature search techniques. Conducting literature searches involves identifying a search strategy. Search strategies typically require health education specialists to:

- identify key search terms;
- identify a period of time to conduct the search (e.g., 2005 to 2010);
- characteristics of the target population (e.g., age, race, gender, geographic location); and
- health conditions (e.g., diabetes, obesity, asthma, teenage pregnancy) of interest.

In many cases, the topics being searched by health education specialists have already been evaluated or researched with a plethora of published results in the literature.

Health education specialists can avoid a duplication of effort by searching the literature specific to a criterion of interest such as study design, methods, or population. Three methods used to evaluate, critique, and report evidence are detailed below.

- Systematic reviews: a published qualitative review of a comprehensive synthesis of publications on particular topics.
- Meta-analyses: a systematic method of evaluating statistical data based on results of several independent studies of the same problem.
- Pooled analyses: a method for collecting all the individual data from a group of studies, combining them into one large set of data, and then analyzing the data as if it came from one big study.

(Brownson et al., 2003)

Key: ◻ Entry ◼ Advanced – level information

Given that systematic reviews, meta-analyses and pooled analyses are not always available, it is sometime useful for health education specialists to seek out other publications in the literature. In this instance, publications on the topic of interest generated since the most recent reviews, or sources that were not included in the most recent reviews, may serve as useful resources. Information can be found in indexes, abstracts, government documents, and computerized databases. Methods for researching the literature are constantly evolving. Computer databases are widely used, because they compile large amounts of information and are easily searched (Cottrell et al., 2009). Databases available today not only catalogue resources, but in many cases provide full text copies of the latest research and evaluation findings. Chapter VI has a list of databases for use in finding research.

The Internet makes available a wide array of interactive information and data that can be used by health education specialists; however, not all information found on the Internet should be considered valid and or reliable (McKenzie et al., 2009). When using the Internet to access information, health education specialists must ensure the information provided by the resource is valid and reliable.

As a literature review is conducted, it is important to understand and evaluate published information for accuracy (Cottrell et al., 2009). The eight questions that can be asked when evaluating research in the literature follow.

- Was the purpose of the study stated?
- Was the research question or hypothesis stated?
- Were the subjects in the study described? Did the literature describe subject recruitment?
- Was the design and location of the study described?
- Were the data collection instruments described?
- Did the presented results reflect the research question or hypothesis?
- Were the conclusions reflective of the research design and data analysis?
- Were the implications meaningful to the priority population?

4.1.5 Synthesize information found in the literature

Research findings and results of program evaluations, including current trends and issues, are made available in published literature. Health education specialists strive to provide evidence of effective approaches to health education problems through a synthesis of professional literature. Health education specialists refer to refereed journals, which publish papers after they have been reviewed by experts in the field or in a specific content area (Cottrell et al., 2009). Published findings can provide useful information about successful study design, data collection methods, as well as data analysis and outcome sharing. While published findings and results vary in direct application and often cannot be generalized to other populations and programs, they may be useful in narrowing the breadth of possibilities for programming, policy development and/or further inquiry. Using published literature appropriately and expeditiously enables the health education specialists to conduct their work with the confidence that it is grounded in up-to-date, peer-reviewed science that will help them establish appropriate protocols for new implementations (Brownson et al., 2003).

Equally as important, using appropriate literature will help reduce the burden of unnecessary paper work or duplicate inquiry for individuals involved. The health education specialist skilled at searching and using literature saves considerable resources by providing guidance and baseline information for minimizing duplication of measurement efforts. To that end, it is important for health education specialists to be able to find, evaluate, and explain the literature findings to their clients (Brownson et al., 2003).

4.1.6 Assess the merits and limitations of qualitative and quantitative data collection for evaluation
4.1.7 ▨ Assess the merits and limitations of qualitative and quantitative data collection for research

Quantitative and qualitative data collection is used for both program evaluation and research are used within the field of health education, and both types of evaluation have practical applications for the health education specialist. Quantitative methodology focuses on quantifying, or measuring, things related to health education programs (Jack, Jr. et al., 2010; McDermott & Sarvela, 1999) through the use of numerical data to help describe, explain, or predict phenomena (Baumgartner & Hensley, 2006). Qualitative methodology is descriptive in nature and attempts to discover meaning or interpret why phenomena are occurring (Baumgartner & Hensley, 2006). Both applications are used to obtain a deeper understanding of the program and its participants.

Often it is advantageous to use a mixed methods approach for data collection to "tell the story" and describe classifications, (e.g. how many, or how much), as well as to indicate why a phenomenon is occurring within a population. Doing so helps the health education specialist make sound recommendations for future programming, and may help introduce new hypotheses for future evaluation and research purposes. Both advanced-level and entry-level health education specialists are responsible for assessing the merits and limitations of qualitative and quantitative data collection for evaluation.

4.1.8 Identify existing data collection instruments
An important initial step in data collection is to identify types and sources of data that will be useful in answering research/evaluation questions. Once evaluation/research questions are established, the evaluator or researcher should consider relevant existing data and use instruments already in existence, when appropriate. A myriad of data collection instruments exists for both qualitative and quantitative inquiry. Many instruments have been validated and tested for reliability and used repeatedly by national, state and local health surveillance programs, (e.g. YRBSS, BRFSS, YTS, NHANES) as well as some parallel on-going programs or inquiries. Health education specialists should be familiar with the existing instruments that are commonly used in the field.

Data collection planning with stakeholders may provide access to existing data and may provide suitable instrumentation for future data collection when comparability and context are desirable. Reviewing the literature, checking the Health and Psychosocial Instruments (HaPI) database, soliciting professional organizations, and accessing organized health education networks prior to data collection can help health education specialists identify useful existing data collection instruments. It may also be useful to review the federal register, an ongoing document by the federal government that contains most routine publications. Parallel projects and programs that are not yet being implemented may be published in the register, and contacting investigators of those proposed projects may help in identification of useful instruments.

4.1.9 Critique existing data collection instruments for evaluation

Program evaluation often focuses on an internal situation, such as collecting data about specific programs, with no intent to generalize the results to other settings and situations. Program evaluations are often conducted using existing data collection instruments. However, using an instrument that has been developed by someone else for use among different populations, in different places, at different times can introduce a level of internal bias that may be problematic. The evaluator should review existing instruments thoroughly, and be sure that each item is appropriate and adequately examines **variables** of interest. Evaluators should be certain there are no extraneous items on instruments that are not relevant to the intent of the evaluation. He or she should be sure that the language is clear and appropriate for the population that the instrument will be administered to as well as assure that the instrument has been tested for validity and **reliability**. Finally, existing instruments should be pilot tested with a sample population before use for evaluation purposes (Trochim, & Donnelly, 2008).

4.1.10 ℕ Critique existing data collection instruments for research

Although there is much discussion about the differences between evaluation and research, it is sometimes difficult to distinguish between them. A major difference between evaluation and research is that research can be conducted with the intent to generalize findings from a sample to a larger population. Research does not always aim for, or achieve, evaluative conclusions, and it is restricted to empirical (rather than evaluative) data. Research bases observed, measured, or calculated conclusions on that data (Jack et al., 2010). The same critical process should be used for existing research instruments that are used as evaluation instruments. Existing data collection instruments should be reviewed thoroughly, and each item should appropriately and adequately examine variables of interest. Researchers should be certain there are no extraneous items that are not associated with the intent of the research. As with critiquing instruments for evaluation, the evaluator should be sure that the language is clear and appropriate for the population to whom the instrument will be administered. In addition, health education specialists should be sure that the instrument has been tested for validity and reliability, and that it has been pilot tested with a similar sample population before being used. (Baumgartener & Hensley, 2006; Jack et al., 2010).

4.1.11 ℕ Create a logic model to guide the evaluation process

Logic models take a variety of forms but generally depict aspects of a program such as inputs, outputs, and outcomes (Healey & Zimmerman, 2010). They offer a scaled-down, somewhat linear, visual depiction of programs. Logic models are used in evaluation to assist in describing key aspects (e.g., inputs, outputs, outcomes) of programs in terms of a simple flow chart. Inputs are the resources, contributions, and other investments that go into a program. Outputs are the activities, services, and products that will reach the participants of a program. Outcomes are often depicted as short-term, intermediate, or long-term. Short-term outcomes are often described as quantifiable changes in knowledge, skills or access to resources that happen if planned activities are successfully carried out. Intermediate outcomes are measured in terms of changes in behaviors that result from achievement of the short-term outcomes. Long-term outcomes are measured in terms of fundamental changes in conditions leading to morbidity or mortality (McKenzie et al., 2009). When logic models are used to help guide the evaluation process, they may range from simple to complex (detailed) logic models. Table 4.1 provides an example of a simple logic model template.

Table 4.1
Sample Logic Model

Inputs/resources	Activities	Outputs	Short-term outcomes	Intermediate outcomes	Long-term outcomes
Human, fiscal, physical, and intellectual resources needed to address the objectives of a program	With the resources available, the following activities will result in measurable, deliverable services and products	Activities, products and services that will influence short-term outcomes	Changes in knowledge or skills among participants of the program	Changes in behaviors or policy	Changes in morbidity or mortality

4.1.12 Develop data analysis plan for evaluation

Developing a data analysis plan is a crucial step for evaluation. By creating a data analysis plan for evaluation, the data that has been collected can be integrated and structured in order to ensure understanding and use of the data. The intended audience, often program personnel or other key stakeholders, may also influence the data analysis plan. Therefore, they may be invited to help develop or create the data analysis plan. The analysis for evaluation depends on the purpose of the evaluation as well as the availability of resources.

4.1.13 ⚊ Develop data analysis plan for research

Data should be collected in accordance with a well-developed analysis plan. The goal of data analysis is to reduce, synthesize, organize, and summarize information to make sense of it (Fitzpatrick, Sanders & Worthen, 2004). Analysis determines if outcomes were different than expected. Planning data analysis is a critical step in research (McKenzie et al., 2009). Research that suffers from methodological problems does not inspire confidence regarding the findings. Analysis planning proves helpful in minimizing errors due to inadequate or inappropriate statistical methods. Data analysis planning should begin with the planning of a program and will guide data collection decisions. Analysis depends on the research questions, data sources and availability, and the intended audience who will use the findings. A comprehensive analysis plan identifies items or observations to be used in answering the research question. It states the level of measurement for each survey question and states what statistical test(s) and/or descriptive data analysis will be used to answer the research questions (Baumgartener & Hensley, 2006).

4.1.14 Apply ethical standards in developing the evaluation/research plan

The health education profession is dedicated to practicing and promoting individual, family, organizational, and community health. Therefore, it is necessary to conduct research or evaluation with human subjects central to the investigations. Regardless of job title, work setting or population served, health education specialists are responsible to the public, the profession and their employer. They are responsible in their delivery of all aspects of health education, research and evaluation, and professional preparation. With attention to propriety, health education specialists acknowledge the value of diversity in society and embrace a cross-cultural approach. They support the worth, dignity, potential, and uniqueness of all people, and are responsible for upholding the integrity and ethics of the profession. Respect for autonomy, promotion of social justice, active promotion of good, and avoidance of harm is the responsibility of each health education specialist (CNHEO, 1999; Bastida, Tseng, McKeever, & Jack, Jr., 2010).

Competency 4.2:
Design instruments to collect evaluation/research data

Data-gathering instruments are used for both quantitative and qualitative data collection methods. Prior to developing data-gathering instruments, researchers consider the type of data collection that is going to occur. Common data collection strategies include face-to-face, telephone, self-administered, traditional mail, and electronic platforms (Johnson & Turner, 2003). Data collection instruments are designed to answer questions that are being asked by the evaluator or researcher (McDermott & Sarvela, 1999). The various data collection instruments available have advantages and disadvantages, and the choice of an instrument depends on priority, the population under investigation, and the resources of those trying to collect data (McDermott & Sarvela, 1999).

Developing data collection instruments can be arduous and time consuming. In many social service sectors there are existing data collection instruments that may be used or adapted to suit the needs of the evaluator/researcher.

When preparing a new data collection instrument for research or evaluation, the developer should keep the following concepts in mind:

- write an easy to understand and complete introduction to the instrument;
- ask only questions that provide useful information in accordance with a well-developed analysis plan;
- ask the most important questions first (demographic questions last);
- organize the questions in logical order;
- use plain, easy-to-understand language;
- avoid technical terms, jargon and acronyms;
- use an even number of responses;
- randomize the order of the response choices;
- avoid unnecessary graphics;
- be sensitive to the feelings of respondents;
- thank respondents; and
- keep it as short as possible.

(Collins, 2003; Presser et al., 2004)

CHAPTER IV

Key: ☐ Entry ☒ Advanced – level information

4.2.1 Identify useable questions from existing instruments

Existing instruments are useful for investigating similar variables in contextually different investigations. It is not always appropriate to use the entire instrument; however, it may make sense to use previously tested, reliable items selected from them. It is imperative that scales and other aspects of the item be retained to maintain validity, especially for research studies. One can check with the developer of the instrument to ascertain validity and reliability information. Before using items from an existing instrument, it is important to consider:

- if the item is appropriate for the intended purpose;
- is the language appropriate for the population;
- whether a test has been performed using a sample from the intended population; and
- to whom you should give credit for using the item.

(Presser et al., 2004)

4.2.2 Write new items to be used in data collection for evaluation

Depending on the goals and objectives set by the health education specialist, a variety of methods can be used to gather data (Cottrell et al., 2009). Health education specialists may choose to use existing data collection instruments as described above, or develop new instrument items to be used for data collection. These may include survey questions, behavior assessment items, interview questions/guides for face-to-face interviews or focus groups, among others (Baker, Crawford & Swineheart, 2004; Saris, van der Veld, & Gallhofer, 2004). Regardless of the method selected, it is the role of the health education specialist to ensure the reliability and validity of the data collection instrument (Jack, Jr. et al., 2010).

Evaluators must decide whether items developed for quantitative methods, qualitative methods or mixed methods will be appropriate and adequate to answer the evaluation or research questions for the program. When quantitative, closed-ended items are indicated, respondents make selections that represent their knowledge, attitude or self-reported behavior from predetermined lists, scales or categories. It is good practice for the evaluator to acknowledge that survey recipients may have a variety of backgrounds. Respondents should be able to clearly understand the purpose of the question items; therefore, it is best to use simple language. When the question requires respondents to use a rating scale, it is best to mediate the scale so there is room for both extremes. At times it may be helpful to relax grammatical standards if the questions sound too formal. There are several **phenomena to avoid:**

- assumptions that everyone has a common basis of knowledge;
- abbreviations;
- leading questions that demand a specific response;
- questions that use two negative words;
- long lists of choices; and
- recall questions over extended time frames.

(Saris et al., 2004)

Key: ◘ Entry ⦚ Advanced – level information

By contrast, open-ended items solicit written or verbal responses to items that cannot be adequately answered with a single word or phrase. Careful composition of qualitative items is as important as with the preparation of quantitative items. Evaluators ask fewer carefully crafted items that require people to respond freely. When composing qualitative items, the same rules apply as with quantitative items, but the evaluator must also be sure the questions provoke respondents to provide insightful information. As with quantitative item development, there are several phenomena to avoid:

- items that ask a "yes/no" question or those that invite a specific (and often brief) answer;
- being too broad to capture useful information;
- being too specific with probing items; and
- asking too many questions.

(Saris et al., 2004)

4.2.3 ⁞⁞ Write new items to be used in data collection for research

Investigators use the findings from research to test hypotheses concerning specific variables established in the planning phases for research plans. They will have determined why they intend to ask the question in accordance with the purpose of the study and research questions. In general, the same rules apply to the development of instrument items for evaluation as for research. Use language familiar to your audience. Education level, age and other relevant cultural characteristics should be taken into account. Items will vary according to the type of information solicited. As with evaluation, there are two basic types of instrument items, open-ended and closed-ended. Open-ended items provide qualitative information that participants offer in their own words and provide descriptive information. Closed-ended items require participants to choose a response predetermined by the researcher; they may be multiple choice, categorical, Likert-scale, ordinal or numerical. The advantage to quantitative questions in research is that they lend themselves more readily to mathematical operations and advanced statistical analysis (Baumgartner & Hensley, 2006).

4.2.4 Establish validity of data collection instruments

Data collection instruments gather data that will describe, explain, and explore a target population in a uniformed or standardized fashion. When considering an instrument's validity, the researcher should consider content, criterion, and construct validity (Jack, Jr. et al., 2010). Content, or face, validity considers the instrument's items of measurement for the relevant areas of interest. Criterion validity refers to one measure's correlation to another measure of a variable. Construct validity ensures that the concepts of an instrument relate to the concepts of a particular theory (Jack, Jr. et al., 2010). Data gathering processes and instruments should be pilot-tested to ensure they are correctly measuring the concepts under investigation (Brownson et al., 2003).

4.2.5 Establish reliability of data collection instruments

Reliability assesses whether the instrument is measuring concepts consistently. Reliability is an issue of concern for observational data collection, as well as with data-gathering instruments (Simons-Morton et al.,1995). Specific procedures are performed to estimate instrument reliability among data gathering

Key: ◻ Entry ⁞⁞ Advanced – level information

instruments. Internal consistency considers intercorrelations among items within an instrument. Test-retest reliability considers evidence of stability over time. Rater reliability considers differences among scorers of items and controls for variation due to error introduced by rater perceptions (McKenzie et al., 2009).

Competency 4.3:
Collect and analyze evaluation/research data

Once the data-gathering instruments have been developed and reviewed, the health education specialist carries out the evaluation or research plan. The plan may be simple or advanced, depending on intended uses and the needs of the program as well as the expectations of the program planners, funding agencies and end users (Cottrell et al., 2009). It is usually desirable to utilize the most rigorous evaluation model or research design available. However, ethics, cost, political and resource realities sometimes indicate a lesser approach to evaluations and research designs. Fortunately, these less rigorous approaches and designs are feasible and adequate to answer some evaluation and research questions when precision might not be as valuable. The evaluator is always professionally and ethically bound to provide the most rigorous design and scientifically sound data information to the target audience.

Analysis of evaluation/research findings detects patterns in evidence by isolating important findings. It is important for the health education specialist to be familiar with statistical terms to be able to synthesize findings from the evaluation/research. Integration of these findings or combining sources of information to reach a larger understanding often requires use of mixed methods. Mixed method evaluation/research entails separate analysis of each evidence element and a synthesis of all sources for examining patterns of agreement, convergence, or complexity. Deciphering facts from a body of evidence involves deciding how to organize, classify, interrelate, compare, and display information. Well-planned evaluations/research usually align with proven models for operations or study designs.

4.3.1 Collect data based on the evaluation/research plan
Evaluation plans are often facilitated using concepts from discipline-specific evaluation models such as those described in Table 4.2: Attainment, Decision-Making, Goal-Free, Naturalistic, Systems Analysis, and Utilization-focused (McDermott & Sarvela, 1999; Neutens & Rubinson, 2010; Patton, 2008). It is important to consider which models will work best for a particular situation and whether evaluation approaches should be combined or used individually. Models help evaluators when making data collection and analysis decisions (McDermott & Sarvela, 1999; Neutens & Rubinson, 2010; Patton, 2008).

Table 4.2
Evaluation Model

Attainment	focused on program objectives and the program goals, serve as standards for evaluation
Decision-making	based on four components designed to provide the user with the context, input, processes and products with which to make decisions
Goal-free	not based on goals; evaluator searches for all outcomes including unintended positive and negative side effects
Naturalistic	focused on qualitative data and uses responsive information from participants in a program; most concerned with narrative explaining "why" behavior did or did not change
Systems analysis	based on efficiency that uses cost-benefits or cost-effectiveness analysis to quantify effects of a program
Utilization-focused	done for and with a specific population

In addition to evaluation models, evaluation frameworks have been developed to summarize and organize the essential elements of program evaluation. These frameworks provide a platform to perform and monitor evaluations. One such framework is the CDC six step framework developed to help guide program evaluation (Table 4.3). The health education specialist should stay abreast of the availability of notable and commonly used evaluation frameworks. Evaluation standards are used as a guide to manage evaluation processes and assess existing evaluations. The standards outline the considerations that must be weighed in formulating an evaluation design (American Joint Committee on Standards for Educational Evaluation, 2008).

Key: ◻ Entry 〴 Advanced – level information

Table 4.3

CDC Six Step Framework for Program Evaluation

ELEMENTS OF THE FRAMEWORK

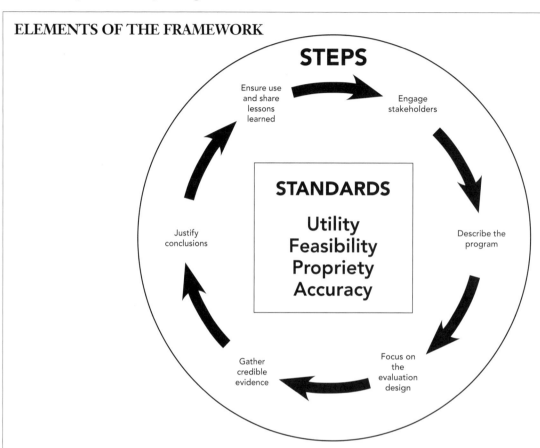

Steps in Evaluation Practice

- **Engage stakeholders**
  Those involved, those affected, primary intended users

- **Describe the program**
  Need, expected effects, activities, resources, stage, context, logic model

- **Focus the evaluation design**
  Purpose, users, uses, questions, methods, agreements

- **Gather credible evidence**
  Indicators, sources, quality, quantity, logistics

- **Justify conclusions**
  Standards, analysis/synthesis, interpretation, judgment, recommendations

- **Ensure use and share lessons learned**
  Design, preparation, feedback, follow-up, dissemination

Standards for Effective Evaluation

- **Utility**
  Serve the information needs of intended users

- **Feasibility**
  Be realistic, prudent, diplomatic, and frugal

- **Propriety**
  Behave legally, ethically, and with due regard for the welfare of those involved and those affected

- **Accuracy**
  Reveal and convey technically accurate information

Note. Adapted from Centers for Disease Control and Prevention. Framework for Program Evaluation in Public Health, Centers for Disease Control and Prevention, 1999; 48(No. RR-11).

Key: ◻ Entry ⫨ Advanced – level information

CONDUCT EVALUATION AND RESEARCH
RELATED TO HEALTH EDUCATION

Research studies are conducted to understand etiologies of health conditions, ascertain effectiveness of programs in terms of stated objectives, explore links between etiologies and interventions or develop and test new research methods (Brownson et al., 2003). Researchers strive to use robust experimental designs whereby the investigator intentionally alters one or more variables or factors to study the effects of doing so. Experimental designs consist of some form of controlled trial. These trials may be randomized where all clusters or participants in the experiment have an equal chance of being allocated to each group of study. Quasi-randomized studies allocate participation in a study based on some scheme, such as an assigned number – odd or even. Non-randomized studies do not use random allocation of participation and groups or individuals are assigned arbitrarily. These non-randomized studies are also termed quasi-experimental studies.

In the absence of an experiment, the investigator may use one of several designs common in health education: a cohort, case control, cross-sectional or ecological approach (Jack, Jr. et al., 2010). Most research plans include research questions and a list of variables that researchers hope to investigate. Data collection methods should be designed to ensure that they measure the effects on variables of interest and should also match data needs, sample size, and resources. Most data collection decisions are dictated by the study design and the purpose of the inquiry.

Study designs in research tend to fall into two broad categories - descriptive or analytic. Descriptive studies (such as cross-sectional) describe the occurrence of disease and disability in terms of person, place, and time using prevalence surveys, surveillance data, and other routinely collected data to describe the phenomena.

Analytic designs explain etiology and causal associations. Analytic studies (such as cohort or case control) aim to estimate the strength of a relationship between an exposure and an outcome. Table 4.4 below highlights the main differences between descriptive and analytic study designs (Aday & Cornelius, 2006).

Table 4.4
Descriptive and Analytic Study Designs

Descriptive	Analytical
Describes	Explains
Is more exploratory	Is more explanatory
Profiles characteristics of group	Analyzes why a group has characteristics
Focus on *what*	Focuses on *why*
Assumes no hypothesis	Assumes a hypothesis
Requires no comparison group	Requires a comparison group

4.3.2 Monitor data collection and management

Data are used to investigate or track progress toward one or more program objectives. Data can also be used to assess the effectiveness of organizations, services, programs and policy. Data collection must be carefully monitored and managed to ensure optimal utility. Prior to the administration of data collection instruments, investigators decide about incentives for participants, respondents as proxies for other people, acceptable

Key: ◻ Entry ⋀ Advanced – level information

response rates, and what documentation or information should be provided to the respondent. Field procedures for carrying out data collections include protocols for scheduling initial contacts with respondents, introducing the instrument to the respondent, keeping track of individuals contacted, and following up with non-respondents when appropriate. Data should be organized in such a manner that they may be analyzed to interpret findings. It often requires statistical understanding and extensive training in order to get optimal use from the collected data. Data collectors should follow all protocols and engage quality control measures when necessary to assure usability of the data collected. Computer assisted data collection requires up-front effort, but can greatly expedite data collection, monitoring, and quality control. It is important that all data are carefully coded and organized into a useable format (McKenzie et al., 2009). Research and evaluation data can help not only to record what changes have occurred, but also to identify what led to those changes (Aday & Cornelius, 2006).

4.3.3 Analyze data using descriptive statistics

Data can be analyzed using descriptive analysis that aims to summarize characteristics of the group of people or the program being studied (Aday & Cornelius, 2006). Descriptive analysis is exploratory in nature and designed to describe phenomena specific to a population using descriptive statistics such as raw numbers, percentages and ratios. Descriptive statistics describe what the data reveals. Descriptive statistics provide simple summaries about the samples' measures. There are a variety of ways to represent descriptive data numerically. Two classifications include continuous data that have the potential for infinite values for variables, or discrete data that are limited to a specific number of values to represent variables. Descriptive data may also be classified as nominal, ordinal, interval, and ratio. Nominal scores cannot be ordered hierarchically but are mutually exclusive (i.e., male and female). Ordinal scores do not have a common unit of measurement between them but are hierarchical. Interval scores have common units of measurement between scores but no true zero. Ratio scores represent data with common measurements between each score and a true zero (Last, 2001).

4.3.4 Analyze data using inferential and/or other advanced statistical methods

Analytic analysis is explanatory in nature and may use both descriptive statistics and inferential statistics to explain phenomena. Inferential statistics are used when the researcher or evaluator wishes to draw conclusions about a population from a sample (Neutens & Rubinson, 2010). This involves inferences about central tendency such as mean, median or mode or any of a number of other aspects of a sample distribution of a population. A variety of sampling methods are common to research and, to a lesser degree, program evaluations. The health education specialist is responsible for knowing terms that relate to using inferential and other statistical methods.

A probability sample, often referred to as a random sample, is drawn when observations and measurements from the total population would be too costly, not feasible, or unnecessary. The term random sample means that each person in a population of interest has an equal likelihood of selection. In random sampling there is no bias involved in the selection of the sample. Any variation between the sample characteristics and the population characteristics is only a matter of chance (Aday & Cornelius, 2006). The larger the sample, the more representative it is considered.

A stratified sample divides a population into segments based on characteristics of importance for the research. Gender, age, social class, education level, and religion are common stratifications. When the population is randomly sampled within each category they are as useful as samples or better than random samples alone, but they require fairly detailed advanced knowledge of the population characteristics, and therefore is more difficult to construct (Aday & Cornelius, 2006).

Non-probability samples are not as representative and are less desirable than probability samples. However; cost, convenience or other factors may prohibit evaluators from probability sampling. To insure that particular segments of a population are represented, an evaluator might use quota sampling by deliberately setting the proportion of strata within the sample. Convenience samples are accidental; however, they are not random. Volunteers would qualify as a convenience sample (Aday & Cornelius, 2006).

4.3.5 Analyze data using qualitative methods

Qualitative research methods include a wide range of data collection strategies (Henderson & Rheault, 2004). The type of qualitative method used depends on the purpose of the evaluation, resources, and use of other techniques. Following are qualitative approaches often used in health education:

- observation/audit;
- participant observation;
- document study;
- interviews; and
- focus groups.

(Henderson & Rheault, 2004)

Analyzing data using qualitative methods helps the evaluator or researcher become more experienced with the variables or phenomenon of interest. Hence, qualitative analysis methods are used to achieve a deep understanding of the issues surrounding items or variables of interest. Qualitative research has special value for investigating complex and sensitive issues. It is extremely useful to achieve deep understanding of how people think about specific topics. It can be especially helpful when the researcher is willing to trade generalizability for contextual detail. Qualitative analysis enables the researcher to describe the phenomena of interest in great detail and in the original language of the research participants (Brownson et al., 2003).

Sample sizes in qualitative data are generally small. Sound qualitative research and evaluation is controlled and systematic. Most analyses involve systematically analyzing content of the data, breaking it into meaningful pieces, and organizing pieces in a way that allows the characteristics and meaning to be better understood. There are several steps involved in qualitative data analysis.

1. *Data reduction*: This step involves selecting, focusing, condensing, and transforming data. The process should be guided by thinking about which data best answers the evaluation questions.
2. *Data display*: This involves creating an organized, compressed way of arranging data (such as through a diagram, chart, matrix, or text). Display helps to facilitate identifying themes, patterns, and connections that help answer evaluation questions. This step usually involves coding, or marking passages in text (or

parts of images, sections of a video, etc.) that have the same message or are connected in some way. An accompanying explanation of what the selected passages have in common is created.

3. *Conclusion drawing and verification*: During this last step, the data is revisited multiple times to verify, test, or confirm the themes and patterns identified. (Miles & Huberman, 1994).

(Jeanfreau, Scharalda, & Jack, in press)

Qualitative analysis is a cyclical and iterative process, with many rounds of investigating evidence, modifying hypotheses, and revisiting the data from a new light. Evaluators and researchers reexamine data repeatedly as new questions, themes, and connections emerge. Evaluators and researchers examine qualitative data to identify:

- patterns, recurring themes, similarities, and differences;
- ways in which patterns (or lack thereof) help answer evaluation questions;
- deviations from patterns and possible explanations for divergence;
- interesting or particularly insightful stories;
- specific language people use to describe phenomena;
- to what extent patterns are supported by past studies or other evaluations (and if not, what might explain the differences); and
- to what extent patterns suggest that additional data needs to be collected.

(Malterud, 2001)

There are several software companies that have produced products that aid in the data management and analysis of qualitative data; however, many evaluators and researchers may still use paper and pen. ATLAS.ti, AnSWR, and NVivo 8 are software packages used for qualitative analysis (Bringer, Johnston, & Brackenridge, 2006; Hwang, 2008).

4.3.6   Apply ethical standards in collecting and analyzing data

When planning and conducting research or evaluation, health education specialists do so in accordance with federal and state laws and regulations, organizational and institutional policies, and professional standards. The Coalition of National Health Education Organizations (CNHEO) provides health education specialists engaged in research or evaluation guidelines for ethical behavior in Article V of the Code of Ethics for the Health Education Profession. Article V outlines the health education specialist's responsibility in research and evaluation (CNHEO, 1999). See Sections 1-7 of the CNHEO Article V below:

Section 1: Health education specialists support principles and practices of research and evaluation that do no harm to individuals, groups, society, or the environment.

Section 2: Health education specialists ensure that participation in research is voluntary and is based upon the informed consent of the participants.

Section 3: Health education specialists respect the privacy, rights, and dignity of research participants, and honor commitments made to those participants.

Section 4: Health education specialists treat all information obtained from participants as confidential unless otherwise required by law.

Section 5: Health education specialists take credit, including authorship, only for work they have actually performed and give credit to the contributions of others.

Section 6: Health education specialists who serve as research or evaluation consultants discuss their results only with those to whom they are providing service, unless maintaining such confidentiality would jeopardize the health or safety of others.

Section 7: Health education specialists report the results of their research and evaluation objectively, accurately, and in a timely fashion.

(CNHEO, 1999)

Institutions, such as universities and hospitals, involved in conducting research that includes human subjects are required to establish an Institutional Review Board (IRB). The IRB functions to protect human subjects involved in research (McDermott & Sarvela, 1999; Neutens & Rubinson, 2010). Since evaluations may have similar ethical considerations, an IRB review and approval is often desired or required prior to data collection (McKenzie et al., 2008). An IRB is at times referred to as an independent ethics committee or a committee that has been formally designated to approve, monitor, and review biomedical and behavioral research involving humans. This type of monitoring and oversight is designed to protect the rights and welfare of the research participants. An IRB performs critical oversight functions for research conducted on human subjects that are scientific, ethical, and regulatory.

Aside from the literature, other forms of secondary data, such as national surveillance data, hospital discharge data, and insurance claim data is appropriate for health education specialists to use to measure the impact of a program or policy on variables of interest. Special attention should be given to legal issues that will affect data sharing with regard to Health Insurance Portability and Accountability Act (HIPAA) laws (PL 104-102), informed consent and commitments to confidentiality (McKenzie et al., 2008). The HIPAA "Privacy Rule" establishes conditions when protected health information may be used for research or program evaluation. Under the Privacy Rule, investigators are permitted information for research with individual authorization, or for limited circumstances without individual authorization (CDC, 2003b).

Competency 4.4:
Interpret results of the evaluation/research

The ability of a health education specialist to interpret results from their own and others' evaluations/research is essential. Uncovering facts regarding a program's performance is not sufficient to draw evaluative conclusions. Interpretation is the effort of figuring out what the findings mean and is part of the overall effort to understand the evidence gathered (CDC, 1999). Ideally health education specialists incorporate evaluation/research findings and scientific evidence into decision-making, policy development and the implementation of programs. The evidence comes from carefully planned reviews of research and evaluation processes (Brownson et al., 2003). Programs steeped in the principles of evidence-based practice have gained favor among professionals practicing health education. Evidence-based practice uses epidemiological insight while studying and applying research, clinical, and public health experience, practice, programs and policies (Anderson et al., 2005). Whatever the source or format, evidence must be interpreted to determine the practical significance of what has been learned. Interpretations draw on information and perspectives that stakeholders bring to evaluation inquiry and can be strengthened through active participation or interaction (CDC, 1999).

Key: ◻ Entry ⑊ Advanced – level information

4.4.1 Compare results to evaluation/research questions

Health education specialists conducting research or evaluation should compare the results of their investigations against the previously developed research/evaluation questions. The questions asked reflect the values held by stakeholders, and those values provide a basis for forming judgments concerning program performance. In practice, when stakeholders articulate and negotiate their values, these become the standards for judging whether a given program's performance will, for example, be considered successful, adequate, or unsuccessful. The evaluation and research questions generated early in the process reflect the stakeholders' values. When operationalized, these standards establish a comparison by which the program can be judged. Data collection methods and analyses determine the probability that findings are not due to chance. The results of the evaluation/research can provide a narrative of experiences, as well as strengths and weaknesses of the investigations. Properly interpreting results will put valuable information in perspective, enabling the evaluator/researcher to compare results and findings to the expected outcomes of stakeholders.

4.4.2 Compare results to other findings

Health education specialists serving as researchers/evaluators should describe, in writing, the results of data analyses clearly so that they can be compared to other programs or studies. Results and statistical data that are appropriately presented provide health education specialists with comparable findings. Findings might be compared to previous reports on the same priority population or with similar programs through parallel studies, surveillance data, online databases, and investigations reported in peer-reviewed articles. A variety of techniques can be used to compare data from different sources (Neutens & Rubinson, 2010). Data comparisons are often presented graphically in tables, figures, bar or line graphs, and pie charts. These graphics should have titles and notes that clarify the meaning of the data presented and tie the graphic presentation to the text (McDermott & Sarvela, 1999; Neutens & Rubinson, 2010). Comparing and contrasting findings with other published literature is useful information for stakeholders and evaluators to consider.

4.4.3 Propose possible explanations of findings

Lessons learned throughout the course of an evaluation or research do not automatically translate into informed decision-making and appropriate action. Deliberate effort is needed to ensure that the processes and findings are used and disseminated appropriately. Understanding and being able to clearly articulate the findings of an evaluation/research investigation provides stakeholders the perspective necessary to make judgments concerning its merit, worth, or significance. Five elements are critical for ensuring use of an evaluation including design, preparation, feedback, follow-up, and dissemination (CDC, 2010). They are:

- design, which refers to how the questions, methods, and overall processes are constructed;
- preparation, which refers to the steps taken to rehearse eventual use of the findings;
- feedback, which is the communication that occurs among all parties;
- follow-up, which refers to the technical and emotional support that users need during the evaluation and after they receive evaluation findings; and
- dissemination, which is the process of communicating either the procedures or the lessons learned from an evaluation to relevant audiences in a timely, unbiased, and consistent fashion.

(CDC, 2010)

Key: ■ Entry ＼＼ Advanced – level information

4.4.4 Identify possible limitations of findings

Even under the best of circumstances, the findings from evaluation and research are subject to systematic error in the sampling, design, implementation, or analysis that compromises the results to some degree. Often this error is referred to as bias. Confounding variables (or factors) are extraneous variables outside the scope of the intervention that can impact the results (Jack , Jr. et al., 2010). In other words, there were variables that affected results that were not accounted for in the study design. Health education specialists need to be able to evaluate sources of error in evaluation or research critically in order to make sense of scientific reports as well as popular media. Health education specialists should be able to identify research errors such as sampling errors, lack of precision, and variability in measurement. They should also be able to spot systematic errors such as selection bias, instrumentation bias, and other internal threats to validity (Friis & Sellars, 2009).

4.4.5 Develop recommendations based on results

Recommendations are actions for consideration resulting from evaluation or research. They help program staff improve programs, make decisions about program operations and move toward program goals. Forming recommendations is a distinct element of program evaluation that requires information beyond what is necessary to form judgments regarding program performance. Recommendations for continuing, expanding, redesigning, or terminating a program are separate from judgments regarding a program's effectiveness. In order to make recommendations, information concerning the context, particularly organizational context in which programmatic decisions will be made, should guide the process. Recommendations that lack sufficient evidence or those that are not aligned with stakeholders' values can undermine an evaluation's credibility. By contrast, an evaluation can be strengthened by recommendations that anticipate political sensitivities of intended users and highlight areas that users can control or influence. Sharing draft recommendations, soliciting reactions from multiple stakeholders and presenting options instead of directive advice increase the likelihood that recommendations will be relevant and well-received (CDC, 2010).

Competency 4.5:
Apply findings from evaluation/research

Findings from evaluation and research can be applied based on the intention of the user. Evaluators should make certain stakeholders have an opportunity to carefully review and discuss findings before applying recommendations to programs or policy. Evaluators translate recommendations to action plans, including who is going to do what about the program and by when. Stakeholders will likely require various reports that may include an executive summary with an explanation of the evaluation goals, methods, and analysis procedures; listing of conclusions and recommendations; and any relevant attachments, including evaluation questionnaires, interview guides, etc. The evaluator may deliver the results in the form of a presentation accompanied by an overview of the report. Evaluators should be sure to record details of the evaluation plan that can be referenced as needed in the future.

Key: ▢ Entry ⦚ Advanced – level information

4.5.1 Communicate findings to stakeholders

An evaluation or research report is the typical form of communication used to disseminate the outcome of the plan set forth by the evaluation or research planners (Neutens & Rubinson, 2010). Although reports take on different styles, it is important for the document to provide user-friendly information to the stakeholders involved (CDC, 2010).

Dissemination is the process of communicating procedures, findings or the lessons learned from an evaluation to relevant audiences in a timely, unbiased, and consistent fashion. Like other elements of the evaluation, the reporting strategy should be discussed in advance with intended users and other stakeholders. Such consultation ensures that the information needs of relevant audiences will be met. Planning effective communication also requires considering the timing, style, tone, message source, vehicle, and format of information products. Regardless of how reports are constructed, the goal for dissemination is to achieve full disclosure and impartial reporting. Developing a checklist of items to consider in creating a tailored evaluation report may help to direct the report content for the audience, explaining the focus of the evaluation, its limitations, strengths and weaknesses (Issel, 2009).

Reporting or communicating research involves detailed documentation. It is often prepared with the intention to publish findings in professional peer reviewed literature for use by other investigators. Although a report may be developed to meet the needs of stakeholders, typically the first part of the report includes an introduction (Neutens & Rubinson, 2010). This may include the front matter (such as the title of the program, names of the evaluators or researchers, and date of the report) and the executive summary (McDermott & Sarvela, 1999). It should also include an explanation of the program's background and the health related and/or other problems addressed by the program (Neutens & Rubinson, 2010).

The second part of the report, the literature review, may include an explanation of relevant studies and an understanding of the background for the study. The literature review will also relate to the purpose of the study, research questions, hypotheses, and the target population. It will provide a theoretical orientation, which may also provide the framework for the review (Neutens & Rubinson, 2010).

The methodology section describes how the evaluation or research plan was carried out. It includes an overview of the procedures, subjects, and data-gathering instruments used in the study (Neutens & Rubinson, 2010). The data analysis plan is often described within the methodology section.

The results section presents evidence tested against the stated hypotheses or research questions, presents the statistical findings, and also includes a discussion of what the findings mean. Findings should be presented in factual and descriptive terms to meet the needs of the intended audience. The results are often communicated in words, numbers, and statistics. The discussion of the data findings typically provides interpretation, implications, and application to practice (Neutens & Rubinson, 2010).

The final portion of the written report may include conclusions, recommendations, or a summary (Neutens & Rubinson, 2010; McDermott & Sarvela, 1999). This section is the part of the report most likely to be read by the stakeholders (Jack, Jr. et al., 2010). The conclusions indicate whether the analysis supports the hypothesis and often includes recommendations for future research and new research questions. The summary briefly restates the problems, procedures and principal findings (Neutens & Rubinson, 2010).

Key: ☐ Entry ⋀⋀ Advanced – level information

4.5.2 ＼＼ Evaluate feasibility of implementing recommendations from evaluation

Robust evaluation designs that utilize randomized control trials, cohort studies and case control/comparison studies provide evaluators and stakeholders with confidence in the validity of the evaluation. These designs can provide recommendations that may be generalized to other similar scenarios. However, most recommendations derived from program evaluation will be specific to the program itself and directed at programmers and stakeholders either involved in the effort or affected by it. The feasibility of implementing recommendations from evaluations depends on cost, other resources, time, politics, and other contextual factors. Programs planned with an evaluation plan and developed with provisions for flexibility allow for early adjustments in programming that may have the potential to maximize desired effects or minimize costs. With sufficient time and strong stakeholder support, feedback on program processes and impacts can serve to improve programming, and improve feasibility of implementing recommendations.

4.5.3 Apply evaluation findings in policy analysis and program development

Current trends indicate the profession of health education is moving towards more involvement in policy and environmental change. As health education specialists engage in the work of policy analysis and program development, they need to come armed with evaluative findings. Policy analysis is defined as the use of any evaluative research to improve or legitimate the practical implications of a policy-oriented program. Among policy-makers, program evaluation is performed when the policy is fixed or unchangeable. However, policy analysis is carried out when there is still a chance that the policy can be revised.

Health impact assessments (HIAs) are used to objectively evaluate the potential health effects of a project or policy before it is developed or implemented. HIAs can provide recommendations to increase positive health outcomes and minimize adverse health outcomes. The HIA framework is used to bring potential public health impacts and considerations to the decision-making process for plans, projects, and policies that fall outside traditional public health arenas, such as transportation and land use.

The major steps in conducting an HIA include :
- screening to identify projects or policies for which an HIA would be useful;
- scoping to identify which health effects to consider;
- assessing risks and benefits to identify which people may be affected and how they may be affected;
- developing recommendations to suggest changes to proposals to promote positive or mitigate adverse health effects;
- reporting to present the results to decision-makers; and
- evaluating to determine the effect of the HIA on the decision.

(Kemm, Parry, & Palmer, 2004)

4.5.4 ＼＼ Disseminate research findings through professional conference presentations

Health education specialists contribute to the profession and to the professional development of other health education specialists by sharing their research/evaluation findings. A common way to disseminate the research findings is through presentations at local, state, national and international health-related conferences.

Key: ⬛ Entry ＼＼ Advanced – level information

Presentations encourage dialog about the processes and outcomes related to evaluation/research. Often, abstracts and objectives of the presentations are required to facilitate a peer-reviewed process for selecting the presentations that appear in conference programs. Conference sessions may include poster sessions, breakout sessions (session time is shared with other speakers), concurrent sessions (session time is dedicated to one presentation), and keynote sessions. If a research/evaluation study will have a major impact in health education, the investigator may be asked to be a keynote speaker.

Key: ◻ Entry ⋀ Advanced – level information

CHAPTER V

Area of Responsibility V
Administer and Manage Health Education

5.1: Manage fiscal resources
Sub-competencies:

5.1.1 ▌▌Identify fiscal and other resources
5.1.2 ▌▌Prepare requests/proposals to obtain fiscal resources
5.1.3 ▌▌Develop budgets to support health education efforts
5.1.4 ▌▌Manage program budgets
5.1.5 ▌▌Prepare budget reports
5.1.6 ▌▌Demonstrate ethical behavior in managing fiscal resources

5.2: Obtain acceptance and support for programs
Sub-competencies:

5.2.1 ▌▌Use communication strategies to obtain program support
5.2.2 ▌▌Facilitate cooperation among stakeholders responsible for health education
5.2.3 ▌▌Prepare reports to obtain/maintain program support
5.2.4 ▌▌Synthesize data for purposes of reporting
5.2.5 Provide support for individuals who deliver professional development opportunities
5.2.6 Explain how program goals align with organizational structure, mission, and goals

5.3: Demonstrate leadership
Sub-competencies:

5.3.1 Conduct strategic planning
5.3.2 Analyze an organization's culture in relationship to health education goals
5.3.3 ▌▌Promote collaboration among stakeholders
5.3.4 Develop strategies to reinforce or change organizational culture to achieve health education goals
5.3.5 Comply with existing laws and regulations
5.3.6 Adhere to ethical standards of the profession
5.3.7 Facilitate efforts to achieve organizational mission
5.3.8 Analyze the need for a systems approach to change
5.3.9 Facilitate needed changes to organizational cultures

5.4: Manage human resources
Sub-competencies:

5.4.1 Develop volunteer opportunities
5.4.2 Demonstrate leadership skills in managing human resources

Key: ◻ Entry ▌▌ Advanced – level information

5.4.3   Apply human resource policies consistent with relevant laws and regulations

5.4.4   Evaluate qualifications of staff and volunteers needed for programs

5.4.5   Recruit volunteers and staff

5.4.6   ℕ Employ conflict resolution strategies

5.4.7   Apply appropriate methods for team development

5.4.8   Model professional practices and ethical behavior

5.4.9   ℕ Develop strategies to enhance staff and volunteers' career development

5.4.10   ℕ Implement strategies to enhance staff and volunteers' career development

5.4.11   Evaluate performance of staff and volunteers

5.5: Facilitate partnerships in support of health education
Sub-competencies:

5.5.1   ℕ Identify potential partners

5.5.2   ℕ Assess capacity of potential partner(s) to meet program goals

5.5.3   Facilitate partner relationship(s)

5.5.4   ℕ Elicit feedback from partner(s)

5.5.5   ℕ Evaluate feasibility of continuing partnership

The Role

Health education specialists are broadly trained to work as systems thinkers with individuals, groups, and communities, and as a result, they can effectively function in multiple roles within the larger context of their institutions or other environments (NCHEC et al., 2010c). The boundaries between the entry- and advanced-levels become permeable when communities, groups, or organizations have roles to fill and few individuals are well-trained and credentialed.

While some administrative functions may fall to the entry-level health education specialist, administration is generally a function of the more advanced-level individual. Health education specialists often become program managers or supervisors of other health education specialists or teams of allied health professionals. Good management incorporates effective leadership skills with managing fiscal resources, task assignments, and performance evaluation. Supervisors obtain acceptance and support for programs from stakeholders such as higher-level management or staff. This role requires effective communication skills, organizational knowledge, and objectivity. Because of their broad training and their understanding of individuals and communities, health education specialists can be effective managers who consider potential partnerships in the larger context of their institution or environment (NCHEC et al., 2010a).

Settings

The following text describes how administering programs is used in different practice settings (NCHEC et al., 2010a).

Community Setting. Health education specialists in a community setting may be responsible for managing a program involving several health education specialists and outreach workers who provide programs and explain health agency initiatives. Advanced-level health education specialists may find themselves providing support for or aligning organizational structure with multiple divisions of their local public health departments, such as mental health services, environmental health services, or health planning efforts.

School (K-12) Setting. In addition to managing students in the classroom, health education specialists in the school setting find themselves identifying and securing fiscal resources to support coordinated school health programs. Serving as curriculum coordinators or project directors, health education specialists may manage curricular and budgetary issues for the school health program, and may work with school health advisory councils in obtaining acceptance and support for content areas to be addressed in the curriculum. A frequent responsibility of the practicing health education specialist is the supervision of pre-service interns (student teachers). As curriculum specialists or program heads, health education specialists serve as team leaders to promote comprehensive health education in their school, throughout the school district, and at the state level.

Health Care Settings. Health education specialists may be the managers of professional development programs in major medical complexes, nursing homes, or transitional facilities. The ability to communicate and facilitate partnerships with a variety of medical professionals, aides, volunteers, clients and family, or community members is very important in this setting. Planning programs that contribute to institutional maintenance of accreditation and compliance with government regulations may also be the task of the health education specialist, who may supervise institutional service learning activities that augment staff efforts.

Business/Industry Setting. In this setting, a health education specialist may lead or be part of a team as a coordinator for an employee assistance program or director of a multi-staff health promotion effort. As an employee, a health education specialist may also supervise or provide support for employed staff, contracted staff, or volunteers in health promotion programs (e.g., smoking cessation, stress management, substance misuse, and weight loss).

College/University Setting. Health education specialists in the college/university setting may be involved in a variety of administrative responsibilities, including coordination of professional preparation programs and chairing of an academic department. In this role, the health education specialists must develop and manage the program budgets. Professional preparation programs also have to align their program goals with the college/university's mission and goals. Responsibilities also might include coordinating and supervising student internships, analyzing the program's curriculum for appropriate goals and objectives, and chairing or facilitating committees.

University Health Services Setting. Health education specialists in the university health services setting may coordinate special campus events, develop campus health initiatives, arrange for campus screenings by other agencies, or develop health education programs for priority populations within the university community. Health education specialists in the college or university setting may also administer health education/promotion programs, or in some cases, the health services center itself. In this role, they must be able to plan, organize the center, administer personnel, secure funds, and manage fiscal resources.

Key: ☐ Entry ▲ Advanced – level information

Key Terms

O➤ **Coalitions** are groups of individuals in an alliance who represent various organizations from within the community who agree to work together toward a common goal (McKenzie, et al., 2009).

O➤ **Culture** can be defined as the combination of thoughts, communications, actions, customs, beliefs, values, and institutions of a group—racial, ethnic, or social—that define how they receive information and how they react to the information that is received (USDHHS, 2001).

O➤ **Cultural competency** is the organization's or individual's capacity to engage effectively within the cultural context of the priority population (USDHHS, 2001).

O➤ **Goals** can be defined as broad statements of intent that provide directions related to where the organization or program should direct its efforts.

O➤ **Ecological approaches** utilize the various dimensions, (e.g., physical, social, and cultural) to affect behavior change. Ecological perspectives take into consideration five levels of influence on health behavior: intrapersonal (individual), interpersonal (group), institutional, community, and public policy (Cottrell, et al., 2009).

O➤ **Mission statements** are concrete, outcome-oriented statements that provide information about the overarching goals of an organization in a broad context (University of Wisconsin, 2009).

O➤ **Organizational Development (OD)** is a term that encompasses strategies and interventions that focus on building capacities and well-being within groups and organizations to achieve maximum effectiveness and efficiency. It includes team building, organizational design, fostering strong and ethical organizational cultures, intergroup relations, group problem solving, and managing organizational change (Robbins & Judge, 2008).

O➤ **Strategic planning** consists of the process of developing strategies to reach a defined set of objectives designed to fulfill the mission of an organization (Kreuter, et al., 2003).

Competency 5.1:
Manage fiscal resources

Health education specialists often have to secure and manage fiscal resources. Skills such as completing funding searches, writing and submitting grants, budgeting, and management of resources are often required of health education specialists in many different settings.

Key: ▢ Entry ⋀⋀ Advanced – level information

ADMINISTER AND MANAGE HEALTH EDUCATION

5.1.1 ⅏ Identify fiscal and other resources

Health education specialists, especially at advanced-levels, may have the responsibility of securing and managing resources for programmed activities. Resources may be procured through participant fees, third-party support, cost sharing, organizational sponsorship, grants and gifts, and a combination of the various sources (McKenzie, et al., 2009). Each source may have different rules that apply to obtaining and using funds. Therefore, health education specialists must understand the policies, rules, and laws that govern these processes.

Health education specialists must also be aware of potential sources of funding that are likely to support their initiatives. Potential sources may include foundations, governmental agencies, corporations, local businesses, and civic organizations.

5.1.2 ⅏ Prepare requests/proposals to obtain fiscal resources

Funding sustainability may be the primary responsibility of advanced-level health education specialists, which means that they must be forward thinking with a broad knowledge of fundraising and other methods of securing fiscal resources, particularly grant writing. Therefore, health education specialists must be prepared to seek and respond to requests for applications/proposals from prospective funders, and respond in an appropriate and timely manner.

Grant proposals typically contain, at a minimum, the following elements:

- Title page – the name of the project, organization, and key contacts;
- Abstract or executive summary – summarizes the proposal;
- Table of contents – the basic layout of the document;
- Introduction – a description of the problem, its magnitude, and the purpose of the funding request;
- Background – a justification for the request (literature, data, evidence, information about the issue for which funds are requested), and information about the requesting organization's experience with the issue;
- Proposed program description – goals, objectives, activities that are to be performed, an evaluation plan, and a timeline for when the objectives and activities are to be accomplished;
- Resources – such as personnel, space, etc.;
- References – list of cited sources;
- Personnel – resumes and job descriptions of personnel associated with the program; and
- Budget – proposed expenditures with a justification for the requested amount.

(McKenzie, et al., 2009)

5.1.3 ⅏ Develop budgets to support health education efforts

Budgets are plans for the use of funds. A budget serves as a tool to help operationalize a program's expenditure of funds. Therefore, a budget serves as a working document that aids organizations to effectively operate and evaluate the proper use of funds (Fallon & Zgodzinski, 2009).

Key: ▢ Entry ⅏ Advanced – level information

Chenoweth (2007) delineates key factors that should be considered when preparing budgets. Health education specialists should be aware of how others in the organization view the project/program. It is important to also be aware of how recent programs/projects and budgets have performed. Health education specialists should be aware of available program analysis outcomes and utilize input from all staff members when making any decision about the budget. Finally, health education specialists should be flexible and keep everything regarding any actual or potential budget changes in perspective.

5.1.4 ⋈ Manage program budgets

Health education specialists are often responsible for developing and monitoring budgets in conjunction with securing or managing fiscal resources. Budgets provide information on estimated or actual revenues and expenditures based upon the needs of the organization. Longest (2004) highlighted the relationship between the evaluation of program performance, fiscal viability, and overall wellbeing of the organization, program, or project.

5.1.5 ⋈ Prepare budget reports

Reports related to project/program budgets are typically prepared and distributed to funding agencies and other key stakeholders on a monthly, quarterly, and/or annual basis. Routinely, reports include information related to fiscal activity during the time period for which it was prepared and total income and expenditures for the budget year (McKenzie, et al., 2009).

Budget reports serve several purposes. Internally, program managers and other organizational leaders utilize accurate and up-to-date budget information in order to make appropriate decisions about organizational operations. However, external stakeholders, such as funding agencies may use the information to assess program feasibility and to assure fiscal and programmatic accountability.

5.1.6 ⋈ Demonstrate ethical behavior in managing fiscal resources

Health education specialists have an obligation to manage fiscal resources in an ethical manner. However, the demonstration of ethics relative to fiscal management is a complex process that encompasses considerations that are more expansive than the legality of specific actions. Part of managing fiscal resources in an ethical manner is being able to understand which programs offer the best value. Therefore, it is important that health education specialists understand, and are able to utilize, the various types of economic analysis – cost analysis (CA), cost-effectiveness analysis (CEA), cost – utility analysis (CUA), and cost-benefit analysis (CBA) (Healy & Zimmerman, 2010; Jennings, Kahn, Mastroianni & Parker, 2003). Health education specialists have an obligation to apply and utilize findings from these various types of analyses to make informed, responsible, and timely programmatic decisions.

Competency 5.2:
Obtain acceptance and support for programs

Obtaining acceptance and support for programs has increasingly become a critical role for health education specialists. Programs require acceptance and support in order to ensure stakeholder involvement from beginning to end. Having acceptance and support from key stakeholders will also help ensure that necessary human and fiscal resources are available in order to maintain program strengths and, if necessary, to address program weaknesses. Health education specialists must work closely with supporters in order to identify ways to sustain programs beyond the project period. Recommended strategies in order to obtain, increase and sustain program acceptance and support are discussed hereafter.

5.2.1 ◖ Use communication strategies to obtain program support

 Organizations that address health education are commonly funded by private donations, contracts, and grants from foundations and/or government agencies. As a result, the health education specialist may be responsible for lobbying, attending hearings, managing fundraising, and participating in grantwriting activities. Competence in this area includes skills in effective communication among individuals, groups, and organizations through written, oral, and nonverbal means (Robbins & Judge, 2008).

Key to program and organizational success is the acceptance and support for programs among internal and external stakeholders/partners. The ability to clearly articulate the aims, goals, and ambitions of the initiative is critical; therefore, the health education specialist should be able to communicate effectively. Effective communication includes developing and selecting appropriate content, formats, and vehicles for formal and informal communications, such as the Internet, telephone calls, meetings, and memorandums of understanding/agreement.

5.2.2 ◖ Facilitate cooperation among stakeholders responsible for health education

Serving as an effective liaison within and between organizations and/or groups necessitates effective "people skills." This cooperation requires ethical behavior, ample knowledge of institutional policy, organizational/group culture, effective communication skills, cultural competence, and objectivity. The health education specialist may aid in the facilitation of cooperation by serving as a representative/liaison and assuring that the primary stakeholders/affiliations participate in, and are appropriately informed about, planned activities both internal and external to the organization. Facilitation requires a familiarity with the culture of stakeholder organization(s), accepted rules of operation for representing their interests, and the ability to respect the organizational structure and modes of interaction.

Key: ◘ Entry ◖ Advanced – level information

CHAPTER V

5.2.3 ⚙ Prepare reports to obtain and/or maintain program support

Health education specialists must possess skills that allow for the collection, synthesis and analysis of information/data for reporting purposes. Furthermore, the health education specialist must possess the ability to organize information in a way that is consistent with the goals, mission, and/or guidelines of the agent from which support is to be obtained. Ultimately the report is developed with the end user in mind. For example, annual reports or quality assurance reports might be required by an organization, while a progress report might be requested by a funding agency.

5.2.4 ⚙ Synthesize data for purposes of reporting

Information/data that is assembled and synthesized for reporting must be consistent with the vehicle through which the process is undertaken and the desired outcomes for which it is developed. Therefore, the health education specialist must be familiar with reporting that is related to human resources, budgets, and program evaluation purposes. This requires skills in data management, analysis, and interpretation.

The health education specialist must be aware of basic guidelines for presenting data in narrative and graphic formats, and be able to effectively and appropriately make written and oral presentations. McKenzie, et al. (2009) have identified basic guidelines for how and when to present reports and data which include: (a) presenting numerical data as graphs and charts, (b) using narrative to interpret graphs/charts, and (c) reporting aggregate data or using other methods to obscure the identities of individuals and organization.

5.2.5 Provide support for individuals who deliver professional development opportunities

Health education specialists may support professional development opportunities through several means. One means includes the health education specialist assisting with curriculum development and/or continuing education opportunities. Health education specialists can also assist with securing fiscal and other resources necessary to deliver professional development activities.

5.2.6 Explain how program goals align with organizational structure, mission, and goals

Program goals and those of the organization should be consistent with the organizational mission. Furthermore, organizational structure, roles, and functions should assure that the goals of the organization are achieved. A common tool used for portraying this alignment is the logic model. A logic model can not only provide a graphic representation of the program, but can also include the organizational mission, the context in which the program operates, as well as external variables that can influence outcomes (Goldman & Schmaltz, 2005; University of Wisconsin-Extension, 2008). Please refer to Chapter IV for more information on logic models.

Key: ⬛ Entry ⚙ Advanced – level information

Competency 5.3:
Demonstrate Leadership

Leadership is the art of anticipating, planning, and managing change (Johnson & Breckon, 2007). Leadership can also be defined as the ability to exercise influence, both formally and informally, in ways that facilitate positive and effective outcomes (Robbins & Judge, 2008).

Health education specialists are called upon to exercise leadership within a variety of contexts, situations, and environments to address health related behavior and systems change within and throughout groups, organizations, and communities. Health education specialists design strategies, lead projects, make decisions, and communicate program inputs and outcomes in order to make sure programs are administered effectively and efficiently (Longest, 2004).

Although administrative functions are primarily performed by health education specialists at more advanced - levels of responsibility, all health education specialists are expected to exemplify the ideals of organizational leadership. Thus, it is imperative that health education specialists conduct themselves according to The Code of Ethics for Health Educators (CNHEO, 1999). Please refer to Appendix A for the Code of Ethics for the Health Education Profession.

CHAPTER V

5.3.1 Conduct strategic planning

Strategic planning should assist the administrative process by analyzing availability of resources in an organization, as well as barriers to implementation of the organizational mission (Kreuter, et al., 2003).

Although planning has been discussed within Chapter II, the scope of "strategic planning" is broader than program planning. However, many of the tools can be used interchangeably. Strategic planning is a process that encompasses individual, group, community, environment, policy, and other systems-level factors that support and/or impinge upon the successful implementation of an organizational mission. The strategic planning process captures the course of managing the constant change that affects almost any organization.

The term is often misused to refer to a specific document, the strategic plan. A strategic plan document is a product of a strategic planning process. The document serves as a road map that can be referred to over time to remind, check assumptions, and measure progress (Kreuter, et al., 2003). Within various strategic planning models, there are four common critical questions:

1. What is the current status of the organization?
2. What is the desired direction of the organization?
3. What steps are necessary to move the organization towards the desired future?
4. What progress is being made?

More specifically, Kreuter, et al. (2003) have specified tools and actions that may be used to implement a comprehensive strategic planning process using the first three questions, with Longest (2004) adding a fourth question that makes the connection between program performance, evaluation, fiscal viability and the overall wellbeing of the organization, program or project. A more detailed discussion of these questions follows.

- *What is the current status of the organization?*
  The answer to this question provides a baseline measure of where the organization stands at the current time. Internal and external relationships are examined in order to assess how well the organization can meet its goals. An internal assessment generally focuses on the strengths and weaknesses of the organization. An external assessment looks at the opportunities and threats outside the organization. One useful tool in assessing the baseline is a stakeholder analysis. This takes into account the following considerations:

  - Who are the key stakeholders for the organization?
  - What do they think of the organization's performance?
  - What criteria do they use in judging the organization's performance?

- *What is the desired direction of the organization?*
  The answer to this question provides a measure of organizational direction. It should consist of short- and long-term time frames, such as one year and four to five years or more into the future. This is designed to capture where the organization should be in a perfect world without real world constraints.

- *What steps are necessary to move the organization towards the desired future?*
  The answer to this question identifies specific steps by which the organization could get to its perfect world ideal, which are described in question two above. It addresses questions such as:

  - What resources are required (money, people, skills, training)?
  - What alternative routes exist, if some or all of these resources are available or are not available, are they available in the quantities needed?
  - What kinds of new or reinforced collaboration may be required?
  - Who will be responsible for it, and when?

- *What progress is being made?*
  Each of the preceding questions has various dimensions, such as funding levels, staff skill sets, new programs, collaborative relationships, and use of resources in the community that are tied to effective outcomes. The nature and complexity of maintaining quality while monitoring costs requires attention to fiscal and human resources, program standards, desired outcomes, and planning with the end in mind. When tracked over time, each of the factors offer insights into how programs are managed, their performance, strengths, weaknesses, and areas for improvement.

Kreuter, et al. (2003) present ten steps that are typically used in a strategic planning process (See Table 5.1).

Key: Entry — Advanced – level information

Table 5.1
Ten Strategic Planning Steps

Step	Activities Performed
1. Initiate and agree on a strategic planning process	• Identify key decision makers. • Determine who should be involved (people, units, agencies).
2. Clarify organizational mandates	• List mandates ("musts") and sources (charters, policies, rules). • Determine implications of mandates for current operations. • Determine whether mandates should be changed.
3a. Identify and understand stakeholders	• Identify internal and external stakeholders. • Determine criteria they use to judge performance. • Determine how they would rate the agency's performance.
3b. Develop/refine **mission statement** and values	• Clarify purpose of organization (why you do what you do). • Respond to key stakeholders. • Define philosophy/core values. • Identify distinct/unique contributions. • List current values and additional values to guide conduct in the future.
4. Assess the environment	• List internal strengths and weaknesses. • List external opportunities and threats. • Identify options for building on strengths and opportunities and minimizing weaknesses and threats.
5. Identify/frame strategic issues	• Identify challenges to the organization that require immediate action, on-going monitoring of strategic issues, or action in the near future. • Identify consequences of not addressing each issue.
6. Formulate tactics to manage strategic issues	• Determine strategies, barriers, and specific actions to address strategic issues. • Develop a first-draft strategic plan listing specific strategies and actions.
7. Review and adopt the strategic plan	• Include key internal and external stakeholders.
8. Establish an effective organizational vision for the future	• Describe the "vision of success" for the organization, based on the mission statement, values, and strategies.
9. Develop an effective implementation process	• List existing programs and services. • Set priorities. • Determine actions, results, milestones. • Decide who is responsible. • Assign dates/resources.
10. Reassess the strategic planning process	• Identify strengths and weaknesses of existing strategies. • Suggest modifications. • Decide which should be maintained, revised or terminated.

CHAPTER V

Key: ■ Entry ■ Advanced – level information

Planning Models

Health education specialists administering programs must be familiar with planning models. Health education specialists will find the use of an ecological framework of particular value in administering programs given that it addresses several important aspects of program planning, implementation, and evaluation. The PRECEDE-PROCEED model represents one of the oldest and most commonly used models in health education and health promotion (Green & Kreuter, 2005). MATCH, Multilevel Approach to Community Health (Simons-Morton et al., 1995); Intervention Mapping (Bartholomew et al., 2006); CDCynergy (CDC, 2003a); and MAPP, Mobilizing for Action through Planning and Partnerships (National Association of County & City Health Officials [NACCHO], 2010) are other examples of planning models used in health education. McKenzie, et al. (2009) offer the Generalized Model for Program Planning, which consists of five integral steps that typify most planning models:

1. assessment;
2. goal setting;
3. intervention planning;
4. intervention development; and
5. evaluation.

The Generalized Planning Model allows for accomplishment of the same major tasks that are presented in the other planning models; however, it utilizes a different approach for accomplishing the tasks.

Logic Models

Logic models, sometimes referred to as roadmaps (Goldman & Schmalz, 2005), not only provide a visual representation of specific programs, but can also include the organizational mission, the context in which programs operate, as well as external variables that can influence outcomes (Goldman & Schmaltz, 2005; University of Wisconsin-Extension, 2002; W.K. Kellogg Foundation, 2004). Please see Chapter IV for a detailed explanation of logic models.

Organizational Assessments and Situational Analysis

Situational analyses are used to assess the context in which programs operate and guide the identification of internal and external strengths and weaknesses of an organization. Internal factors include human, physical, and financial resources, activities and processes, as well as past experiences. External factors include future trends, economy, funding sources and opportunities, demographics, physical environment, legislation, and local, national, and/or international events. The information from the analysis can also help with the development of strategic plans and aid in making decisions about organizations and programs. As such, strategic planning should assist the administrative process by analyzing the availability of resources in an organization, as well as barriers to implementing the organizational mission (Kreuter, et al., 2003). SWOT (strengths, weaknesses, opportunities, and threats) (Longest, 2004) and VMOSA (Vision, Mission, Objectives, Strategies, and Action Plans) (University of Kansas, 2009) are two situational analysis tools that may be used to identify the internal and external variables that contribute to or impede the organization's ability to fulfill its vision, mission, and objectives.

Key: ◻ Entry ⦚ Advanced – level information

5.3.2 Analyze an organization's culture in relationship to health education goals

Organizations are a collection of people who are intentionally organized to achieve goal(s). Organizational culture, the aggregate of affiliated individuals' singular and collective beliefs, values, and norms, is also influenced by its core mission, goals and the internal-external cultural, economic, and political environment in which it operates. For example, a health education specialist working within a government agency, university, or school setting should be aware of its culture, understand the role and function of the organization within the context of other agencies, from local to national, and have knowledge of the government regulations, codes of conduct, and organizational structure.

Planning models that accommodate the assessment of both internal and external influences (e.g., PRECEDE-PROCEED and MATCH) along with multi-system (intrapersonal, interpersonal, community, organizational) **ecological approaches** can guide the health education specialist as they assess and monitor individuals and groups to achieve successful program development, sustainability, and change.

Organizational development is a specific discipline with its own theories, research, and practices. It can contribute much to the management of complex environments within organizations and their relationships to their goals and those of their partners (Butterfoss, Kegler, & Francisco, 2008). Robbins and Judge (2008) have reviewed relevant literature and identified seven characteristics that can facilitate the assessment of an organizational culture and its capacity for change along a continuum from high capacity to low capacity:

1. innovation and risk taking;
2. attention to detail;
3. outcome orientation;
4. people orientation;
5. team orientation;
6. aggressiveness; and
7. stability.

5.3.3 ⫰ Promote collaboration among stakeholders

Informed, engaged, and capable personnel are key to the success of health-related organizations and programs (McKenzie, et al., 2009). Therefore, health education specialists should take steps to make sure all stakeholders understand the desired outcomes, support and contribute to planning, and balance desired results with stakeholder preferences (Longest, 2004). It is equally important for administrators to promote cooperation by providing feedback to personnel. When leading programs and projects, health education specialists need to facilitate participation by individuals and groups connected to the program to achieve the planned outcomes. Establishing positive relationships with internal and external stakeholders helps to match the program to the requirements and expectations of those stakeholders. Memorandums of understanding (MOU) or memorandums of agreement (MOA) can be used to document the expectations of stakeholders and help facilitate effective collaboration among organizations with competing interests.

CHAPTER V

Key: ⬛ Entry ⫰ Advanced – level information

Team approaches, which require and contribute to cooperation, are commonly used in health education. In order to perform effectively, teams need to operate within an environment that engenders trust, has the resources necessary to carry out their responsibilities, has effective leadership, has an organizational structure that supports the work of the team, and offers incentives to reinforce the team's efforts (Robbins & Judge, 2008).

Longest (2004) presents information on the stages involved in building teams. At each of the stages, leadership must be undertaken to address specific issues. The stages of team development and leadership actions that must be undertaken are presented below:

1. Forming is the stage of establishing the team. Team members determine their individual and other team members' roles, respectively. During this stage team members also attempt to determine acceptable and unacceptable behaviors. Therefore, leadership must clearly direct the team, which includes guidance in establishing objectives.

2. Storming is the stage in which team members experience conflict or there is the greatest potential for conflict. Leadership must ensure that processes and structure are established and effectively implemented to minimize conflict.

3. Norming is the stage in which team members reach agreement about their roles and the roles of other team members. Leadership must help the team take responsibility for progression toward meeting goals and objectives.

4. Performing is the stage in which the team has developed to a level where they are able to accomplish the tasks they set out to accomplish. Leadership can begin to delegate more tasks to the team.

5. Adjourning is the final stage in programs that have established periods of time for operations or programs that are discontinued due to other reasons. Leadership needs to assure that team members are recognized regardless of the circumstances under which the team reaches the final stage.

5.3.4 Develop strategies to reinforce or change organizational culture to achieve health education goals

Culture can be defined as the combination of thoughts, communications, actions, customs, beliefs, values, and institutions of a group–racial, ethnic, or social–that define how they receive information and how they react to the information that is received (USDHHS, 2001).

Organizational culture is a neutral term, and as a result, an organization's culture may serve as a barrier to, or an enhancer of, health education goals. The culture can be weak, strong, or transitory (Butterfoss, Kegler & Francisco, 2008). Health education specialists must consider organizational culture in their efforts and develop and implement effective strategies to manage or change it, as appropriate. Five aspects that contribute to the culture of an organization are: (a) assumptions, (b) values, (c) behavioral norms, (d) behavioral patterns, and (e) symbols and rituals that portray its message.

Key: ◻ Entry ⚍ Advanced – level information

Rowitz (2009) presents a systems approach to organizational change that includes:

- values clarification;
- construction/revision of the mission/vision;
- goals and objective identification;
- action plan development;
- action plan implementation; and
- evaluation.

Diffusion of Innovations theory provides insights relative to systems and strategies towards organizational change. The health education specialist needs to be aware of active and passive strategies for the diffusion of new ideas, thoughts, and behaviors and the systems through which they are disseminated (Oldenburg & Glanz, 2008). They also need to be aware of the use of Diffusion of Innovations for reviewing policy and management strategies related to actual or anticipated change within an organization (Greenhalgh, Robert, MacFarlane, Bate, & Kyriakidou, 2004). Oldenburg and Glanz (2008) provide an extensive overview of the Diffusion of Innovations and several other organizational change theories and concepts including stage theory, organizational development theory and interorganizational relations theory.

5.3.5 Comply with existing laws and regulations

Health education specialists must comply with all laws and regulations that apply to the profession and the context in which they practice. The laws and regulations may be executed at the federal, state, or local levels, and they may be in a broad range of categories and specific to the setting, such as laws related to employment practices, and laws related to business operations. For example, the health education specialist within the health care setting must be familiar with the policies related to confidentiality, compliance, and government regulations related to institutional accreditation. Another example in school settings might be the health education specialist's responsibility for implementing obesity prevention activities. Health education specialists in this instance must be aware of state laws, school district regulations, and school expectations regarding time allowed for physical activities and student exposure to nutrition education.

5.3.6 Adhere to ethical standards of the profession

Professional ethics guide health education specialists in the performance of their duties. The CNHEO have worked together to develop a Code of Ethics for the Health Education Profession (1999). The articles of the code are as follows:

1. Responsibility to the Public
2. Responsibility to the Profession
3. Responsibility to Employers
4. Responsibility in the Delivery of Health Education
5. Responsibility in Research and Evaluation
6. Responsibility in Professional Preparation

For more information on the Code of Ethics, please refer to Appendix A

Key: ⬚ Entry ⑊ Advanced – level information

5.3.7 Facilitate efforts to achieve organizational mission

Health education specialists contribute to the fulfillment of organizational missions and visions in several ways. Health education specialists can provide technical assistance, advocacy, strategic planning, and building and supporting teams that plan and implement interventions/strategies. Further, health education specialists can help "discover possibilities" within organizations with which they are affiliated (University of Kansas, 2010).

5.3.8 Analyze the need for a systems approach to change

Organizational change is a term encompassing the complexity of moving organizations towards more effective and efficient operations. It also focuses on the roles of change agents, both internal and external to the organization.

Modeste and Tamayose (2004) define a systems approach as a school of thought postulating that most outcomes are the result of systems, not individuals. It attempts to improve efficiency, as well as quality, by emphasizing how information flows and the interrelatedness of the parts of the whole. A systems approach to change involves breaking the project into interconnected, logical parts and undertaking a study of the parts to determine how they perform (Johnson & Breckon, 2007). Once this occurs, shortcomings in the various parts can be addressed.

5.3.9 Facilitate needed changes to organizational cultures

Health education specialists may often find themselves in situations in which they are required to facilitate needed organizational changes. In this role they may be an organization's staff member (internal change agent) or work in a consulting capacity (external change agent). In order to be a successful change agent, a health education specialist must develop strategies to reinforce or change organizational culture to achieve health education goals as suggested in Sub-competency 5.3.4.

Competency 5.4:
Manage Human Resources

The management of human resources is integral to working with any health agency, association, or organization. The health education specialist has to be aware of the division of work to be accomplished within the context of designated roles and functions within the organization. The entry-level health education specialist may be responsible for building, leading, and sustaining teams/work groups within and between organizations. The advanced-level health education specialist is likely to be placed in the unique position of developing job descriptions, selecting staff for program or organizational roles and functions, forming teams, and guiding other leaders. Both the entry- and advanced-level health education specialists may be responsible for facilitating and supporting the work of people who are internal and external to their direct line of operations within the organization. For example, human resources responsibilities can include managing coalitions, facilitating community based initiatives, and forming/sustaining interagency collaborations. Effectively managing human resources within organizations requires familiarity with participatory forms of leadership that consider diverse work styles, respect the talents of group members, and incorporate the strengths of team members to achieve the organizational and programmatic mission.

Key: ◻ Entry ⦚⦚ Advanced – level information

Human resources for which a health education specialist may be responsible include paid staff, consultants, volunteers, and interns/service learning students. Internal resources, individuals from within a planning agency/ organization or members of its constituency, are responsible for planning, implementation, and/or evaluation of the program. Health education specialists may serve as a community resource and interface with navigators/ natural helpers. Peer educators, staff, and community health outreach workers are individuals with specific knowledge pertinent to educating their peers and are examples of internal resources that health education specialists may interact with. When an agency or organization has a gap between program goals, objectives, or outcomes, an external resource, such as a consultant, may be necessary to ameliorate the gap (McKenzie, et al., 2009), and the health education specialist may be responsible for interactions with the external agent.

5.4.1 Develop volunteer opportunities

The key word within this Sub-competency is "develop." Within an organization, institution, or community, the health education specialist develops and/or coordinates programs and activities that are designed to change individuals, organizations, and systems to promote and support health. An inherent responsibility of health education specialists is creating opportunities for change by using the extensions of volunteers, both internal and external to the organization. Through community outreach efforts, such as the interface between a health care agency and community group or within a church or civic organization, the health education specialist works within and across groups to identify and manage the resources that are available through volunteers.

Many of the groups that are involved in health education and promotion rely on volunteers (Simons-Morton, et al., 1995). Health education specialists must be fully aware of the advantages and disadvantages of the use of internal human resources, such as staff, and external human resources, such as volunteers. Due to the advantages and disadvantages to using internal and external human resources, many agencies use combined resources to achieve desired outcomes (McKenzie, et al., 2009).

Working with volunteers
Minelli & Breckon (2009) identified four key tasks in working effectively with volunteers: recruiting, training, supervising, and recognizing. Personal contact, invitation, and media are ways to recruit volunteers for regular or specific tasks. For volunteers to be effective, it is important to conduct training to help them understand the tasks that you expect them to accomplish. They should also understand the mission, goals, and objectives of the organization, as well as their role as a volunteer. In addition to letting volunteers know what is expected of them, it is important to supervise them in a professional and caring manner, and to recognize them for their important contribution. Wurzbach (2004) identifies the following tips for working with volunteers:

- determine the organization's specific need for volunteers and hours served;
- create job descriptions outlining responsibilities of volunteers;
- use media and personal contacts to promote the organization to attract volunteers;
- interview and train volunteers with the same rigor as paid employees;
- provide performance feedback and evaluation;
- praise volunteers for their community service; and
- recognize their achievements publicly.

5.4.2 Demonstrate leadership skills in managing human resources

Leadership has been defined by many individuals in many different ways. The Dictionary of Public Health Promotion and Education Terms and Concepts (Modeste & Tamayose, 2004) defines leadership as the process of intentionally influencing others to work toward the goals and objectives of the organization, group, or program. In their day to day activities, managers have to influence others to ensure goals and objectives are accomplished. This may be undertaken through transactional approaches that rely on the leaders' promises of rewards and benefits; transformational approaches in which the leaders ask followers to place their own interest second to the good of the group, organization, or society; or a combination of approaches (Fottler, Hernandez, & Joiner, 1994). Regardless of which approach is used, managers must demonstrate the ability to utilize leadership skills in human resource management to ensure stated goals and objectives are achieved.

5.4.3 Apply human resource policies consistent with relevant laws and regulations

Program managers must be familiar with federal, state, and local laws, regulations, and policies that govern human resources. State and local laws, regulations, and policies vary, and all laws, regulations, and policies are updated periodically. The program manager is responsible for investigating and becoming familiar with current laws, regulations, and policies that apply to their area of operations. Current major federal laws, regulations, and policies that apply to human resource management in all organizations include the following: (Fottler, et al., 1994; Sengupta, Calman & Hripcsak, 2008)

- Statutes Prohibiting Discrimination in Employment
  - *Title VII of the Civil Rights Act of 1964*
  - *Civil Rights Act of 1991*
  - *Age Discrimination in Employment Act*
  - *Americans with Disabilities Act of 1990*
  - *Rehabilitation Act of 1973*
  - *Pregnancy Discrimination Act of 1978*
  - *Vietnam Veterans' Readjustment Assistance Act of 1974*
  - *Fair Credit Reporting and Disclosure Act*
  - *Immigration Reform and Control Act of 1986*
- Employment Rights
  - *Family Medical Leave Act of 1993*
  - *Workers Compensation*
- Employee Benefits and Compensation
  - *Fair Labor Standards Act*
  - *Employee Retirement Income Security Act of 1974*
  - *Consolidated Omnibus Budget Reconciliation Act (Cobra)*
  - *Unemployment Compensation*
  - *Equal Pay Act of 1963*
- Other Federal Laws
  - *National Labor Relations Act of 1935*
  - *Worker Adjustment and Retraining Notification Act of 1988*
  - *The Occupational Safety and Health Act of 1970*
  - *Health Insurance Portability and Accountability Act of 1996 (HIPAA)*

Key: ◻ Entry ⚍ Advanced – level information

5.4.4 Evaluate qualifications of staff and volunteers needed for programs

In order to have successful programs, managers must select appropriate individuals to fill positions within an organization/program. Fottler, et al. (1994) and DeCenzo and Robbins (1999) indicate there are a number of instruments that can aid in the evaluation of staff and volunteer qualifications that will assist managers in selecting appropriate personnel. Instruments commonly used by health organizations include: tests, interviews, reference checks, job simulation, work sampling, credentialing, licensing, application forms, resumes, and assessment centers. Each of the methods has strengths and weaknesses. Therefore, each method should be carefully examined to determine which is most appropriate for the category of personnel, level and type of organization.

5.4.5 Recruit volunteers and staff

The recruitment of volunteers and staff is essential to the successful achievement of goals and objectives. The recruitment process consists of planning, implementation, and evaluation during which six questions must be answered (Fottler, et al., 1994).

- •Planning Phase
  - ▪ Why is a position required?
  - ▪ What are the qualifications required of the individual(s) needed to fill the position(s)?
  - ▪ When are the services of these individuals required?
  - ▪ Who will be responsible for recruiting for the position?
- •Implementation Phase
  - ▪ Where will potential volunteers/staff be recruited?
  - ▪ Who in the organization will attract potential individuals to fill the positions?
  - ▪ Determine who will be the appropriate individuals to fill the positions.
- •Evaluation Phase
  - ▪ Determine if the strategy resulted in the selection of appropriate personnel.

5.4.6 ▨ Employ conflict resolution strategies

Organizations can be affected by intra- or inter-personal, intra- or inter-group and inter-organizational conflict. Effective leadership includes negotiating, mediating, proactive planning, program design, and communicating effectively to prevent or minimize its effect on the organization's climate and performance (Hellriegel & Slocum, 2004).

Conflict resolution directs individuals and organizations to see the similarities and differences that exist between them and then leads them to focus on reducing or eliminating differences in order to accomplish goals and objectives. Rowitz (2009) presents an eight step process for conflict resolution that can be applied in most situations:

1. create an atmosphere that is effective for goal or objective accomplishment;
2. clarify the perceptions of all parties involved;
3. focus on the needs of the individuals and organizations as separate entities, as well as the needs of collective individuals and organizations;

Key: ▢ Entry ▨ Advanced – level information

4. build shared positive power;
5. work toward and with a future orientation, but learn from past activities;
6. create options;
7. develop goals, objectives, and activities that can be accomplished; and
8. make sure that there are benefits for all involved parties.

Negotiation between two or more individuals or organizations may be part of the conflict resolution process. Among the models for negotiation, a 14-step model developed by Schoenfield and Schoenfield incorporates many of the strategies from other models (Rowitz, 2009). The steps of this model are outlined below.

Pre-negotiation:
1. information gathering
2. goal determination
3. issues identification
4. analysis
5. assessment of strengths and weaknesses
6. estimation of the parties' positions
7. consideration of outcomes that present wins for both/all parties

Negotiation:
8. setting the opening position
9. setting the bottom line
10. selection of strategies
11. concession consideration
12. agenda determination
13. timing analysis
14. selection of communication modes

5.4.7 Apply appropriate methods for team development
Teams of individuals or groups from different departments or organizations may be brought together to accomplish goals and objectives. In order for the individuals and groups to work effectively together, activities to enhance members' trust and openness may have to be undertaken. Activities to help build individuals and groups into effective teams involve:

- goal setting;
- interpersonal relationship development;
- role and responsibility clarification; and
- process analysis.

(DeCenzo & Robbins, 1999)

Key: ◻ Entry ⑊ Advanced – level information

5.4.8 Model professional practices and ethical behavior

Health education and promotion professionals may come from a variety of disciplines. In order to ensure individuals in the profession act appropriately, a guide has been created to eliminate some of the ambiguity surrounding what ethical behavior is and is not. Please refer to Appendix A for the Code of Ethics for the Health Education Profession and the importance of adhering to ethical standards in the profession.

5.4.9 ▨ Develop strategies to enhance staff and volunteers' career development

Employee and volunteer training and development, and career development are among the myriad of tasks that health education specialists must manage. Training and development are important tasks because:

- they may improve employee performance;
- employees need to continuously update their skills due to changes in technology, organizational changes, and managerial changes;
- solutions to organization problems may be facilitated during the process;
- employees may be prepared for promotion; and
- they can serve as a mechanism for the orientation of new employees.

(Fottler, et al., 1994)

Employee/volunteer training focuses on assisting the individuals with acquiring and/or improving the skills required to perform in their current position. Development is designed to assist the organization and the employee with preparing for future needs within the organization. Strategies to accomplish this task may include, but are not limited to: job rotations, acting as an assistant to the individual filling the position, committee assignments, lectures/seminars, and simulations (DeCenzo & Robbins, 1999). Career development is designed to assist employees with advancement in their career, but it focuses on the long-term career effectiveness and success of an individual versus the more immediate/intermediate effectiveness that is the focus of training and development programs (DeCenzo & Robbins, 1999).

5.4.10 ▨ Implement strategies to enhance staff and volunteers' career development

Employee and volunteer training may be in the form of on-the-job training or off-the-job training.

On-the-job training steps are as follows:

1. tell the trainee about the job to prepare them for the experience;
2. provide them with instructions ensuring that essential information is provided;
3. allow the trainee to demonstrate their understanding of the information that has been provided; and
4. place the trainee on-the-job, but inform them of who to call if they need assistance.

Off- the-job training includes:
- classroom lectures,
- video viewing,
- simulation exercises,
- computer-based trainings,
- training away from the job site utilizing actual equipment that will be used on the job, and
- programmed instruction.

(DeCenzo & Robbins, 1999)

5.4.11 Evaluate performance of staff and volunteers

Evaluating the performance of staff and volunteers is an essential aspect of management and provides organizational leadership with important information. This may include:

- information to aid in making administrative decisions;
- information about the performance of various segments of the organization;
- information on various employees' skills and abilities;
- information about supervisors' abilities; and
- information on management's ability to bring about change in employee performance.

(Fottler, et al., 1994)

There are various methods of conducting performance appraisals including: comparative methods, straight rankings, alternative rankings, paired comparisons, and forced distribution. Human resource departments of organizations generally evaluate the various methods and make decisions about which methods the organization will use (Fottler, et al., 1994). The role of the program manager is to understand the method that is employed by the organization and to undertake the evaluation process in a manner that is sincere and honest (DeCenzo & Robbins, 1999).

The following steps may aid a manager in conducting sincere and honest appraisals that meet the needs of the organization, the manager, and the employee or volunteer:

1. schedule appraisals and prepare for them;
2. provide the individual who is being appraised a supportive environment and take actions to put the individual at ease to increase feedback receptiveness;
3. provide the individual being appraised with information about the purpose of the appraisal;
4. have a two-way dialogue with the individual about the appraisal and allow the individual to conduct self-evaluation;
5. focus on work-related behaviors;
6. provide specific examples to support your evaluation;
7. provide positive and negative feedback;
8. check with the person being appraised to ensure understanding of the appraisal; and
9. prepare a development plan that outlines actions that should be taken in the future.

(DeCenzo & Robbins, 1999)

Key: ☐ Entry ⋀⋀ Advanced – level information

Competency 5.5:
Facilitate partnerships in support of health education

Organizations are finding increased benefits from working in partnership or collaboration with others. Benefits range from optimizing the public's health, leveraging resources, improving reach, reductions in service and effort duplication, a broader-base of support, increased creditability, and increased appeal to funding organizations (Healey & Zimmerman, 2010).

Collaborations may come in the form of advisory committees, commissions, coalitions, consortia and alliances, networks, and task forces (Turnock, 2004). Health education specialists must be able to effectively facilitate the various partnerships in order to successfully execute their duties and responsibilities.

Coalitions, one of the most common partnerships in public health, are groups of individuals or organizations that join forces to address a specific issue or multiple issues (Modeste & Tamayose, 2004). The joining of forces in a coalition, dependent upon its structure, may allow for a sharing of human and fiscal resources that may lead to better overall outcomes.

Effective partnerships require preparation, planning, implementation, evaluation, and sustainment (Healey & Zimmerman, 2010). Health education specialists must be familiar with these activities as they may be called upon to manage the partnership process.

The principles for the creation of effective partnerships include:
- building trust;
- utilizing champions;
- having an end goal in mind;
- using data effectively;
- sharing accountability;
- building beneficial relationships for all partners;
- establishing a plan for operation of the partnership/collaboration;
- making sure meetings have results;
- acknowledging and celebrating progress;
- addressing the relationship of resources to membership equity and inclusion;
- being realistic about what can be accomplished; and
- addressing and minimizing "turf" issues.

(Healey & Zimmerman, 2010)

5.5.1 \\ Identify potential partners
Groups from other disciplines, sectors, and organizations may be involved in addressing the same issue; although, they may not be addressing it from a health education perspective. Human and fiscal resources may be used to create coalitions and collaborations that achieve common visions and missions. Potential partners

Key: ▢ Entry \\ Advanced – level information

include businesses, community and faith based organizations, social organizations, educational institutions, government agencies, and foundations. After organization identification is undertaken, the leaders of the respective organizations can determine if they should pursue a partnership (Healey & Zimmerman, 2010) and help identify other potential partners.

5.5.2 ◖◗ Assess capacity of potential partner(s) to meet program goals

Assessing needs of the community, the capacity and resources within the organization to address those needs, and prioritizing during the strategic planning process improve an organization's current operations, as well as its vision for the future (O'Donnell, 2002). As part of the development of partnerships, leaders must assess the appropriateness of potential partners. As part of the assessment, an examination of the potential partner's history, capabilities, resources, and vision/mission needs to be undertaken to determine if they are a good fit for the partnership (Healey and Zimmerman, 2010). In this role, health education specialists' responsibilities may include conducting assessments, selecting appropriate evidence-based strategies and interventions, and using assessment information to adapt the selected interventions to respond to the priority population's or organization's needs. Logic models may also be used as a tool to facilitate the capacity of an organization to meet its goals.

5.5.3 Facilitate partner relationship(s)

Organizations that embrace a health agenda commonly form internal and/or external advisory boards/committees to assure that community concerns are addressed in ways that are consistent with the values and expectations of their constituencies.

With increasing numbers of organizations and institutions incorporating partner relationships through "community engagement," administering partnerships may be facilitated through:

- community based participatory research;
- interfacing with community based, nonprofit, and/or voluntary organizations that have common agendas;
- working with special interest groups to expand the reach of the initiative; and/or
- providing critical links between community members and institutions/organizations to assure coordination, congruence, and sustainability.

Fallon and Zgodzinski (2009) put forth the following method to identify partners and establish relationships:

- arrange a meeting with leaders from various organizations who have the ability to make decisions;
- have the leaders identify where coordination is required or beneficial and where various resources can be utilized;
- identify common interests; and
- develop memorandums of agreement or understanding after trust and other issues have been resolved.

ADMINISTER AND MANAGE HEALTH EDUCATION

The health education specialist may also contribute perspectives that include factors that are external to the community, yet affect programming or sustainability. An advanced-level health education specialist may play a key role in the implementation of a health impact assessment as a facilitator of community dialogues, conducting assessments, translating technical information, and undertaking other processes that enhance community participation within the broader context of programs and operations.

5.5.4 ⚊ Elicit feedback from partner(s)

Just as health education programs are evaluated, partnerships and collaborations should be evaluated to determine their effectiveness. A plan should be established to evaluate partnership or collaboration activities before they begin. A determination needs to be made about what will be measured, when measurements will occur, and who will do the measurements. Healey and Zimmerman (2010) provide the following as a guide for evaluating partnerships and collaborations:

1. develop an evaluation plan;
2. evaluate progress toward goal and objective achievement;
3. record and track data based on established timeline;
4. report the results;
5. determine the levels of goal, objective and other achievements;
6. use the findings for program improvement;
7. prepare evaluation reports; and
8. broadly share achievements as a mechanism for partnership promotion.

5.5.5 ⚊ Evaluate feasibility of continuing partnership

After partnerships have been evaluated, health education specialists have to decide if the partnership should be sustained. Weighing the results of the evaluation against resources used or saved in the partnership, as well as a reevaluation of the mission and goals of each organization, will allow health education specialists to make informed decisions regarding the utility of continued partnerships.

Key: ⬛ Entry ⚊ Advanced – level information

CHAPTER VI

Area of Responsibility VI
Serve as a Health Education Resource Person

6.1: Obtain and disseminate health-related information
Sub-competencies:
6.1.1   Assess information needs
6.1.2   Identify valid information resources
6.1.3   Critique resource materials for accuracy, relevance, and timeliness
6.1.4   Convey health-related information to priority populations
6.1.5   Convey health-related information to key stakeholders

6.2: Provide training
Sub-competencies:
6.2.1   ‖ Analyze requests for training
6.2.2   ‖ Prioritize requests for training
6.2.3   Identify priority populations
6.2.4   ‖ Assess needs for training
6.2.5   ‖ Identify existing resources that meet training needs
6.2.6   ‖ ◻ Use learning theory to develop or adapt training programs
6.2.7   ‖ Develop training plan
6.2.8   ‖ Implement training sessions and programs
6.2.9   ‖ Use a variety of resources and strategies
6.2.10   ‖ Evaluate impact of training programs

6.3: Serve as a health education consultant
Sub-competencies:
6.3.1   Assess needs for assistance
6.3.2   Prioritize requests for assistance
6.3.3   Define parameters of effective consultative relationships
6.3.4   Establish consultative relationships
6.3.5   ‖ Provide expert assistance
6.3.6   Facilitate collaborative efforts to achieve program goals
6.3.7   ‖ Evaluate the effectiveness of the expert assistance provided
6.3.8   Apply ethical principles in consultative relationships

Key: ◻ Entry ‖ Advanced – level information

The Role

The setting in which the health education specialist functions largely determines the nature of the resources provided. When requested, health education specialists need to serve as a resource for valid and reliable health information and materials. They must be: aware of a variety of community resources at the local, state, and national levels; familiar with computer-based retrieval systems and national **online databases**; and skillful at locating valid information through Internet searches. In addition, the health education specialist needs to be able to evaluate and select appropriate resource materials for dissemination to individuals and groups. Being a resource person also means that the health education specialist must be able to establish consultative relationships and develop the skills necessary for serving as a liaison for networking and for facilitating collaborative efforts (NCHEC et al., 2010a).

Settings

The following text describes how acting as a resource is used in different practice settings (NCHEC et al., 2010a).

Community Setting. Community settings may include work with community-based organizations, local voluntary health organizations, churches, civic organizations, neighborhood associations, and other non-for-profits. In the community setting, health education specialists might be asked to serve on various community-wide coalitions to help identify and implement strategies to improve health. Health education specialists can serve as a resource and link to current health related data (Behavioral Risk Factor Surveillance System, Youth Risk Behavior Surveillance System), research studies, and published best practices in health promotion and disease prevention. In addition, health education specialists can provide suggestions on relevant literature findings, audiovisual materials, educational pamphlets, and posters for distribution.

School (K-12) Setting. A health education specialist in the school setting might participate in the work of a curriculum committee formed to identify and select educational materials that would be in compliance with state legislative mandates and school district policies. The health education specialist might be asked to provide expert assistance to committee members in examining state laws and codes, establishing criteria for the evaluation of instructional materials, and recommending placement of the topic in the overall curriculum scope and sequence plan. After selection of the material, the health education specialist might also arrange preview sessions for interested parents and community members.

Health Care Setting. Health care settings may include hospitals, clinics, medical centers, and satellite health clinics. A health education specialist in the health care setting might serve as a consultant to a community group in developing chronic disease prevention and control education programs. The health education specialist would provide information on successful or evidence-based programs, help identify culturally and linguistically appropriate materials, conduct focus groups to assist in planning interventions, identify expert speakers, and help identify media and other communication channels for disseminating information about the program to the community.

Key: □ Entry ⋀⋀ Advanced – level information

Business/Industry Setting. Physical fitness and nutrition programs are frequently featured in worksite health promotion programming. As a resource person, the health education specialist would be responsible for disseminating information to employers and employees about the program in a timely manner. Health education specialists can identify and organize resources needed for the implementation and continuation of the fitness or other health promotion programs and policy changes at the worksite to promote health. They can identify research data to present to concerned personnel and monitor the plans of those responsible for conducting the program to ensure that its activities match the stated goals and objectives. They can also find relevant posters and brochures about healthy eating and physical activity to display in break rooms and distribute to employees.

College/University Setting. The professor or instructor teaching a course in a health education professional preparation program might have students serve as consultants to a local school district to help district team members assess their coordinated school health program using the CDC's School Health Index. As the students work with the local district, they are sharpening their consulting and networking skills, as well as conveying health related information to key stakeholders in the schools.

University Health Services Setting. The health education specialist in the university health services setting might establish a Web site where students and staff can obtain information about health-related topics, such as nutrition; alcohol, tobacco and other drugs; sexuality; stress reduction; and physical activity. The Web site should contain links to a number of sites containing current and reliable health information.

CHAPTER VI

Key Terms

- **Code of ethics** is a framework of shared values of the profession that help guide the behaviors of a health education specialist (CNHEO, 1999).

- **Consultation** is the process by which the knowledge of one person is used to help another make better decisions (Simons-Morton et al., 1995; Dickert & Sugarman, 2005).

- **Informal consulting** does not require a written agreement or formal contract. This type of consulting consists of acting as a resource person responsible for organizing health education materials and responding to requests for health education information and literature/materials (Simons-Morton et al., 1995; Dickert & Sugarman, 2005).

- **Formal consulting** requires a contract or written agreement between two parties, the client and consultant. A formal consultant is hired for his/her expertise in a particular area for which the client needs assistance, advice, direction, etc. Formal consulting follows the steps of diagnosis, recommendation, action, evaluation, and termination (Simons-Morton et al., 1995; Dickert & Sugarman, 2005).

- **Evidence-based** refers to program or strategies that have been evaluated and are found to be effective (National Cancer Institute [NCI], 2006).

Health literacy is defined as the extent to which individuals have the ability to obtain, process and understand basic health information and care services to make appropriate health decisions (USDHHS, 2000).

Health numeracy is the ability to understand numbers (Peters, Hibbard, Slovic, & Dieckman, 2007).

Online database refers to any systematically organized information accessible on the Internet, which may be used by health education specialists to obtain health knowledge and/or resources for the health education process. An online database may include text documents, citations, abstracts, images, audios, videos, and/or Web links.

Primary data sources are publications of descriptions of research studies or data written by the individual(s) who participated in the studies (Teddlie & Tashakkori, 2009).

Secondary data sources are publications of research studies or data written by an individual who did not participate in those studies (Teddlie & Tashakkori, 2009).

Tertiary data sources are publications such as encyclopedias or other compendia that sum up secondary and primary sources (Teddlie & Tashakkori, 2009).

Competency 6.1:
Obtain and Disseminate Health-Related Information

Health resources are critical to health promotion, and health education specialists are often gatekeepers to them for other professionals and the community. Health information can be obtained from a variety of sources, including professional journals, textbooks, government publications (local, state, federal), colleges/universities, medical centers, professional conferences, public health agencies, associations, and the Internet. Health information may be converted into electronic documents and images including digital audio, video, and multimedia formats.

6.1.1 Assess information needs
Health education specialists should start by defining the information needs of a population, which may include statistics for community assessment or formative research, educational materials, evidence-based programs or strategies for program planning, survey tools for data collection or evaluation, or topic-specific health information. They can use a variety of software and/or Web applications to save and retrieve data and/or literature necessary for program planning, assessment, implementation, or evaluation.

The health education specialist needs to know where to obtain the resources and materials needed to effectively implement programming. Resource materials can increase awareness and enhance learning. Select the most appropriate materials and resources from credible, reliable sources that match audience needs.

Key: ◻ Entry \\\\ Advanced – level information

Regardless of where health information originates, the following are steps for identifying the information needed for dissemination:

1. identify the need;
2. match the need to likely source;
3. pursue lead;
4. judge the quality and quantity of the information found; and
5. organize the available material in a format most useful to the user.

6.1.2   Identify valid information resources

There are a variety of health information resources available to health education specialists. **Primary data sources** include published studies or experiments written by individuals who conducted the study. **Secondary data sources** include articles or study summaries written by individuals who were not part of the study or data collection. **Tertiary data sources** include reference tools (such as pamphlets or fact sheets) compiled from primary and secondary sources (Cottrell et al., 2009; Teddlie & Tashakkori, 2009). As a resource person, the health education specialist needs to be able to locate the information needed and interpret the findings.

Two primary sources for population and health statistics are the U.S. Census and the National Center for Health Statistics (NCHS). The U.S. Census offers quality data about the people and economy in the U.S. It has tables of data, searchable queries and maps of data. The data includes the results from the Population and Housing Census, Economic Census, American Community Survey, and Economic Indicators (http://www.census.gov/). The NCHS is a rich source of information about the health status of the population and monitors trends in health status and health care delivery (http://www.cdc.gov/nchs/). Health education specialists can access data and also health questionnaires for NCHS' major surveys.

Leading government health agencies provide information about health topics and access to electronic or printable health promotion materials, campaigns, or reports. Some examples of these are the following:

- United States Department of Health and Human Services (http://www.dhhs.gov);
- Centers for Disease Control and Prevention (http://www.cdc.gov);
- National Institutes of Health (http://www.nih.gov);
- Government Printing Office (GPO) Access (http://www.gpoaccess.gov/); and
- United States Government's Web site (http://www.firstgov.gov/).

Organizations can also be good sources of health statistics and information. Health education specialists can search for local resources in their community including telephone directories, public libraries, wellness councils (group of businesses interested in health promotion), health coalitions/partnerships, city and county health departments, neighborhood health centers, colleges and universities, and community organizations (Wurzbach, 2004). Other resources include governmental agencies, quasi-governmental agencies, and nongovernmental agencies (voluntary, philanthropic, service, religious, and professional) (Cottrell et al., 2009). Government health agencies are part of national, state, or local structures (McKenzie et al., 2008).

Key: ⬛ Entry ⑃ Advanced – level information

The World Health Organization, located in Geneva, Switzerland, is the most recognized international health organization, and provides a variety of health information and data on their website (http://www.who.int/en/). Some other sources of information are voluntary health agencies and foundations. Voluntary health agencies are organizations that deal with health needs and may rely heavily on donations or volunteers to function (Cottrell et al., 2009). Examples of voluntary health organizations are the American Cancer Society, American Lung Association, American Red Cross, and American Heart Association. Foundations are charitable organizations that donate funds or assets for a specific purpose. The Foundation Center provides program details for thousands of foundations (http://fconline.fdncenter.org/). For example, the Robert Wood Johnson Foundation publishes reports and other documents from its funded public health projects.

In addition, the Internet is a source for many excellent health education resources when evaluated for accuracy and currency. Several authoritative sources of consumer health information exist: MedlinePlus, Healthfinder and Health on the Net (HON). A description of each source follows.

- MedlinePlus is the National Library of Medicine's Web site (in both English and Spanish) for consumer health information. It includes health topics, a medical encyclopedia, interactive health tutorials, and health news. (http://medlineplus.gov).
- Healthfinder is a Department of Health and Human Services Web site for consumer access to information from governmental agencies and their partners. It offers links to online journals, medical dictionaries and prevention and self-care. (http://www.healthfinder.gov).
- Health on the Net (HON) is non-profit medical information portal that links to reliable and trustworthy medical sites on the Internet. (http://www.hon.ch/HONcode/).

Examples of evidence-based interventions that have been proven to work can be found at several Web sites. They provide information about evidence-based strategies (e.g., one-on-one education for cancer screening) or programs, and also may have the packaged program materials available or a link to the program developer's site. Some of these sites include:

- National Cancer Institute's (NCI) Research-tested Intervention Programs (RTIPs) (http://rtips.cancer.gov/rtips/);
- Diffusion of Effective Behavioral Interventions (DEBIs) for HIV programs (http://www.effectiveinterventions.org/);
- SAMSHA's Guide to Evidence-based Practices (EBP), (http://www.samhsa.gov/ebpwebguide/); and
- National Registry of Evidence-based Programs and Practices (NREPP) (http://nrepp.samhsa.gov/).

Health education specialists can also employ professional associations/organizations such as the Society for Public Health Education (SOPHE) or American School Health Association (ASHA) and their Web sites or electronic mailing lists to acquire recommendations and information sources from colleagues in the field. To reach experts on topical issues, professional associations are effective channels. They may have a directory that is searchable by members' areas of interest. Professional associations for health education include Society for Public Health Education (SOPHE), the Public Health Education and Health Promotion (PHEHP) Section of the American Public Health Association (APHA), and the American Association for Health Education (AAHE).

Electronic mailing lists can be used by health education specialists to broadcast messages and questions to other health education specialists via E-mail. Examples are:

- HEDIR (International Electronic Mail Directory of Health education specialists - http://www.aahb.siu.edu/HEDIR/Menu.html); and
- HEALTHPROM (Health Promotion - http://www.healthprom.org/).

Health education specialists can use online resources to locate educational materials for a variety of populations. Some materials are free to health education specialists, while some are available at minimal charge. The following Web sites readily provide health education materials:

- *GEM (The Gateway to Educational Materials)* is a searchable Web site that provides educators with quick and easy access to thousands of educational resources found on federal, state, university, nonprofit, and commercial Internet sites. Health education specialists can select health subjects and refine their search. Its search page is accessible at http://thegateway.org/.

- *HRSA (Health Resources and Services Administration)* of the U.S. Department of Health and Human Services (USDHHS) provides a wide variety of health education materials free of charge. Its search page is accessible at http://www.ask.hrsa.gov/Search.cfm.

- *National Health Information Center* offers a referral source for health information and has a Health Information Resource Database. It is located at http://www.health.gov/nhic/.

Online health information, such as journals, other documents, and databases can be accessed using indexed retrieval systems at libraries. Web browsers access search engines to review relevant records in response to a query for a keyword, title or phrase. The following bibliographic databases offer access to health information in published journals.

- *MEDLINE:* Although this database contains primarily medical journals, many health education journals are also indexed. PubMed is its online searchable interface through the Web site of the National Library of Medicine (NLM). It offers free access to citations from MEDLINE and other journals. Users can search health information by keywords in title, author, abstract, source, and other search fields. The results are provided in the form of article sources, abstracts, and sometimes Web links to retrieve full text documents. This database is free and can be accessed at http://www.ncbi.nlm.nih.gov/PubMed. Full-text articles may require a fee from the publisher.

Key: ◻ Entry ⫶⫶ Advanced – level information

- *ERIC (Education Resource Information Center):* This database contains journals related to school health, school-aged children, and education in its broadest sense. Often, ERIC includes articles from professional journals and documents, which are available online in full text or on microfiche in large libraries, especially at colleges or universities. ERIC documents are materials that are not found in journal literature, such as proceedings from conferences or policies. This database is free and can be accessed at http://www.eric.ed.gov/.

- *CHID (Combined Health Information Database):* This database is produced through the combined efforts of several federal agencies organized by the National Institutes of Health (NIH) and the Health Resources and Services Administration (HRSA). It provides descriptions of health education and health promotion programs in progress at the state and local levels, bibliographic citations and abstracts of journal articles, full-text articles, books, reports, pamphlets, audiovisuals, and other health promotion and education materials. This database is free and can be accessed at http://www.chid.nih.gov.

- *CINAHL (Cumulative Index for Nursing and Allied Health Literature):* This is a database for health education information indexes, major health education journals, and journals from nursing and many other disciplines. The use of CINAHL may involve a fee for subscription. This database can be accessed at http://www.cinahl.com/.

- *EBMR (Evidence-based Medicine Reviews):* This is a collection of databases that offer evidence-based strategies, programs and medicine such as Cochrane Database of Systematic Reviews, The Database of Abstracts of Reviews of Effectiveness (DARE), Health Technology Assessments (HTA), methods and article reviews. Each database from the EBMR collection is a separate file and must be browsed separately. For example the Cochrane Library offers full reports that provide the evidence for and against the effectiveness and appropriateness of treatments such as education and medication. It is located at http://www.ovid.com.

- *HaPI (Health and Psychosocial Instruments):* This database collects rating scales, questionnaires, checklists, tests, interview schedules, and coding schemes/manuals for health and social sciences. Health and psychosocial instruments in this database are used and/or published in literature and often recognize reliability and validity concerns. Health education specialists may use these instruments for assessment and/or evaluation purposes. The use of HaPI may involve a fee for subscription. This database can be accessed at http://www.ovid.com.

- *PsycInfo:* This database includes a summary of journal articles, books, dissertations and technical reports from professional and academic literature in psychology. The database can be found at http://psycnet.apa.org/.

Health education research or practice articles can be found in some leading journals in the field: *Health Education & Behavior, Health Promotion Practice, American Journal of Health Education, American Journal of Health Promotion, American Journal of Health Behavior, Health Education Research, Journal of School Health, Journal of Community Health, Journal of American College Health* and *Patient Education and Counseling*, among others. Along with information collected regularly by government agencies, these are good sources of health information.

6.1.3 Critique resource materials for accuracy, relevance, and timeliness

To determine if the health information source is credible and reliable, the health education specialist should be mindful of the following: purpose of the source, scientific methodology, qualifications of the author, standing of the publication or organization in the profession, as well as the quality of references and sources (Cottrell et al., 2009).

Health education specialists need to be aware of the types of electronic health-related resources available, and how to make decisions about when to use each one based on the information needed. Whether the resource is a bibliographic database or a Web-based information source, health education specialists need to analyze and evaluate the worthiness of the information retrieved, as some information on the Web is inaccurate or untruthful. Health education specialists should look for sites hosted by reputable sources, consider biases reflected in the information, and determine if the information is outdated or misleading.

It is important to evaluate the quality and significance of the information in relation to the needs of the priority audience. When assessing online information, consider the following:

- Who is responsible for the site?
- What is the site's funding source?
- What is the purpose of the site?
- Does it contain evidence-based references?
- Is the information current and up-to-date?
- Does it track users as subscribers or members?

(NCI, 2005)

Some additional considerations for evaluating the quality of online resources are detailed in the Table 6.1 on the next page.

CHAPTER VI

Key: ☐ Entry ◣ Advanced – level information

Table 6.1

Additional Consideration for Evaluating Quality of Online Resources

Element	Application of Element
Web site purpose	Intention of the site consistent with the institutional affiliation and author credentials
Domain name	The URL ends in .org, .gov, or .edu. A site's domain name and extension may offer information about the credibility of the source. Those sites ending in .org (organization) or .gov (government) tend to offer more valid information than those with a .com (commercial) extension
Priority population	Content of the Web site is appropriate for the audience whether consumer, professional or both (Cottrell et al., 2009)
Site's appropriateness	Review of sources and timeliness of information
Site's accuracy	Content of the site is backed by empirical research or facts and verified by expert opinion. References are available for statistics and information. (Eysenbach, Powell, Kuss, & Sa, 2002)
Site's adequacy	Determine if site's research was conducted independently (Doyle et al., 2010)
Site's currency	Health information changes constantly; data updated regularly (National Library of Medicine, 2009)
Readability	Reading level of the content of the site is acceptable to audience (Eysenbach et al., 2002)
Reputable affiliations	Type of organizations sponsoring the site; materials being published consistent with the agency's mission
Author/administrative names	Qualified people writing the information posted (professional credentials)
Author contact information	A mailing address, phone, fax or E-mail information available on the site (Cottrell, et al., 2009)

Key: ◻ Entry ⋀ Advanced – level information

SERVE AS A HEALTH EDUCATION RESOURCE PERSON

In addition to knowing where to find and how to access health information, the health education specialist must be able to evaluate the appropriateness and effectiveness of materials for the priority population, group or client. Resource materials for any program, such as handouts, brochures, fact sheets, talking points, and Frequently Asked Questions should be carefully reviewed to make sure they enhance message appeal (Barnes et al., 2003).

Resources and materials should be selected based on the client/community's needs and the program objectives. When evaluating resources, consider the following:

- Does the resource contain the information that the client/community wants to know?
- Can the client/community understand the information contained in the resource? (Doak, C.C., Doak, Gordon, & Lorig, 2001; Doak, C.C., Doak & Root, 2002)
- Is the information current and accurate?
- Is the format appropriate and the information culturally appropriate?
- Will the resource meet program objectives? (NCI, 2008)
- What is the reading level of the materials?

Materials can also be assessed in terms of **health literacy**. Health literacy is defined as the extent to which individuals have the ability to obtain, process, and understand basic health information and health care services to make appropriate health decisions (USDHHS, 2009). Some consequences of poor health literacy are inappropriate or no usage of health care services, improper use of medicines, poor health outcomes, or poor self-management of chronic conditions (Zarcadoolas, Pleasant, & Greer, 2006). Individuals with lower literacy tend to read slowly, take words literally, skip over uncommon or unknown words, have short attention spans and hide their limited abilities to read (Jacobson, Cucchi, & Morton, 2006). In verbal communication, health education specialists should:

- speak slowly;
- focus on and repeat key messages;
- explain things in plain language (i.e., avoid jargon);
- use analogies that people may already know;
- avoid using too many statistics;
- allow time for questions;
- use the "teach back" technique in which the person has a chance to show that he or she is understanding the messages; and
- use other communication materials or strategies to compliment the interaction.

Health education specialists should assess the literacy and health literacy levels of their audience to choose appropriate materials. For individuals with lower literacy, health education specialists can pick resources that use simple language and have short sentences, define medical or technical terms, and supplement the education with other materials such as videos and pictures (NCI, 2008). Materials that are distributed may require lower reading levels. The materials also should have few multisyllabic words and simple sentences, have few technical terms or phrases, and use graphics to visualize health messages (Jacobson et al., 2006). Educators can use literacy methods like SMOG (Simple Measure of Gobbledygook), Fry Readability formula, or Flesch-Kincaid readability tests to evaluate the reading level of a material. Another government effort to

Key: ☐ Entry ╲╲ Advanced – level information

increase effective communication to the public is known as plain language in materials development. The Web site, http://www.plainlanguage.gov/, provides tools and examples of plain language.

The Institute of Medicine (2004) proposes a model of health literacy that includes four concepts: a) cultural and conceptual knowledge, b) oral literacy in terms of listening and speaking, c) print literacy in terms of writing and reading, and d) numeracy. **Health numeracy** is the ability to understand numbers (Peters et al., 2007) which affect individuals' health care decisions and behaviors. Some strategies to assist people in their numeracy processing is to: present fewer health statistics, reduce the need for inferences and calculations, use visual cues or displays to show numbers and use analogies with which people are familiar. Other strategies include focusing on one numeric idea at a time (one per sentence), using analogies or physical items to represent quantity (e.g., fist as a serving size for fruits), or teaching with stories. For example, in teaching about walking two times a day for 30 minutes, a health education specialist can talk about a man who takes a long walk around his neighborhood after breakfast and dinner.

When reviewing written resource materials, consider the following questions:

- Is the information accurate and up to date?
- Does the material have audience appeal?
- Is it complete? Is there sufficient, too much, or too little information?
- Is it written in a logical, clearly developed, easy-to-follow format?
- Is the message supportive, positive, and personal?
- Does it attract and keep the reader's attention?
- Is the physical appearance (color, layout, print, illustrations) appropriate for the audience?
- Are the graphics simple, clear, and compatible with the text?
- Is the vocabulary appropriate for the audience? Are new terms defined, and has jargon been avoided?
- Is the reading level appropriate for the audience?

(Kickbusch, 2001; Plomer & Bensley, 2009)

The materials should be compiled and evaluated through a quick review process. An Educational Materials Review Form (Wurzbach, 2004) or a modified version may have health education specialists inventory the materials and determine which is most relevant and appropriate for your community group. The form assesses these aspects of the materials:

- form;
- length;
- topic;
- mode of delivery;
- setting;
- target audience;
- language;
- readability;

•scope of the material (national to local);
•pre-test or evaluated;
•availability; and
•language.

6.1.4   Convey health-related information to priority populations

Health education specialists have to present health information to priority populations or communities across different settings. It is important to consider communication objectives and best strategies for the presentation of the data. Some examples are presentations, discussions, lecture, demonstrations, printed educational materials, or posters. For statistical health data, it may be more effective to present graphical data instead of tabulations of numbers in tables for the lay audience. It is helpful to ask people who are knowledgeable about the population for the presentation style that would be best received by the audience. Remember that simplicity is best to increase the understanding of the information. While certain methods are acceptable to one group or culture, they might be less acceptable to others. Therefore, it is important to match the methods to the content and audience needs.   In addition, if time permits, a health education specialist could pilot strategies with small audiences to receive feedback and evaluation of the best methods of presentation.

6.1.5   Convey health-related information to key stakeholders

Key stakeholders are individuals who are interested in the health information. They may be community, business, religious, health agency or other leaders. A health education specialist should communicate with stakeholders regularly to increase the utilization of the health-related information. The presentation methods could include: an oral presentation, a one or two page executive summary, a short report, graphs or tables of data, or an oral presentation with a PowerPoint.

The health education specialist should consider if the presentation will be formal (i.e., at an organized function), semiformal or informal. Some steps for conducting effective presentations are:

1.   prepare for the presentation;
2.   understand the presentation setting;
3.   open the presentation;
4.   use effective skills in delivering the presentation;
5.   end the presentation; and
6.   respond to the audience's questions.

(Wagenschutz & Rivas, 2009)

Competency 6.2:
Provide Training

Health education specialists should have the skills and abilities to analyze, prioritize, deliver and evaluate training provided to interested groups. In this capacity, health education specialists will utilize their skills to develop a variety of training experiences that can address issues ranging from improving self-efficacy regarding diabetes management, conflict resolution skills among youth, car seat safety for children, teambuilding, and strategic planning in the workplace. Regardless of the area around which training is intended, health education specialists play an important role in delivering such training and should have the necessary skills to lead training sessions. Please refer to Chapter III for more information on training personnel to deliver health promotion programs.

6.2.1 ℕ Analyze requests for training
Trainings are delivered to individuals or groups to increase the knowledge, skills, or proficiency in a topic area to help improve job performance. Health education specialists may get requests for training from a variety of different organizations or for in-service training. Requests for training should be collected and assessed to determine if they fit the needs of the organization and produce positive outcomes for participants.

6.2.2 ℕ Prioritize requests for training
Once it has been determined that trainings need to be conducted, the health education specialist may have to prioritize the multiple requests for training. Different criteria may assist in making decisions on which trainings will occur first. Then the health education specialist can schedule and plan for high priority requests. Some considerations in prioritizing requests include the following:

- urgency of the need for education;
- objectives of the training;
- potential impact on the organization or community;
- projected return on investment;
- training design needs;
- size of the audience and/or training;
- costs of the training;
- importance of the requester; and
- projected workload associated with the training.

(Lawson, 2008)

6.2.3 Identify priority populations
Health education specialists should select priority populations for the training. Some considerations for identifying these populations include: who will benefit most from the training or has unmet needs for knowledge and skills, who are the primary stakeholders, and which groups may have the greatest impact on the organization after receiving the training (Lawson, 2008). Past and current training needs assessment data and discussions with the stakeholders for the training can inform the selection of priority training populations. In addition, administrative factors may be taken into consideration as well, including time, budget, and staff capacity.

Key: ◻ Entry ℕ Advanced – level information

6.2.4 Ⅱ Assess needs for training

A training needs assessment is conducted to identify the gap between the actual and desired performance in organizations (Lawson, 2008). The five recommended steps in conducting a training needs assessment are to:

1. identify the need or problem;
2. determine the needs assessment design;
3. collect data;
4. analyze data; and
5. provide feedback.

(Lawson, 2008)

In the identification of needs, health education specialists can learn about the organizational context, perform a gap analysis, and set objectives for the assessment. Next, health education specialists can establish criteria for the needs assessment design and evaluate the advantages and disadvantages of methods. The criteria for choice of data collection methods may be dependent on time, staffing, preference of the leaders of the organization, number of stakeholders, workplace disruptions, complexity of training issues, the validity and reliability of methods and the training audience themselves. Data are then collected through a variety of methods, including interviews, surveys, document reviews (e.g., procedures, organizational plans, reports or audits), proficiency tests, performance appraisals, training evaluations, job descriptions or observations (Lawson, 2008).

Some examples of training assessment questions are:

- What training have you received to prepare you for your job?
- What additional training would help you do your job better?
- What are the most difficult aspects of your job?
- What skills, knowledge, or behaviors do you think your participants/employees need to receive or improve upon in order to do their jobs better?
- What trainings have been offered in the past?
- What are barriers to the training efforts?

In the data analysis step, health education specialists conduct qualitative and/or quantitative analyses and determine some potential solutions or recommendations for training. Finally, they can disseminate needs assessment findings by writing a report or making oral presentations. The data and implications can be shared with the organization and other stakeholders to determine the next steps (Lawson, 2008). Information collected through past training efforts, training needs assessments with the intended audience, training records, performance evaluations, and other organizational data will provide the basis for developing training goals and objectives.

6.2.5 ⬛ Identify existing resources that meet training needs

Health education specialists may also receive requests for information about skills-related training or professional development in health promotion. They can start by evaluating if current training resources meet the needs of the organization. Training resources are often provided for professional development through workshops or conferences from local, regional, or national professional associations. Professional organizations may also offer annual meetings, workshops, distance learning and Webinars (presentations delivered through the Internet), about health promotion issues. Health education specialists can locate training resources that fulfill continuing education requirements for CHES credentialed individuals through the Web site of the National Commission for Health Education Credentialing (NCHEC) located at http://www.nchec.org/.

Health education or public health-related training may be offered by local health departments, colleges or universities, local or regional professional associations, extension services, area health education centers (AHECs) or through national professional associations. Some of these organizations or governmental agencies may also offer online training courses. The Community Tool Box also has practical information and skills for health education. It is created and maintained by the Work Group on Health Promotion and Community Development at the University of Kansas (http://ctb.ku.edu/en/). The Public Health Foundation has a learning resource center that has high quality training and health promotion materials (http://www.phf.org/). It also offers TRAIN (TrainingFinder Real-time Affiliate Integrated Network), a Web-based learning management clearinghouse of distance and on-site training for local, state, or national arenas. It is located at https://www.train.org/DesktopShell.aspx. Materials are in a variety of formats, including print, computer-based and video.

6.2.6 ⬛⬛ Use learning theory to develop or adapt training programs

Learning theories are incorporated into the development or adaptation of training programs to make learning more effective. These theories may provide a foundation for how learning occurs or offer strategies to employ in training sessions. Training based on theoretical principles or concepts may have increased effectiveness. The following are examples of some learning theories that are more commonly used in training.

Adult Learning Theory (Andragogy)
Learning is defined as the process of gaining knowledge or expertise (Knowles et al., 2005). Knowles et al. (2005) outline some important principles to consider in teaching adults.

> Although the advanced-level health education specialist is typically responsible for utilizing learning theories in the development and adaption of training programs, the entry-level health education specialist should have knowledge of learning theories concepts that are commonly used in health education.

- Adults are motivated to learn when they have needs and interests that learning can satisfy.
- Adults are oriented to learning that is life-centered (i.e., based on life situations).
- Experience is the richest source of learning for adults.
- Adults are self-directed learners.
- Adult education considers individual differences as people age such as differences in time, place, and pace of learning.

It is helpful to allow adults learners to be part of the decision making in the planning of learning and ensure the training content is relevant to the participants' work or job. In addition, health education specialists should explain why the participants are learning a topic, explain the immediate value of the new knowledge and skills, and approach teaching through problem-solving techniques to engage the learner when developing training.

ARCS (Attention, Relevance, Confidence, Satisfaction) Motivation Model
The ARCS model is a compilation of guidelines from many motivation theories. Causes of motivation may be either extrinsic (external to the learner) or intrinsic (internal to the learner). The intent of the ARCS model is to provide learners with the necessary time and effort to acquire new knowledge and skills (Gagne, Briggs, & Wager, 1992). The motivational categories of the ARCS Model are presented in Table 6.2 below (Gagne et al., 1992).

Table 6.2
Application of the Motivational Categories

Category	Application of the Motivational Category
Attention	• Capture the learners' interest • Maintain their attention
Relevance	• Know the learners' needs • Provide learners with opportunities to match activities that match their motives for learning • Tie the instruction to learners' past experiences (e.g., analogies, prerequisite knowledge)
Confidence	• Build positive expectations of learning • Provide methods for learning to achieve success in mastery of knowledge and skill
Satisfaction	• Provide reinforcement to learners' successes • Encourage use of new knowledge and skills

Gagne's Theory of Instruction
Gagne presents a comprehensive view of instruction. He identifies categories of learning: a) verbal information, b) cognitive strategies, c) intellectual skills, d) motor skills, and e) attitudes. He further proposes the nine events of instruction that provide conditions for learning. The nine events are presented below (Gagne, 1985). These hierarchies can help with developing the sequencing of instruction during trainings (See Table 6.3).

CHAPTER VI

Table 6.3
Events of Instruction

Event of Instruction	Application to Training
1. Gain attention	Describe why training is important. Ask stimulating questions. Present a problem to be solved.
2. Inform learners of the objectives	Present the learning objectives.
3. Build on prior knowledge	Associate new content with prior knowledge.
4. Present the stimulus	Present the training content.
5. Provide guidance	Give illustrative examples, analogies, mnemonics, or basic steps in performance to help learner retain new knowledge or skill.
6. Elicit performance	Provide opportunities to practice new skill or behavior.
7. Provide feedback	Give immediate feedback on performance during the training.
8. Assess performance	Assess knowledge/skills gained.
9. Enhance retention and transfer	Provide supplemental materials (e.g., worksheets, problem sets, case scenarios, training manual) to reinforce learning. Discuss or ask how knowledge and skills can be applied on the job.

Bloom's Taxonomy

Bloom's Taxonomy relates to the classification of learning objectives developed for learners. He proposes that learning in the cognitive domain should apply the higher order processes instead of lower order objectives that are traditionally seen. Instruction should have higher ordered objectives that are mentally demanding. Table 6.4 presents the taxonomy, skills demonstrated, and examples of verbs for that level of objectives (Gronlund, 1995). Health education specialists can use these levels of skills when writing training objectives.

Table 6.4
Taxonomy and Skills Demonstrated

Classification	Skills Demonstrated	Verbs
Knowledge	Recall of information or major ideas Mastery of the subject matter	Define Describe Label List State Tell
Comprehension	Understand information	Explain Outline Restate Summarize
Application	Use information Solve problems using knowledge or skills	Apply Construct Demonstrate Illustrate Show Use
Analysis	Identification of components Recognition of patterns	Analyze Distinguish Compare Contrast Explain
Synthesis	Relate knowledge from several areas Predict and draw conclusions	Construct Create Devise Formulate Plan
Evaluation	Compare and discriminate between ideas Decide based on arguments	Choose Judge Justify Debate Assess

CHAPTER VI

Key: ☐ Entry ◪ Advanced – level information

Maslow's Hierarchy of Needs

Maslow developed a hierarchy of basic human needs. Each level of needs must be met before the individual can move to the next levels. The levels of needs start at physiological needs and move up to self-actualization. The hierarchy of needs and how it applies to training adults are presented in Table 6.5 below.

Table 6.5
Maslow's Hierarchy of Needs

Need	Application to Training
Physiological needs (food, water, warmth)	• Provide breaks and snacks/meals. • Set a comfortable room temperature.
Safety needs (security and safety)	• Offer safe training environment. • Permit learners to asks questions throughout.
Needs of love (sense of belonging)	• Create a feeling of group dynamics and feeling of acceptance.
Esteem (status, achievement)	• Recognize achievements. • Positively reinforce learning.
Self-Actualization (personal fulfillment)	• Offer work or training that challenges learner. • Offer skills to make progress on long-term goals.

6.2.7 ⚊ Develop training plan

Trainings can enhance the knowledge and skills of professionals and communities. Effective training programs should follow these major steps:

1. determine training needs;
2. set objectives ;
3. determine subject content to accomplish the objectives;
4. select participants;
5. determine the best schedule;
6. select appropriate facilities;
7. select appropriate instructors;
8. select and prepare audiovisual aids;
9. coordinate the program; and
10. evaluate the program.

(Kirkpatrick, D.L., & Kirkpatrick, 2009)

The training needs assessment or other formative research can help with steps 1-6. The health education specialist can determine if it is appropriate to deliver training or if other content experts need to be recruited to best present the training content. Then, the health education specialist should prepare the training curriculum based on training objectives and using appropriate strategies from learning theories to make learning successful. Please refer to Sub-competency 6.2.9 for a description of strategies.

The trainer should take into consideration:

- priority audience;
- where training will be held;
- goals and objectives of the initiative/intervention;
- planned activities for the program; and
- materials needed.

6.2.8 Implement training sessions and programs

Once the training plan is finalized, it needs to be implemented. The implementation plan should involve the following:

- administrative details;
- promotion of the training;
- recruitment of the audience;
- schedules and venue selection;
- training objectives, curriculum and supporting materials;
- assignment of the trainers;
- evaluation procedures and instruments; and
- budget.

(Piskurich, Beckschi, & Hall, 1999)

Although one individual or group may take the lead in a training event, several individuals or groups could be involved in the marketing and arrangements related to the training event (McKenzie et al., 2009).

6.2.9 Use a variety of resources and strategies

Training may involve a variety of strategies based on its goals and audience. Some common strategies such as teaching and peer education strategies are presented below (McKenzie et al., 2009; Piskurich et al., 1999). Audiovisual materials, multimedia and printed educational materials often support the instruction (See Table 6.6).

CHAPTER VI

THE HEALTH EDUCATION SPECIALIST | 149

Key: ◻ Entry ◤◤ Advanced – level information

Table 6.6
Examples of Teaching Strategies

Teaching strategies	Lecture Brainstorming Case studies Coaching Group or cooperative learning Debates Demonstrations Discussion Drills Guest speakers Panel Simulations and games Role playing Problem solving
Peer	Peer teaching Group discussions
Audio visual materials	Charts, pictures, posters Computer Television Overheads and overhead projector Slides and slide projector
Printed educational materials	Handouts and worksheets Pamphlets Study guides Text and reference books Workbooks Posters
Multimedia	CD-ROMs DVDs Internet Videos Video conferencing Distance learning
Training simulations	Training on equipment Training simulators Computer simulation Gaming

Key: ◻ Entry ⫽ Advanced – level information

6.2.10 ⫼ Evaluate impact of training programs

Conducting an evaluation will help prove the worth of the training programs. D.L. Kirkpatrick and Kirkpatrick (2009) recommend three primary reasons that training programs must be evaluated: a) to justify the existence of the training and its contribution to the organization or participants, b) to determine whether to continue the training program, and c) to collect information on how to improve the training. Four levels of training and what they measure are proposed in Table 6.7. Evaluation should start at level one and move sequentially down the other levels.

Table 6.7
Levels of Training

Level	Description	Tools
Level 1 – Reaction	Participants' feelings about the training	Surveys Feedback forms
Level 2 – Learning	Extent to which participants change attitudes, improve knowledge or competencies, and/or increase skills because of the training	Survey before and after the intervention
Level 3 – Behavior	Extent to which participants are employing the skills on the job	Interviews and observations over time
Level 4 – Results	Effects on the organization because of the training	Archival review of documents for the indicators of success

Competency 6.3:
Serve as a health education consultant

Sometimes health education specialists are asked by outside organizations and agencies to assist with a particular health or health education issue. Consultants might be asked to facilitate organizations in planning, implementing, or evaluating programs. Consultants might also be asked to give educational seminars on a health topic, or might be asked to deliver a program, such as a smoking cessation program, to employees of a company that does not have a health education specialist on staff.

6.3.1 Assess needs for assistance

An effective consultative relationship requires knowledge about the health issue/problem, as well as resources, a helping attitude, and skills to provide advice and direction to meet programmatic goals and objectives of an organization. The need for **consultation** should be established by meeting with key stakeholders of the

Key: ◻ Entry ⫼ Advanced – level information

organization, discussions of the reasons for consultation and review of organizational documents supporting the need. Once this information is gathered, a health education specialist can better assess the need for assistance and begin the consultative relationship.

6.3.2 Prioritize requests for assistance

Sometimes the demand for consulting services may exceed resources; therefore, a number of considerations are taken into account in prioritizing these requests. These considerations may include:

- if the request matches the skills of the health education specialist;
- if it falls into the major category of services offered;
- what the scope and nature are of the request for assistance;
- the level of commitment of the clients or organizations involved; and
- presence of other consultants who may also provide the same services.

6.3.3 Define parameters of effective consultative relationships

Health education specialists often work as a liaison between individuals in systems, such as the local or state health department, voluntary health agencies or health care facilities. They may collaborate with staff within their place of employment or with individuals in differing agencies and organizations. The health education specialist, when acting as a consultant, shares his/her knowledge and expertise with individual clients, groups, organizations, and community leaders. The expertise shared with the client includes:

- health education and health promotion information;
- program assessment, planning and evaluation skills;
- health education resources and materials; and
- professional guidance on health-related procedures.

Through this interpersonal process of consultation, the health education specialist can provide technical assistance and special information to those clients or organizations in need of help. The health education specialist can act as either an *internal consultant* (informally advising colleagues within an agency) or an *external consultant* (outside of the agency, more formal). As an internal consultant, the health education specialist acts as a resource person who responds to information requests and organizes materials (Dickert & Sugarman, 2005; Simons-Morton et al., 1995).

On the other hand, external consulting usually requires a contract between the consultant and the client; and the services provided are more technical assistance or process-oriented. As a direct health education service, formal consulting with outside groups requires the health education specialist to provide technical expertise, current theory, and specialized knowledge.

The steps in formal consulting include:

1. assessment of the clients' needs;
2. reports or suggestions for action;
3. implementation of agreed-upon actions;
4. evaluation of the suggested actions; and
5. final reporting of results.

(Simons-Morton et al., 1995; Dickert & Sugarman, 2005)

A consultant generally assists in defining the health issue and developing a plan of action based on the current appraisal of all available information. Once the information is gathered, the consultant helps the client understand the concerns surrounding the health problem, analyze the implications of the problem, and develop an appropriate plan of action to effectively deal with the problem. After the consultation is completed, health education specialists can review the accomplishments, evaluate the consultative process and make recommendations in the final report.

Requests for information and materials often come from outside organizations. Health education specialists must be able to answer specific questions, distribute educational resources, or make appropriate referrals to other agencies. The effective health education consultant in the role of a liaison will ensure that the learning environment is comfortable and positive, that he or she is available as a facilitator or teacher, and that the clients are open to learning (Simons-Morton et al., 1995; Dickert & Sugarman, 2005).

When working among staff or outside groups, the health education specialist focuses on:

- trusting and respecting other leaders and groups;
- engaging individuals and groups;
- empathizing with individuals and groups; and
- supporting individuals and groups.

Health education specialists should also exhibit cultural competence or the ability to interact and provide effective care to people of different cultures. Cultural competence is important in the delivery of consultative services for health promotion. They should have knowledge of different cultures and how culture affects health status (e.g., cultural competence training), suggest that materials be in the language of the intended audience, and advocate for services that reflect awareness of cultural beliefs and practices or a diverse staff and linguistic services, if needed, when working with outside groups (USDHHS, 2001).

6.3.4 Establish consultative relationships

Health education specialists act as liaisons between individuals, groups, and health care provider organizations. Often, when a health education specialist serves as a liaison, group fears and experiences regarding a health issue are addressed. The health education specialist may also consider how the involved parties listen, reflect, and summarize ideas and questions.

Key: ◘ Entry ▨ Advanced – level information

A health education consultant serving as a liaison between groups and organizations needs the following skills: facilitation, presentation, data collection, meeting management, resource material evaluation, networking and report writing. The consultants may be asked to liaise among different groups and coordinate communication among and linkages with other public health agencies in the area. Consultants analyze and synthesize information about the problem or concern, and interpret it for the client. They meet regularly with the client or other stakeholders, and assess the quality and appropriateness of resource materials. They must be able to write detailed reports covering problem diagnosis, actions and recommendations, while keeping in mind barriers and the political climate of the client's organization (Simons-Morton et al., 1995; Dickert & Sugarman, 2005).

6.3.5 ⫴ Provide expert assistance

After the consultative relationship has been established, the health education specialist will then provide the assistance needed and outlined in the consultation agreement. Often the tasks will involve the common skills of health education specialists, including assessing individual and community needs; planning, implementing and evaluating effective health education programs; coordinating the provision of health education services; acting as a resource person; or communicating health and health education needs and resources. Health education specialists should keep in communication with the client or organization frequently as defined in the consultation agreement. Monitoring progress and keeping open communications with the client will make the relationship more effective.

6.3.6 Facilitate collaborative efforts to achieve program goals

Often, health education specialists may be asked to serve as partners, individuals or groups who work with or convene other organizations to accomplish a shared goal to promote the health of the community. These may be called partnerships, collaboratives or coalitions. Some benefits of partnering are:

- increasing credibility beyond individual organizations;
- leveraging or maximizing resources;
- improving the reach to the community;
- increasing broad support for an effort; and
- minimizing the duplication of efforts.

(Olson, 2010)

Skillful networking can provide the health education specialist with an extensive contact list of other professionals working in a variety of settings who can be called upon for guidance, such as opinions, answers, and referrals, when appropriate. Many agencies, organizations, hospitals, and businesses (especially those that cannot afford full-time, in-house, technical experts) hire consultants to create interventions, conduct evaluations, or make program recommendations. Health education specialists often use the expertise of health education consultants when planning or modifying their programs.

6.3.7 ▌ Evaluate the effectiveness of the expert assistance provided

Evaluation should be ongoing in the consultative relationship. Generally, it is divided into three steps:

1) identification of the evaluation questions or criteria;
2) assessment of the achievement of the questions or criteria; and
3) dissemination of findings.

In the evaluation, data can be gathered from the client, consultant, and other stakeholders. Different methods may be employed to evaluate the consultation, including qualitative methods, such as observation; organizational documents; checklists; and/or quantitative methods including surveys or databases. Using multiple methods allows for triangulation of results from different sources.

Some examples of evaluation questions of consultation include:
- To what extent have the goals of the contract been met?
- To what degree has the timeline for the consultation plan been achieved?
- In what ways has the organization changed as a result of the consultation?
- How does the organization feel about the consultant's behavior throughout the consultative relationship?
- What is the level of satisfaction with the consultant and their reports?

Formative evaluation allows for continual assessment of the relationship throughout. It allows for monitoring progress, troubleshooting, and corrective actions. Some specific items that can be evaluated are:

- number and length of contacts between consultant and client;
- progress made to date;
- degree client is satisfied with what has happened;
- client's impression of consultant; and
- any changes needed in the manner that the consultation is being conducted.

Summative evaluation focuses on the outcomes or products of the consultation. Once evaluation questions are defined, collected and analyzed, then the results can be shared with all parties to discuss their implications and make recommendations for improvements in the relationship or next steps (Dougherty, 2008).

6.3.8 Apply ethical principles in consultative relationships

Consultants must have a set of principles that defines ethical behavior and guides their actions toward those behaviors. Ethical practice may be based on deciding what is right and wrong and then performing the right behavior. Therefore, health education specialists must practice integrity in the conduct of health education. A **code of ethics** presents the obligations of practitioners in meeting their social responsibility (Cottrell et al., 2009). Please see Appendix A for the Code of Ethics for the Health Education Profession.

Key: ▢ Entry ▌ Advanced – level information

Some other important issues in ethical practice are informed consent and privacy of information. Informed consent means that people are given sufficient information about a project, program, or medical procedure to make an informed decision about whether or not to participate. Informed consent typically should have the following components:

- information about the program, procedure or research project;
- the individuals' roles or responsibilities;
- the risks and benefits to participation; and
- voluntary agreement.

A health education specialist may have to submit a proposal to an agency's or university's Institutional Review Board (IRB) for review and approval of their procedures, data collection instruments and informed consent documents. Furthermore, once individuals participate in health education services, it is the duty of the health education specialist to protect the information provided by any participants, or privacy of information. The enactment of the Health Insurance Portability and Accountability Act of 1996, also called HIPAA, stressed the importance of standards and use of participant or patient information (Cottrell et al., 2009).

Some important ethical guidelines to consider when working with organizations are listed below.

- Do no harm to your client. Health education specialists should, in their actions and work with other organizations, protect clients and other stakeholders from harm.
- Keep client information private or confidential unless the client or law requests otherwise.
- Avoid conflicts of interest. For example, health education specialists should not represent two opposing interests at one time.
- Do not act in the official capacity as an advocate for your client.
- Do not go beyond your own expertise or qualifications. Health education specialists should know their level of competence with various health education skills and perform actions that match their own education, training or professional experiences (i.e., not exceeding those boundaries of competence).
- Respect others. Consultants should respect the opinions, values and beliefs of others different from their own.
- Ensure that all participation in research and data collection is voluntary and has informed consent.
- Represent accurately potential services and outcomes to their employers.
- Maintain competence in their field of practice.

(American Psychological Association, 2002; Authenticity Consulting, 2005; Taub, Kreuter, Parcel, & Vitello, 1987)

Key: ☐ Entry ℕ Advanced – level information

CHAPTER VII

Area of Responsibility VII
Communicate and Advocate
for Health and Health Education

7.1: Assess and prioritize health information and advocacy needs
Sub-competencies:
7.1.1   Identify current and emerging issues that may influence health and health education
7.7.2   Access accurate resources related to identified issues
7.1.3   Analyze the impact of existing and proposed policies on health
7.1.4   Analyze factors that influence decision-makers

7.2: Identify and develop a variety of communication strategies, methods, and techniques
Sub-competencies:
7.2.1   Create messages using communication theories and models
7.2.2   Tailor messages to priority populations
7.2.3   Incorporate images to enhance messages
7.2.4   Select effective methods or channels for communicating to priority populations
7.2.5   Pilot test messages and delivery methods with priority populations
7.2.6   Revise messages based on pilot feedback

7.3: Deliver messages using a variety of strategies, methods and techniques
Sub-competencies:
7.3.1   Use techniques that empower individuals and communities to improve their health
7.3.2   Employ technology to communicate to priority populations
7.3.3   Evaluate the delivery of communication strategies, methods, and techniques

7.4: Engage in health education advocacy
Sub-competencies:
7.4.1   Engage stakeholders in advocacy
7.4.2   Develop an advocacy plan in compliance with local, state, and/or federal policies and procedures
7.4.3   Comply with organizational policies related to participating in advocacy
7.4.4   Communicate the impact of health and health education on organizational and socio-ecological factors
7.4.5   Use data to support advocacy messages
7.4.6   Implement advocacy plans
7.4.7   Incorporate media and technology in advocacy
7.4.8   Participate in advocacy initiatives
7.4.9   ▨ Lead advocacy initiatives
7.4.10 ▨ Evaluate advocacy efforts

Key: ◪ Entry ▨ Advanced – level information

7.5: Influence policy to promote health

Sub-competencies:

7.5.1 ℕ Use evaluation and research findings in policy analysis

7.5.2 Identify the significance and implications of health policy for individuals, groups, and communities

7.5.3 Advocate for health-related policies, regulations, laws, or rules

7.5.4 ℕ Use evidence-based research to develop policies to promote health

7.5.5 Employ policy and media advocacy techniques to influence decision-makers

7.6: Promote the health education profession

Sub-competencies:

7.6.1 Develop a personal plan for professional growth and service

7.6.2 Describe state-of-the-art health education practice

7.6.3 Explain the major responsibilities of the health education specialist in the practice of health education

7.6.4 Explain the role of health education associations in advancing the profession

7.6.5 Explain the benefits of participating in professional organizations

7.6.6 Facilitate professional growth of self and others

7.6.7 Explain the history of the health education profession and its current and future implications for professional practice

7.6.8 Explain the role of credentialing in the promotion of the health education profession

7.6.9 Engage in professional development activities

7.6.10 Serve as a mentor to others

7.6.11 Develop materials that contribute to the professional literature

7.6.12 Engage in service to advance the health education profession

The Role

Health education specialists are charged with the responsibility of providing information to diverse audiences. Whether through individual, small group, or mass communication techniques, health education specialists use their professional background to interpret and prioritize needs for health information and advocacy efforts. They also communicate to others the unique foundations of, and contributions offered by, health education professionals across a range of employment settings. To that end, health education specialists consider the value systems of the intended audience in delivering messages using a variety of strategies, methods and techniques, as well as engaging in health education advocacy. Through advocacy and promoting the profession, health education specialists promote health for individuals, groups, and communities (NCHEC et al., 2010a).

Settings

The following text describes how communication and advocacy are used in different health education practice settings (NCHEC et al., 2010a).

Key: ◘ Entry ℕ Advanced – level information

COMMUNICATE AND ADVOCATE
FOR HEALTH AND HEALTH EDUCATION

Community Setting. In a community setting, lay health education specialists (also referred to as promoters, community health advocates, and community health advisors) might act as lay health education specialists for an asthma program reducing environmental triggers in the home, for example. The health education specialist would work with the lay health education specialists to develop asset maps of the community, define goals and objectives, and develop program materials in appropriate languages at appropriate reading levels. The health education specialist would recruit, train and support the lay health workers as they conduct health education-related activities. Health education specialists can also act as advocates for community health needs, such as lobbying the local government to use funds in ways that help promote the community's health, or to create local laws or ordinances that promote community health.

School (K-12) Setting. When employed in a school setting, a health education specialist might be responsible for promoting the coordinated school health approach by presenting curriculum information and student health information needs and concerns to groups of parents. In the event of parental concerns, the health education specialist would take into consideration the multiple value systems represented by the group and would employ appropriate strategies to communicate the material and respond to parents' questions. Depending on the topic, the health education specialist might use illustrations from classroom instruction, student presentations, videos, or Web technology to enhance the presentation. Health education specialists can also advocate for student or faculty health in a school setting by creating school health councils, or by suggesting ways to modify a curriculum.

Health Care Setting. In this setting, the health education specialist might be responsible for a program to support patients' smoking cessation efforts. The health education specialist would need to communicate with providers the importance of the program, as well as the health education specialist's appropriateness for launching such an effort. The health education specialist could advocate for corporate responsibility to engage in health promotion and prevention efforts. With the providers' understanding and support, the health education specialist would be responsible for informing the priority population of the program's availability in ways consistent with organizational policy and the values of the intended audience. Brochures, posters, flyers, public service announcements, and various electronic media might be considered.

Business/Industry Setting. A health education specialist employed in the workplace might become aware of some previously unrecognized health need among workers. The health education specialist would communicate that need (e.g., insufficient opportunity for physical activity) to management. Using his or her background in behavioral and biological sciences, the health education specialist would interpret the problem for management and articulate the possible ways of addressing the problem, such as offering a program or screening, or changing organizational policy. Acknowledging concerns specific to management, the health education specialist could then communicate ways in which a health education program or policy might benefit management and the worker.

College/University Setting. A health education specialist in a college/university setting might be faced with the challenge of ensuring health education's "place" in the college curriculum. Recognizing multiple perspectives on expected student learning outcomes, the health education specialist would consider colleagues' professional backgrounds and use that information in formulating presentations on the importance of health

Key: ☐ Entry \\\\ Advanced – level information

education programs in the university environment. Communication might be handled through reports to curriculum committees, presentations to administrators, electronic communications or small group discussions with students and faculty. University health education specialists may develop an advocacy plan in order to improve the health of current and future students.

University Health Services Setting. In a university health services setting, the health education specialist interfaces with students, health care providers, faculty, and other stakeholders. In this arena, the health education specialist might be charged with providing an educational program or social norm campaign to improve students' decision-making about use of drugs and alcohol. The health education specialist would communicate to health care providers the need for such a campaign, and contribute to the program to ensure the providers' support and participation. The health education specialist would communicate the educational purpose of the program and/or relevant social norms data to students and interpret its value relative to their health education needs and concerns. This communication could be handled through electronic or print channels to individual students, posters placed around campus, and presentations before small groups within dormitories. The health education specialist might also work with select student organizations to encourage policy development regarding alcohol consumption on campus, alternatives to alcohol consumption, and advocate for local laws or ordinances that stiffen alcohol or drug-related offenses for businesses.

Key Terms

O—▼ **Advocacy** is "the pursuit of influencing outcomes – including public policy and resource allocation decisions within political, economic, and social systems and institutions that directly affect people's lives" (World Health Organization, 2010).

O—▼ **Culture** involves ideas, beliefs, values, customs, and norms that are learned from family and community, and are passed down from generation to generation (Doyle and Ward, 2010).

O—▼ **Cultural Competency** refers to an ability to interact effectively with people of different cultures. Cultural competence comprises four components: (a) awareness of one's own cultural worldview; (b) attitude towards cultural differences; (c) knowledge of different cultural practices and worldviews; and (d) cross-cultural skills. Developing cultural competence results in an ability to understand, communicate with, and effectively interact with people across cultures (Martin & Vaughn, 2007).

O—▼ **Cultural Sensitivity** is understanding, valuing, and respecting the similarities and differences between culturally based attitudes, beliefs, and behaviors (Vaughn, 2008).

O—▼ **Health communication** informs and influences practices, behaviors or policies in an effort to improve individual or community health (Schiavo, 2007).

O—▼ **Health marketing** is the creation and delivery of health promotion programs using multidisciplinary, evidence-based strategies to motivate the public toward positive health practices (CDC, 2006a).

Key: ◻ Entry ⋀⋀ Advanced – level information

○━► **Lobbying**, according to federal law, is any attempt to influence specific legislation (Vernick, 1999).

○━► A **lobbyist** is a person who tries to influence legislation on behalf of a special interest (Doyle et al., 2010).

○━► **Persuasive communication** involves tailored health-related messages to meet audience needs, and persuades them to adopt healthy attitudes and behaviors (Doyle et al., 2010).

○━► **Policies** are sets of rules and objectives to guide activities (Doyle et al., 2010).

○━► **Social Marketing** is using marketing principles in planning, implementation, and evaluation of health education programs designed to bring about social change. The ultimate objective of marketing is to influence action (Siegel & Lotenberg, 2007).

○━► **Web 2.0** refers to the second generation of Internet tools that are user-centered and interactive (Bennet & Glasgow, 2009).

Competency 7.1:
Assess and prioritize health information and advocacy needs

Assessing and prioritizing health information and health education are essential skills for health education specialists. Increasingly, health education specialists are placed in positions where advocating for health education programs has become an important component of their work experience. This section will: identify emerging issues that influence the field of health education, describe how to access accurate resources to address issues in health education, outline the importance of analyzing the impact of proposed policies on health education, and convey the relevance of analyzing factors which influence decision-makers.

7.1.1 Identify current and emerging issues that may influence health and health education

It is a responsibility of health education specialists to effectively communicate important, timely information to key decision-makers. Information needs are based on an understanding of factors that influence health status including medical care, public health, and socio-behavioral and environmental factors.

Evidence-based decision-making is a key component in delivering effective health education. Systematic reviews that summarize the evidence are helpful to translate findings into practice. In order to influence policy-makers, reviews and reports need to present the information in a concise, understandable format. To facilitate using this information, the health education specialist may develop tools, such as guidelines, educational materials, practice recommendations, talking points, and translation of reports into activities (Atkins, Fink, & Slutsky, 2005).

CHAPTER VII

7.1.2 Access accurate resources related to identified issues

When determining advocacy resources to be used, it is important to select sources based on characteristics of data needed, and also to select sources that are credible with the advocate's partners and policymakers the advocate wishes to influence. Please refer to Chapter IV for more information on research and locating relevant data. Sources might include:

- Peer-reviewed publications which provide the background and science behind issues and planned action. However, there can be a time gap between the research and publication that causes the information to be seen as dated.

- Health education professional organizations (see list in Sub-competency 7.6.4 in Table 7.4) provide position papers, resolutions, model policies and tool kits addressing multiple health education issues.

Federal Web sites can be used, such as the National Institutes of Health, which has 27 institutes and centers (http://www.nih.gov/icd/index.html). The Centers for Disease Control and Prevention's 11 centers and other offices provide reports, evidence-based tools and best-practice resources. From either of these sites the health education specialist can subscribe to RSS feeds. These sites provide health topic information, data sources, model policies, and news. Federal Web sites provide timely and credible information often updated in nearly real time.

National non-governmental organization's Web sites: The American Heart Association, American Lung Association, and American Cancer Society offer a broad range of content and policy tools and advice. Research!America and Trust for America's Health are examples of credible national sites focused on environmental change and policy.

- Nationally recognized health philanthropies such as the Robert Wood Johnson Foundation and Kellogg Foundation maintain Web sites with white papers and model programs, policies and practices that are highly credible.

- Professional organizations of policymakers are information sources valued as credible and practical by policymakers. The National Governors Association and National Conference of State Legislatures monitor policy initiatives across the country and provide resources. National health policy resources include the Association of State and Territorial Health Officials and the National Association of County and City Health Officials, the national organization representing local health departments.

- State health agency Web sites and state health and human services agencies provide background and policy tools relevant to each state.

7.1.3 Analyze the impact of existing and proposed policies on health

National health policies guide the establishment of health program priorities. Important considerations in health policy development include community needs assessment and a scientific assessment of the results, impacts of current programming, and available resources to support and maintain the policy (Doyle et al., 2010).

Key: ☐ Entry ⋀ Advanced – level information

7.1.4 Analyze factors that influence decision-makers

Legislative advocacy, media advocacy, and grassroots activities are ways to influence decision-makers (Doyle et al., 2010).

Legislative advocacy is contacting a policy-maker to discuss a public health problem. Health education specialists can provide well-documented data and empirical evidence to help decision-makers create laws and regulations to support health (Lachenmayr, 2009).

Media advocacy attempts to change the normative behavior of the media to alter public policy/practice and create environmental change. The first step is to set the agenda to garner media attention in order to alter the public's perception of the importance of a public health issue. The next step is to frame the issue by selecting specific content to present as important (Doyle et al., 2010).

Media advocacy is a powerful tool for health education specialists and their advocacy efforts. They are effective in gaining support for health education efforts and initiatives. When health education specialists are developing the strategies for the media advocacy efforts, they should ask the following questions:

- What is the problem they are trying to solve?
- What is the possible solution to the problem?
- Who will support the effort?
- What needs to be said and how can attention be gained?

(Dorfman, 2009)

Methods such as news, press, video, or radio releases, interviews, letters to the editor and media alerts are all strategies to build support and communicate the need for health programs or health policy change and implementation (Schiavo, 2007).

Grassroots activities are efforts that originate from individuals within a community, rather than originating with health agencies. Health education specialists can help individuals and communities organize efforts to reach health-related goals (Doyle and Ward, 2010).

Although television and radio reach a broad population, these methods tend to offer insufficient details for the target audience. Web 2.0 and Internet resources, such as MySpace, Facebook, Twitter, LinkedIn and others, can spread the message about an issue quickly as individual users pass on content. Additionally, information can instantaneously be updated and can be tailored for intended audiences (NCI, 2008).

Key: ◻ Entry ⫝̸ Advanced – level information

Competency 7.2:
Identify and develop a variety of communication strategies, methods, and techniques

In order to engage stakeholders in health and health education, it is often necessary for health education specialists to develop a variety of communication strategies, methods, and techniques. Health education specialists are often required to use behavioral theories to design communication strategies and determine the best channel through which to disseminate messages. Please refer to Chapter III for a description of common behavior change theories and models. The following Sub-competencies discuss:

- the importance of using communication theories and models to develop messages;
- tailoring messages to align with priority populations;
- using images to enhance messages;
- selecting methods and channels to communicate with target populations;
- pilot testing messages and delivery methods; and
- revising messages utilizing feedback from stakeholders.

7.2.1 Create messages using communication theories and models

Research indicates that there is a need for better health care provider-patient communication, and consumers are increasingly seeking health information not only about disease treatment but also about disease prevention and health promotion (ODPHP, n.d.). Few people understand the concept of health-risk or scientific research. Public perceptions about health-related messages are influenced by the following characteristics: ease of solution and immediate results, perceived susceptibility, and personal beliefs (NCI, 2008). A consumer-focused health education specialist learns as much as possible about the target audience and influences behavior change by meeting consumer needs. Using the social marketing process, the health education specialist can analyze the problem situation, environment and resources; segment the target audience; create strategies; and evaluate the results (Goldman, 2003).

Utilizing the social marketing approach, health education specialists listen to the needs and wants of the consumer by looking at the marketing mix, traditionally consisting of the 4 "P's":

- Product: health behavior, program, or idea;
- Price: financial, physical, psychological, time;
- Place: how and where learning will take place; and
- Promotion: approach used to reach the audience.

(Siegel & Lotenberg, 2007)

Siegel & Lotenberg (2007) add a fifth "P," Partners. This "P" refers to the importance of mobilizing resources by working with other organizations.

Key: ◻ Entry ∿ Advanced – level information

COMMUNICATE AND ADVOCATE
FOR HEALTH AND HEALTH EDUCATION

It is important for the health education specialist to recognize the importance of community involvement in the health decision-making process, and avoid the top-down process of health communication. Some tips include:

- involve the community/priority audience early in the process;
- clarify the community/audience's role as early as possible;
- ask the community/audience how they wish to be involved; and
- identify and respond to the needs and interests of a variety of community groups.

(Agency for Toxic Substances and Disease Registry, n.d.)

7.2.2 Tailor messages to priority populations

Almost half of American adults read at or below basic levels, and messages to priority populations need to be readable and attractive to the audience. A variety of barriers, including language barriers, prevent people from understanding the health materials, information, and services needed to make good consumer health decisions (Schiavo, 2007). Those with the greatest need for health education may have the least access to information and services. Individuals in low income and or low education status groups may lack access to communication technologies, such as the Internet, creating a knowledge gap and digital divide. People with low health literacy skills have an inability to read and understand health literature, navigate the health care system/health marketplace, and critically evaluate health messages in the media. Populations with low literacy report poorer health, incur higher health care costs, and possess lower knowledge of medical conditions than populations with higher health literacy skills (ODPHP, n.d.). Approximately 75 million American adults reported Basic or Below Basic health literacy levels. Older Americans and those with lower educational levels were most at risk (National Center for Educational Statistics [NCES], 2006).

To reach audiences with low literacy, it is important to:

- keep materials short, simple and organized;
- use examples and graphics;
- be clear and concise;
- generate a consistent message;
- pretest materials with the target audience;
- summarize or highlight the main points;
- include a balance of white space with words and pictures;
- use few polysyllabic words; and
- maintain the readability at about a fourth grade reading level.

(NCI, 2008)

There are several readability formulas that help measure vocabulary difficulty and sentence length to generate an estimated reading level, e.g., Fry Readability Formula, Flesch-Kincaid, Fog-Gunning Index, and SMOG. These formulas can be used to ensure the language on print materials meet the intended audiences' reading levels.

Key: ◻ Entry ⁊⁊ Advanced – level information

Culture influences the perception of health messages. It is important to be aware of the advantages of segmenting the population into the priority audience according to behavioral, cultural, demographic, physical, and psychographic characteristics. The health education specialist should respect the diversity between cultures, understand attitudes and values related to cultures, and involve the target audience in material and message development and testing (NCI, 2008).

Effective campaigns are audience-centered and developed by professionals with specific knowledge of the psychographics and demographics of the target audience. Targeting and tailoring the messages for the audience takes into consideration the cultural practices and needs of the priority audience and improves the effectiveness of the campaign (ODPHP, n.d.). Every culture has a value system in which health practices are reflected. When serving multicultural and diverse populations, health education specialists train providers to work toward **cultural competency**. For example, they may seek to overcome language barriers by involving bilingual community members, and create partnerships with community resources and coalitions (Doyle et al., 2010).

In summary, important cultural principles include:

- remembering that everyone is a member of a culture or cultures;
- acknowledging that culture affects health beliefs and practices; and
- being both culturally sensitive and culturally competent are essential to effective communication.

(Doyle et al., 2010)

7.2.3 Incorporate images to enhance messages

The congruence between images and health messages is essential. Images should only be included if they improve the impact of the print or electronic messages for the audience. The health education specialist must also consider ethical use of images, obtaining rights or permission to use images or using images from public or commercial sources. Public image libraries that are provided online at the CDC, and other sites can provide images in the public domain. The health education specialist must also assure that images are culturally appropriate. Conducting focus groups with the intended audience can help assure the value added by use of specific images.

In practice, health education specialists "should: (1) ask, 'how can I' use pictures to support key points?; (2) minimize distracting details in pictures; (3) use simple language in conjunction with pictures; (4) closely link pictures to text and/or captions; (5) include people from the intended audience in designing pictures; (6) have health professionals, not artists, plan the pictures; and (7) evaluate pictures' effects by comparing response to materials with and without pictures" (Houts, Doak, C.C., Doak, & Loscalzo, 2006, p. 173).

Photovoice is a powerful way to use images for communication and advocacy. Developed by Caroline C. Wang and Mary Ann Burris (1997), photovoice blends a grassroots approach to photography and social action. It provides cameras not to health specialists, policy makers, or professionals, but to people with least access to those who make decisions affecting their lives. Photovoice has three main goals:

- to enable community members to record both their concerns about and the strengths of their community;
- to promote dialogue about the issues addressed in the videos; and
- to reach policy makers.

(Wang & Burris, 1997)

7.2.4 Select effective methods or channels for communicating to priority populations

A health education specialist should take into consideration the advantages and disadvantages of different methods of disseminating educational materials (NCI, 2008) as described in Table 7.1.

Table 7.1
Communication Channels and Activities: Pros and Cons

Type of Channel	Activities	Pros	Cons
Interpersonal channels	• Hotline counseling • Patient counseling • Instruction • Informal discussion • Fact sheet with a list of questions for patients to ask health care providers • How-to booklets and points for discussions in private homes or within the family • Videos for discussion	• Can be credible • Permit two-way discussion • Can be motivational, influential, supportive • Most effective for teaching and helping/caring • Can supply messages in culturally sensitive format	• Can be expensive • Can be time-consuming • Can have limited intended audience reach • Can be difficult to link into interpersonal channels
Organizational channels	• Organizational meetings and conferences • Workplace campaigns • Newsletters • Educational programs (in-person, audiovisual, computerized, print) • In-house radio or video broadcasts • Add-ons to regular communication (e.g., messages handed out with paychecks or organization notices)	• May be familiar, trusted, and influential • May provide more motivation/support than media alone • Can offer shared experiences • Can reach larger intended audience in one place	• Can be time consuming to establish • May not provide personalized attention • Organizational constraints may require message approval • May lose control of message if adapted to fit organizational needs

Key: ☐ Entry ⫼ Advanced – level information

Community channels	• Town hall meetings and other events • School campaigns • Faith based organization campaigns • Educational programs • Speeches • Kiosks or displays in shopping malls, post offices, or other public venues	• May be familiar, trusted, and influential • Can reach larger intended audience in one place • Requires collaborative approach • Can evaluate knowledge change in some cases	• Can be time consuming to establish • Difficulties with establishing lead agency in collaboratives can arise • Evaluating behavior change is difficult • No or limited one-on-one time with intended audience
Mass media channels *Newspapers*	• Advertisements • Inserted sections on a health topic (paid) • News • Feature stories • Letters to the editor • Op-Ed pieces • Cartoons/comics • Newspaper inserts • Media kits	• Can reach broad intended audiences rapidly • Can convey health news more thoroughly than TV or radio and faster than magazines • Intended audience has opportunity to clip, reread, contemplate, and pass along material • Small circulation papers may take Public Service Announcements (PSA)	• Coverage demands a newsworthy item • Larger circulation papers may take only paid ads and inserts • Exposure usually limited to one day • Article placement requires contacts and may be time-consuming • Stories can be difficult to "pitch"
Mass media channels *Radio*	• Ads (paid or public service placement) • News • Public affairs/talk shows • Dramatic programming (entertainment education) • Audio news releases • Media kits • Music news releases/music videos	• Range of formats available to intended audiences with known listening preferences • Opportunity for direct intended audience involvement • Can distribute ad scripts that are flexible and inexpensive • Ads or programming can reach intended audience when they are most receptive • Paid ads can be relatively inexpensive	• Reaches smaller audiences than TV • Public service ads run infrequently and at low listening times • Many stations have limited formats that may not be conducive to health messages • Difficult for intended audiences to retain or pass on material

Key: ◻ Entry ⫼ Advanced – level information

Mass media channels *Television*	• Ads (paid or public service placement) • News • Public affairs/talk shows • Dramatic programming (entertainment education) • Audio or video news releases • Media kits • Music news releases/ music videos	• Largest audience reach • Visual combined with audio good for emotional appeals and demonstrating behaviors • Can reach low income intended audiences • Ads or programming can reach intended audience when most receptive • Ads allow message and its execution to be controlled	• Ads can be expensive • PSAs run infrequently and at low viewing times • Message might be difficult for audience to retain • Promotion can result in overwhelming demand
Mass media channels *Internet*	• Web sites • E-mail lists • Chat rooms • Newsgroups • Ads (paid or public service placement) • Social Networking sites	• Large reach • Can instantaneously update and disseminate information • Can control and tailor information • Can be interactive and visually appealing • Can use banner ads to direct intended audience to your program's Web site	• Can be expensive to design and maintain • Intended audiences may not have access to the Internet • Newsgroups and chat rooms may require monitoring • Can require maintenance over time

(Note. Adapted from NCI, 2008).

Health communication informs and influences health-related decisions (NCI, 2008). A health communication campaign can support a multi-component approach to solving public health problems. Prior to campaign material distribution and promotion, remember to carefully define the market, segment the market, analyze the segments, and choose a target market with shared consumer preferences (CDC, 2006a). The health education specialist is in a unique position to determine the format/type of materials to be developed by evaluating the nature and function of the message, as well as how it best fits with the channels selected.

7.2.5 Pilot test messages and delivery methods with priority populations

It is important to pilot test (using focus groups, interviews, questionnaires, readability tests) draft materials to make sure they are understandable and relevant (Plomer & Bensley, 2009). The pilot testing methods should

Key: ☐ Entry ▨ Advanced – level information

fit the program's budget and timeline. Include individuals who share similar characteristics as the intended audience such as gatekeepers, opinion leaders, and community influences as test segments where appropriate. Pilot testing can be used to assess comprehension and recall, determine personal relevance, and evaluate controversial elements, but the health education specialist needs to consider the time it takes to revise the communication message based on the findings of the pilot test (NCI, 2008).

The CDCynergy Social Marketing Version outlines steps for piloting and revising materials (CDC, 2003a).

1. Test creative concepts with intended audiences to see if the ideas resonate.
2. Pretest specific messages with intended audiences to ensure that they hear what you want them to hear.
3. Pretest products and materials with intended audiences to ensure that your products and materials elicit the intended response and produce the desired actions.
4. Choose pretest settings – the places where you hope to provide your service(s) or expose your audience to messages.
5. Pretest product distribution plans.

7.2.6 Revise messages based on pilot feedback

After pilot testing messages and delivery methods with priority populations, it is important to revise messages based on pilot feedback. After modifications, the communication message should be tested again. Pilot testing and modification should be integrated into the overall timeline to ensure that products, services and communication materials will be ready for program launch. The creation of materials, including the pretesting process, can be time-consuming (Plomer & Bensley, 2009). However, feedback received is necessary to improve message efficacy.

Health education specialists responsible for revising health education communication materials based on the feedback acquired from the pilot must take into consideration the following:

- the nature of the message (e.g., style, sensitivity, complexity);
- the function of the message (e.g., calling attention to an issue or teaching a new skill);
- goals and objectives of the message;
- activities and channels to reach (e.g., senior centers, schools, universities, churches, health clinics);
- additional effort and implications by modifying the message;
- costs and accountability; and
- budget and/or in-kind resources from other sources.

(CDC, 2000; NCI, 2008; Selden, Zorn, Ratzan & Parker, 2000)

Depending on the extent of revisions, costs may range from minimal to extensive. In order to minimize cost, program planners should share revised messages with the priority population to ensure changes are appropriate. Also, results from pilot testing will help program planners to identify new, old, or a combination of new and old channels through which revised messages will be disseminated.

Key: ☐ Entry ⫼ Advanced – level information

Regardless of the channel utilized to disseminate revised messages, they must be scientifically accurate, consistent, clear, credible, and relevant to the intended audience (NCI, 2008; Kreps, Barnes, Neiger, & Thackeray, 2009). Revised messages should take into account key primary cultural factors that include: race, ethnicity, language, nationality and religion (Schiavo, 2007). In addition, other secondary cultural factors such as age, gender, educational level, occupation, and income level (NCI, 2008) should be taken into consideration. Program planners must stay in touch with the norms, perceptions, and views of their priority populations. Therefore, through the use of a participatory approach, it is necessary to periodically revise messages in order to enhance their effectiveness and reach to priority populations.

Competency 7.3:
Deliver messages using a variety of strategies, methods and techniques

After identifying and developing a variety of communication strategies, methods, and techniques, health education specialists must deliver a variety of approaches and techniques. This section describes three important approaches that include: a) employing techniques that help empower individuals and their communities; b) utilizing technology to communicate to key stakeholders; and c) the importance of evaluating the delivery of communication strategies, methods and techniques.

7.3.1 Use techniques that empower individuals and communities to improve their health

At the individual level, effective health communication can help increase awareness, motivation, skill development, and positive attitudes—all of which help empower individuals and communities to improve their health (NCI, 2008). On the community level, effective health communication can influence public policy, promote environmental change, improve health service delivery, empowerment, and assist in creating healthy social norms (NCI, 2008).

Health education specialists may be called upon to interpret information between health care providers and patients. Different levels of communication, including one-on-one instruction, media messages, brochures and support groups, may occur between health education specialists and clients (Cottrell et al., 2009). Improved communication between health education specialists and clients can lead to improved patient satisfaction, patient compliance, and quality of life changes.

On the *social network level*, effective health communications can change group communication patterns, usually through influencing the group's opinion leader. On the *organizational level*, effective health communications can support organizational efforts and support policy change. On the *societal level*, effective health communications can influence norms, policies, laws, and environments (NCI, 2008).

Persuasive communication tailors health-related messages to audiences' needs in an effort to persuade them to adopt healthy attitudes and behaviors (Doyle & Ward, 2010). A major challenge in persuasive communication is identifying the most appropriate and effective channel, context, and message content to motivate community members to seek and use health information (ODPHP, n.d.).

Key: ◻ Entry ⦚ Advanced – level information

Health education specialists can use the Health Communication Campaign Model to analyze the community health problem, identify the priority audience's needs and appropriate strategies to reach them, use communication theories and marketing techniques, select the settings, channels, and activities to be included in the message, and evaluate the outcomes (Kreps et al., 2009).

7.3.2 Employ technology to communicate to priority populations

Electronic communication

In addition to traditional health communication campaigns using mass media, printed materials, integration of mass media with community programming, and incorporation of social marketing techniques – campaigns are increasingly relying upon digital technologies and are shifting from individual to community-level change strategies (ODPHP, n.d.). Interactive digital media include E-mail, Web surveys, Internet, interactive television, bulletin boards/newsgroups/electronic mailing lists, chat rooms, teleconferencing, Web blogs, CD-ROMs, social networking, Web 2.0 and other evolving media. Media can be used to send tailored messages and receive audience feedback. Credibility and access are issues, however. Interactive health communication and telehealth can create risks associated with poor or inaccurate information and privacy/confidentiality concerns (ODPHP, n.d.).

Advantages of *interactive media* (computers and digital technologies) compared to traditional mass media include:

- customized health information;
- information access on-demand;
- wider distribution/faster content updates;
- increased choices;
- access to experts on-demand;
- convenient; and
- viral spread.

(ODPHD, n.d.)

Educational media

Educational media can enhance and/or supplement instruction. It can be used to emphasize key points and for skill acquisition practice. Audiovisual aids help the audience remember/comprehend important points using visual association. Examples of aids include: charts/graphs, illustrations/diagrams, maps, movies/videos, slides, field trips/site visits, posters, photographs, handouts, models, flipcharts, displays and PowerPoint presentations.

For aids to be effective, they need to be able to:

- stand alone;
- illustrate only one key point on each aid;
- use pictures/charts/graphics with short key words; and
- represent facts in a clear, uncluttered manner.

(ATSDR, n.d.)

7.3.3 Evaluate the delivery of communication strategies, methods, and techniques

Evaluation can and needs to occur on many different levels, including evaluation of communication strategies, methods or techniques. This can include several surveillance and evaluation efforts. For example, since 2002, evaluation of the statewide Strategic Tobacco Retail Effort (STORE, n.d.) Campaign, a campaign designed to look strategically at tobacco retail licensing to minors, has consisted of several surveillance and evaluation efforts, including: tobacco purchase surveys, point of marketing surveys, law enforcement surveys, surveillance studies, media tracking, opinion polls, and ordinance tracking, among others.

Competency 7.4:
Engage in health education advocacy

The word advocate comes from the Latin word for "voice." Advocacy has been defined as a way to systematically alter policy and infrastructure (Caira et al., 2003). Advocacy skills are essential for the health education specialist, because advocacy embraces the concept of influencing organizational decision makers as well as public officials or the legislative body. It is essential for health education specialists to build advocacy skills and become active participants in the process. Individuals can take small steps in supporting advocacy efforts. Health education specialists must find and use their "voice" in important issues within your community, state, or nation. (Galer-Unti, Tappe, & Lachenmayr, 2004).

7.4.1 Engage stakeholders in advocacy

By conducting key informant interviews, holding focus groups, reviewing case studies and conducting surveys of settings that are specific to political context, health education specialists begin the process of building an evidence-based public health policy campaign and to build their stakeholder base for this campaign. Once an advocacy issue is identified, health education specialists can ask the following questions when engaging stakeholders:

- What community resources are available?
- Who are the allies and adversaries on this issue?
- Who else shares the problem?
- What would those groups who share the problem gain or lose by joining the campaign?

(adapted from Lachenmayer, 2009, p. 337)

7.4.2 Develop an advocacy plan in compliance with local, state, and/or federal policies and procedures

Brownson, Chriqui and Stamatakis (2009) describe three areas of policy development:

1. policy process investigates options to increase adoption;
2. policy content uses data to investigate effective elements; and
3. policy outcomes evaluate the impact of policy.

CHAPTER VII

Key: ◻ Entry \\\\ Advanced – level information

In policy development, a health education specialist is tasked with collecting and analyzing quantitative and qualitative data, selecting effective tools, and evaluating the impact of policy decisions (Brownson et al., 2009).

The process of building an effective campaign strategy incorporates the early steps of documenting the public health problems and the political environment and selecting the issue focus. Once an issue is selected, the core group determines campaign goals, organizational resources and needs, allies and opponents, targets and tactics. Taken together, these form the campaign strategy. In this case, "strategy" means the overall design for building the power to compel a government official, who otherwise would not support local policies or regulations when he or she does not otherwise want to (STORE, n.d.).

Health education specialists should be aware of advocacy policies and procedures for the setting in which they work. For example, non-profit agencies can perform lobbying as long as that lobbying meets the federal guidelines and does not exceed a certain percentage of the non-profit's activities. However, health education specialists working for some state and federal agencies are not allowed to conduct lobbying activities.

7.4.3 Comply with organizational policies related to participating in advocacy

Federal, state and organizational laws and policies affect the health education specialist's ability to participate in certain types of advocacy efforts while "on" organizational time. It is the health education specialist's responsibility to comply with state and federal law, as well as the organizational policy, regarding such activities. Formal organizational policy, as well as departmental or individual management policy, may apply.

The Code of Ethics for the Health Education Profession (CNHEO, 2006) states that health education specialists have a responsibility to promote, maintain, and improve individual, family, and community health. The Health Education Code of Ethics encourages actions and social policies that support and facilitate the best balance of benefits over harm for all affected parties. That begins with advocating for programs, interests or populations and organizational policy and procedures within the health education specialist's own organization.

Outside of their daily role, a health education specialist can strengthen advocacy efforts as a member of a professional organization that advocates and may lobby for issues of interest. Health education specialists can also use the organization's name in support of an issue, if that organization has an established position on the issue, and approves such use.

An individual acting as a private citizen can participate in any level of advocacy or lobbying. Care must be taken not to use any resources (time, computers, phones, letterhead, etc.) that belong to an employer when acting as a private citizen. It may also be necessary to declare when one's views are in fact their own and not that of the organization from which they are employed.

7.4.4 Communicate the impact of health and health education on organizational and socio-ecological factors

Health education plays an important role in identifying the impact of multiple determinants on health (e.g., physical, social, organizational, institutional, economical, societal, and political). Health education specialists are therefore responsible for communicating about the role of the profession in implementing, evaluating,

Key: ☐ Entry ⩘ Advanced – level information

translating, and disseminating effective health education and promotion practices (Poland, 2009). In addition, health education specialists must communicate the role of health education in generating policy changes that lead to creating optimal conditions that promote health. Across multiple determinants of health at the individual (e.g., behaviors, attitudes), family (e.g., structure, support), neighborhood or community (e.g., toxins, crime, poverty), cultural groups (e.g., shared beliefs, values), and organizational (e.g., educational system, health care, *policies*) levels, health education specialists play an important role in identifying strategies around which to improve the conditions that promote health—all of which should be communicated at local, state and national levels (Schulz, 2004; Quinn & Green, 2006).

7.4.5 Use data to support advocacy messages

Though it is recommended that health education specialists monitor effects of public policy, such data does not always exist to inform new policy (Brownson et al., 2009). Hartsfield , Moulton and McKie (2007) reviewed public health laws, identifying over 100 public health laws covering a variety of topics, most commonly tobacco control, injury prevention, and school health (Brownson et al., 2009). However, only 6.5% of the reviewed laws provided research evidence supporting such legislation (Brownson, et al., 2009).

The health education specialist's role often includes preparing data for quick and practical dissemination. For success in the process, one often needs to proactively analyze and assemble data in order to ensure evidence is ready when a policy window or opportunity emerges (Greenlick, Goldberg, Lopes, & Tallon, 2005).

Data needs to be in a form that:

- shows public health burden;
- demonstrates priority of an issue over many others;
- shows relevance at the local (voting district) level;
- shows benefits (or sometimes harms) from an intervention (Freudenberg, Bradley, & Serrano, 2009);
- personalizes an issue by telling a compelling story of how peoples' lives are affected; and
- estimates the cost of the intervention (Brownson, Royer, Ewing, & McBride, 2006).

(Brownson, et al., 2009, p. 1580)

7.4.6 Implement advocacy plans

An advocacy plan includes five elements: a) goals, b) organizational considerations, c) constituents, allies and opponents, d) targets, and e) tactics. In the first two steps, health education specialists should identify the goals of the advocacy effort, and identify organizational issues that can facilitate or impede efforts. Health education specialists should then begin to identify their allies, constituents and opponents. Allies are a critical part of any campaign and therefore play an essential part in the implementation of your advocacy efforts. Allies are the way that health education specialists have connections to, and influence over, their targets.

Once health education specialists know their campaign goals, organizational issues and have developed a list of allies and opponents, a list of the targets for their campaign needs to be developed. Health education specialists must also identify which individuals can make the final decision, and should keep good records of whether these individuals are considered a target, supporter, opponent, or are undecided on the issue.

Key: ◻ Entry ∖∖ Advanced – level information

As a final step to the development of an advocacy campaign, health education specialists need to begin to strategically think about the tactics that they can use with their allies that will influence their targets and help them to achieve their campaign goal. A good resource to utilize in the development and implementation of advocacy plans is the Health Education Advocate site (http://www.healtheducationadvocate.org/). The Health Education Advocate site is a joint project of several national health education organizations.

7.4.7 Incorporate media and technology in advocacy

Capwiz and other Internet action networks are vital resources for the health education specialist to utilize when working on advocacy issues (available at: http://capitoladvantage.com/capwiz). For example, there are E-advocacy tools to help mobilize their members to send letters to members of congress electronically. Often these action network sites have various components that can be utilized, for example the APHA capwiz network offers:

- *Mega Vote* <www.capwiz.com/apha/megavote/> is a weekly E-mail regarding political voting.
- *Elected Official Finder* <www.capwiz.com/apha/officials> contains biographical information on elected officials.
- *Issues and Legislation* <www.capwiz.com/apha/issues/> contains information about health-related legislation.
- *Media Guide* <www.capwiz.com/apha/dbq/media/> allows members to send electronic letters to local media.
- *Legislative Action Center* <www.capwiz.com/apha/home> posts regular updates on legislation, and allows members to E-mail local political representatives.

In addition to internet action networks, mobile technologies can also be used as tools for advocacy efforts. These involve "any device and application that uses cellular (or wireless) technology to send information or communication across distances to other devices or people" (Lefebvre, 2009, p. 491).

7.4.8 Participate in advocacy initiatives

Advocacy initiatives are designed to influence policy and law, and often include activities such as education, lobbying, and mobilization, among others (Fagen, Reed, Kaye, & Jack, 2009). Advocacy strategies can also be categorized into six areas:

1. voting behavior (register to vote and encourage others to do the same);
2. electioneering (contributing to the campaign of a candidate supportive of public health and health education);
3. direct lobbying (contacting a policy maker);
4. grassroots lobbying (starting a petition drive to advocate for a specific policy);
5. use of the Internet to access information on health issues; and
6. media advocacy (responding to members of the media for health-related information).

(Galer-Unti et al., 2004)

7.4.9 ℕ Lead advocacy initiatives

Making public policy and leading advocacy initiatives is a continuous process that relies heavily upon proven approaches and other factors that include resources, personal experiences, ideology, interest groups, and advocacy organizations. Health education specialists must become and remain committed to staying current on effective approaches to mobilize their stakeholders; disseminate success with other health education specialists; and participate in training opportunities to sharpen skills and abilities to lead advocacy initiatives. Leading advocacy initiatives requires health education specialists to demonstrate leadership in prioritizing key issues in public health and education, identifying appropriate social networks, mobilizing other health education organizations, fund raising, strategic planning, and evaluating advocacy efforts.

7.4.10 ⚑ Evaluate advocacy efforts

Since advocacy has become a more common activity for health education specialists, it is becoming increasingly important to evaluate those efforts (Fagen et al., 2009). Because successful implementation of advocacy strategies is determined in real-time and, by nature, must be responsive to continuously shifting social and political environments, advocacy evaluation is most likely to be proactive than retrospective in approach and emphasize assessing continuous progress over time toward the policy goal (Fagen et al., 2009).

Common advocacy evaluation questions include:

- How are advocates building their professional capacities by learning skills such as communications, media relations, strategy development, and campaign planning?
- Based on influential factors in the political, social, and economic environments, what advocacy strategies are likely to be most effective for policy change efforts?
- How can multiple agencies work together effectively to advocate for mutually desirable policy changes?
- How can advocacy strategies be changed during a campaign to more effectively influence desired policy changes?

(Fagen et al., 2009, p. 483)

Table 7.2 below describes resources to assist the health education specialist in developing competency in advocacy evaluation.

Table 7.2
Advocacy Evaluation Resources

Innovation Network www.innonet.org	Free clearinghouse of more than 100 advocacy evaluation resources; free newsletter Advocacy Evaluation Update; free report *Speaking for Themselves: Advocates' Perspectives on Evaluation*
The California Endowment www.calendow.org	Sections of Web site on advocacy and evaluation; free downloadable materials including *The Challenges of Assessing Advocacy: Parts I and II*
The Evaluation Exchange www.hfrp.org/evaluation/the-evaluation	Free downloadable publication from the Harvard Family Research Project, Evaluation Exchange Spring 2007 issue focused on advocacy evaluation

(*Note*. Adapted from Fagen et al., 2009, pp. 483-484)

Key: ◻ Entry ⚑ Advanced – level information

CHAPTER VII

Competency 7.5:
Influence Policy to Promote Health

The role of health education specialists influencing health policy to promote health is very important. This section will provide the reader with information on:

- use of evaluation and research findings in policy analysis;
- implications of health policy for individuals, groups, and communities;
- importance of advocating for health-related policies, regulations, laws, or roles;
- use of evidence-based research to develop policies to promote health; and
- use of policy and media advocacy techniques to influence decision-makers.

7.5.1 ⚊ Use evaluation and research findings in policy analysis

Health education specialists should use evaluation and research findings in policy analysis to inform health policy debates and to help address decision makers' information needs regarding longstanding critical issues, such as people who lack health insurance, efficient operation of government health insurance programs, effective care delivery, chronic disease and long-term care, health care financing, and public health. Further, the utilization of evaluation and research findings can help health education specialists assess needs of their stakeholders that remain unmet. Use of evaluation and research findings in policy analysis will serve as a key resource to help health education specialists to remain current with reported policy implications, the identification of solutions, and translating effective policy and media advocacy techniques to influence decision makers into practice.

7.5.2 Identify the significance and implications of health policy for individuals, groups and communities

As professionals, health education specialists interact with a variety of individuals ranging from legislative correspondents, health care providers, and patients. The health education specialist has to be skilled in written and verbal communication, as well as in understanding and interpreting mass media.

Conceptually, health policy includes factors and forces that affect the health of the public. Policies play a major role in delivering and financing health care and public health efforts in the United States; they influence or structure health care, communities, and society.

The organizing, financing, and delivery of health-related policy are affected by the following forces: Congress, federal health agencies, states, health care providers, businesses, and local communities (Barr, 2002). Because health policy is an ever-changing endeavor, it is essential for health education specialists to stay abreast of developments for advocacy work and policy change.

Key: ▢ Entry ⚊ Advanced – level information

7.5.3 Advocate for health-related policies, regulations, laws or rules

Before contacting an elected official, it is important to have an understanding of the issue being discussed. Prepare brief and clear "talking points" that state the problem, proof of the problem, and the solution being advocated. Many individuals contact their elected officials by phone, E-mail, fax, letter, or in person. E-mailed or faxed letters are a preferred written method, because - unlike mailed letters - they do not have to go through a bioterrorism screening process. Because of the changing dynamics of mail screening processes, one should check for the best way to contact an elected official.

Prior to a first meeting with a legislator, it is vital for the health education specialist to conduct research on the legislator. This will help the health education specialist identify personal and professional information about the legislator, as well as identify endorsers, committees, sponsors and influencers of the legislator.

After contacting a legislator, advocacy efforts are not over. It is important to take the time to show appreciation with a "thank you" and to follow-up with the representative or an appropriate staff person. Find others who support the issue and encourage them to make a phone call, write a letter, sign a petition, or schedule a meeting. By using a variety of strategies to advocate for health issues, a health education specialist has the potential to shape and change policy to impact the health of many people (Galer-Unti et al., 2004).

Health education specialists conducting media advocacy can follow some basic steps to improve effectiveness: develop a strategy, understand the media, develop messages, and attract journalists' attention and trust (Dorfman, 2009).

Individuals involved in advocacy work and policy change often question their impact on the system. Evaluating the progress of policy change created by advocacy efforts can be challenging. The California Endowment (Guthrie, Louis, David & Foster, 2006) recommends the following key steps in a policy evaluation approach:

1. adopting a conceptual model for understanding the process of policy change;
2. developing a theory about how and why planned activities lead to desired outcomes;
3. selecting benchmarks to monitor progress; and
4. measuring progress toward benchmarks and collecting data.

The California Endowment also advocates creating benchmarks to represent key milestones in creating change. Table 7.3 represents an example of a benchmark framework:

Key: ◻ Entry ⫶⫶ Advanced – level information

Table 7.3

Example of Benchmark Development from Framework

Benchmark Category	Project-Specific Interim Benchmarks of Progress
Changing definitions/reframing	Change official purpose of vending machines to include providing nutritious food for students
Community or individual behavior	Recruit 100 students to submit requests for healthy snack choices into the school suggestion box
Shifts in critical mass	Have four of seven school board members to make a motion to hold a hearing on the issue of vending machines in schools
Institutional policy	School board passes a resolution banning sodas from being sold in school vending machines
Holding the line	Stop vending machine lobby from introducing resolution to allow vending machines in junior high and high schools

(Guthrie et al., 2006)

Research regarding health care policy provides evidence-based information that affects health care outcomes. In addition, quality, cost, use, and access to public health and health care are influenced. The research background helps public health stakeholders to make informed decisions and improve the quality of health education and public health efforts.

7.5.4 ▨ Use evidence-based research to develop policies to promote health

The Guide to Community Preventive Services is a free resource to help practitioners choose programs and policies to improve health and prevent disease at the community level. Systematic reviews are used to answer these questions:

- Which program and policy interventions have been proven effective?
- Are there effective interventions that are right for my community?
- What might effective interventions cost; what is the likely return on investment?

Key: ▢ Entry ▨ Advanced – level information

Laws and policies can affect population health and reduce long-term medical and other costs. Examples include:

- broad-based policies, such as smoking bans and laws;
- targeted laws, such as child safety seat laws;
- educational requirements, such as vaccinations for child care and school attendance; and
- community-wide interventions, such as water fluoridation.

(CDC, 2006b)

The Community Guide (http://www.thecommunityguide.org/uses/policy_development.html) provides information on public health interventions and policies that have been proven to work. As a result, legislators, policy makers, community leaders, and community members interested in specific issues can use it to:

- identify what laws and policies promote public health and at what cost; draft evidence-based policies and legislation;
- justify funding decisions and proposals; and
- support policies and legislation that promote the health of their communities and change policies and legislation that do not.

7.5.5 Employ policy and media advocacy techniques to influence decision-makers

Building relationships with the decision makers who control the means to the change sought, as well as those who influence the decision makers and decision makers' constituents can help health education specialists influence health policy. Determine policy issue areas of interest and the kind of media that can reach key decision makers.

Competency 7.6:
Promote the Health Education Profession

This section will discuss several ways health education specialists can promote the profession including:

- developing a personal plan for professional growth and service;
- being able to describe state-of-the-art health education practice;
- being able to explain major responsibilities of health education specialists;
- developing professional literature; and
- engaging in service to advance the health education profession.

CHAPTER VII

Key: ☐ Entry ◣◣ Advanced – level information

7.6.1 Develop a personal plan for professional growth and service

Health education specialists provide an array of information to diverse audiences in a variety of settings. In planning continuing education, one should take into account the setting in which one is practicing health education or wants to practice in the future. These settings may include community, school (K-12), health care, business/industry, college/university or university health services.

Sources of professional growth for the health education specialist can come through job experience and training, other professional experiences, formal academic preparation, and obtaining individual certification. Professional development opportunities include:

- reading professional journals;
- attending professional meetings;
- taking courses;
- authoring journal articles, chapters, or books;
- presenting at professional meetings; and
- participating in other professional development activities.

At some point, a health education specialist who does not already have an advanced degree, may consider going on for master or doctoral degrees. Typical graduate degrees include:

- Master of Education (MEd);
- Master of Science (MS);
- Master of Arts (MA);
- Master of Public Health (MPH);
- Master of Science in Public Health (MSPH);
- Doctor of Philosophy (PhD); and
- Doctor of Public Health (Dr.PH).

The individual's personal plan for growth should help inform the choice of degree and college or university. In pursuing continuing education opportunities, health education specialists should be cognizant of how the activities may further develop their knowledge and skills in the Seven Areas of Responsibility. Many health education specialists choose to gain the nationally recognized CHES and/or MCHES certification to promote, demonstrate and continue their professional development. Please refer to Sub-competency 7.6.8 for more information on credentialing.

7.6.2 Describe state-of-the-art health education practice

The question of what health educations specialists do in practice was recently confirmed in the Health Educator Job Analysis-2010 (HEJA-2010) that is described in more detail in Sub-competency 7.6.7. In a national survey, health education specialists rated tasks and knowledge performed within the most recent

12 months in terms of frequency and importance. The updated model comprises 223 Sub-competencies, organized into 39 Competencies within Seven major Areas of Responsibility. Of the Sub-competencies, 61 were validated as advanced-level only (NCHEC et al., 2010).

Research establishes what is true regarding a policy program or practice. Evaluation describes the value of a policy program or practice, and the application of health education ethics determines whether or not that valued, proven policy, program or practice should be used. To describe state-of-the art health education, the health education specialist must know the theory behind health education practice, the unified code of ethics, and the basis of program, policy and practice evaluation.

7.6.3 Explain the major responsibilities of the health education specialist in the practice of health education

Seven Areas of Responsibility of health education specialists include:

I. Assess needs, assets, and capacity for health education
II. Plan health education
III. Implement health education
IV. Conduct evaluation and research related to health education
V. Administer and manage health education
VI. Serve as a health education resource person
VII. Communicate and Advocate for health and health education

(NCHEC et al., 2010a)

The U.S. Department of Labor Bureau of Labor Statistics (BLS) (2009) defines health education specialists (SOC 21-1091.00) as those who promote, maintain, and improve individual and community health. The BLS recognizes that health education specialists are responsible for a range of responsibilities that include:

- assisting individuals and communities to adopt healthy behaviors;
- collecting and analyzing data to identify community needs prior; and
- planning, implementing, monitoring, and evaluating programs.

They may also serve as a resource to assist individuals, other professionals, or the community, and may administer fiscal resources for health education programs (BLS, 2009).

Key: Entry / Advanced – level information

7.6.4 Explain the role of health education associations in advancing the profession

Professional associations in health education carry out many of the functions necessary for continuing education in the profession. Their purposes include, but are not limited to, conducting continuing education programs, disseminating research findings, legislative advocacy, and establishing ethics and standards for the profession (Cottrell et al., 2009).

The Coalition of National Health Education Organizations (CNHEO), is a collaboration of membership organizations. Members of the CNHEO are listed in Table 7.4. The primary mission of the CNHEO is "the mobilization of the resources of the health education profession in order to expand and improve health education, regardless of the setting"(CNHEO, n.d.). The CNHEO functions with the following objectives:

- facilitates national-level communication, collaboration, and coordination among the member organizations;
- provides a forum for the identification and discussion of health education issues;
- formulates recommendations and takes appropriate action on issues affecting member interests;
- serves as a communication and advisory resource for agencies, organizations, and persons in the public and private sectors on health education issues; and
- serves as a focus for the exploration and resolution of issues pertinent to professional health education specialists.

(CNHEO, n.d.)

Table 7.4
Members of the Coalition of National Health Education Organizations

Member	Mission	Project-Specific Interim Benchmarks of Progress
American Association for Health Education (AAHE)	To serve health education specialists and other professionals who promote the health of all people. AAHE encourages, supports and assists health professionals concerned with health promotion through education and other systematic strategies.	*American Journal of Health Education* *International Electronic Journal of Health Education* *http://www.aahperd.org/aahe/*
http://www.aahperd.org/aahe/		
American College Health Association (ACHA)	ACHA is the principal advocate and leadership organization for college and university health.	*Journal of American College Health* *http://www.acha.org/*
http://www.acha.org/		

Key: ☐ Entry ⋀⋀ Advanced – level information

American Public Health Association's Public Health Education and Health Promotion Section (APHA-PHEHP)	To be a strong advocate for health education, disease prevention and health promotion directed to individuals, groups and communities in all activities of the association. To set, maintain and exemplify the highest ethical principles and standards of practice on the part of all professionals whose primary purpose is health education and disease prevention.	*American Journal of Public Health* *The Nation's Health*
http://www.jhsph.edu/hao/phehp/		
American Public Health Association's School Health Education and Services Section (APHA-SHES)	To provide a section within the American Public Health Association that works independently with other association substructures and external organizations toward the improvement of early childhood, school, and college health programs.	*American Journal of Public Health* *The Nation's Health*
http://www.apha.org		
American School Health Association (ASHA)	To protect and promote the health of children and youth by supporting coordinated school health programs as a foundation for school success.	*Journal of School Health* *Health in Action*
http://www.ashaweb.org/		
Directors of Health Promotion and Education (DHPE)	To strengthen, promote and enhance the professional practice of health promotion and public health education nationally and within State health departments.	*The Voice*
http://www.dhpe.org/		

CHAPTER VII

Key: ◻ Entry ＼＼ Advanced – level information

Eta Sigma Gamma (ESG)	To foster professional competence and dedication of members in the health education profession.	*The Health Educator* *Eta Sigma Gamma Student Monograph*
http://www.etasigmagamma.org/		
Society of State Directors of Health, Physical Education and Recreation (SSDHPER)	To provide leadership in facilitating and promoting initiatives to achieve national health and education goals and objectives. The society promotes effective school programs and practices that involve collaboration with parents and community groups to positively impact healthy and active lifestyles.	*The Society Page*
http://www.thesociety.org/		
Society for Public Health Education (SOPHE)	To provide leadership to the profession of public health education and to contribute to the health of all people and the elimination of disparities through advances in health education theory and research, excellence in professional preparation and practice, and advocacy for public policies conducive to health.	*Health Promotion Practice* *Health Education and Behavior*
http://www.sophe.org/		

Key: ◻ Entry ＼＼ Advanced – level information

7.6.5 Explain the benefits of participating in professional organizations

Professional organizations perform many of the essential functions that make an occupation a profession (Simons-Morton, Greene, & Gottlieb, 1995). The establishment of professional standards and a credentialing process raises the level of practice in the profession. Membership in one or more of the professional organizations in Table 7.4 allows the health education specialist to update skills and knowledge, network with peers and mentors and identify collaborators for research and publication opportunities. In addition, many associations provide job banks which assist members both in locating a new position and in recruiting professional talent. Joining state and local professional organizations can increase networking that supports the health education specialist's ability to influence local and state policy and grow and maintain supportive partnerships.

7.6.6 Facilitate professional growth of self and others

For health education specialists practicing in the academic realm, facilitating professional growth of others is the guiding mission. Creating a learning community with peers and students in academic settings facilitates the growth of both faculty and students. Professional growth can also result from additional formal education. Additional course work can be selected to strengthen skills and deepen knowledge or to expand into complementary areas of study. Practitioners can participate in research to practice efforts and serve as preceptors for undergraduate and graduate health education students. For both academics and practitioners, professional growth opportunities include providing and participating in continuing education opportunities via professional organizations at the state and national level. In any setting, health education specialists can function as both a mentor, sharing skills and expertise, or mentee open to the opportunity for acquisition of new knowledge and skills.

7.6.7 Explain the history of the health education profession and its current and future implications for professional practice

The history of health education in the United States dates back to the late 19th century with the establishment of the first academic programs preparing school health educators (Allegrante et al., 2004). Interest in quality assurance, and the development of standards for professional preparation of health educators emerged in the 1940s. Over the next several decades, professional associations produced guidelines for preparing health educators, and accreditation efforts were introduced. Yet it was not until the 1970s that health education began evolving as a true profession in terms of sociological perspective (Livingood & Auld, 2001). In addition to defining a body of literature, efforts were initiated to promulgate a Health Education Code of Ethics, a skill-based set of competencies, rigorous systems for quality assurance, and a health education credentialing system (NCHEC et al., 2010).

Beginning in the mid 1970s, the health education profession began the process of developing the steps necessary to establish the credentialing of health education specialists. This process is outlined in more detail in the publication, *A Competency-Based Framework for Health Education Specialists – 2010* (NCHEC et al., 2010a). Through a series of conferences, workshops, and the landmark Role Delineation Project (United

Key: ▢ Entry ◪ Advanced – level information

CHAPTER VII

States Department of Health, Education and Welfare, 1978), which was officially funded in 1980, the responsibilities, functions, skills, and knowledge expected of the entry-level health education specialist were delineated, and the concept of the "generic role" of all health educators, regardless of work setting, emerged and formed the basis for the credentialing process for health education specialists (NCHEC et al., 2010a).

The 1978 Workshop on Commonalities and Differences recommended the formation of a planning committee, which became the National Task Force on the Preparation and Practice of Health Educators (NTFPPHE). Competencies were developed and released in the 1985 document *A Framework for the Development of Competency-Based Curricula for Entry-level Health Educators*. NTFPPHE formally became incorporated as the National Commission for Health Education Credentialing, Inc (NCHEC) in 1988. In 1989, experienced health education professionals had the opportunity to become Certified Health Education Specialists via a chartership process that included a review of documented experience. The first CHES exam was administered in 1990 and is now offered twice a year at more than 120 testing locations nationwide.

The role of the health education specialist was further defined in a six year (1998-2004) study known as the National Health Education Specialist Competencies Update Project (CUP), which outlined the roles of entry- and advanced-level health education specialists (Gilmore et al., 2005). Results from the CUP study led to the release of new publications in 2006 and 2007, and revisions to the CHES exam in October 2007 to reflect the updated Responsibilities, Competencies and Sub-competencies of the entry-level health education specialist. Very significantly, the CUP model introduced a hierarchical model in which advanced-level builds on the entry-level (Gilmore et al., 2005). This finding paved the way for the introduction of an advanced-level certification, identified as Master Certified Health Education Specialist (MCHES) by NCHEC commencing in 2010 (NCHEC, 2010a).

In June of 2008, the CHES exam was granted accreditation by the National Commission for Certifying Agencies (NCCA), a government-recognized accrediting body for professional certification organizations. This signifies that the CHES exam complies with stringent testing and measurement standards among certification organizations.

The next phase of research was known as Health Educator Job Analysis-2010 (HEJA-2010), an 18-month project, sponsored by AAHE, SOPHE, and NCHEC, to validate the contemporary practice of entry- and advanced-level health education specialists. The updated model is comprised of 223 Sub-competencies, organized into 39 Competencies within Seven major Areas of Responsibility. Of the Sub-competencies, 61 were validated as advanced-level only (NCHEC et al., 2010a; NCHEC et al., 2010b). The HEJA-2010 results are the basis of this publication, *The Health Education Specialist: A Companion Guide for Professional Excellence, 6th Edition*.

Key: ☐ Entry 〴 Advanced   level information

Health Education History Timeline

1978 National Task Force developed

1980 Role verification – project officially initiated

1985 Competencies established

1988 NCHEC incorporated as a nonprofit organization

1989 Charter certification initiated - work history

1990 First CHES exam given

1997 CHES exam offered twice a year

2000 Code of Ethics for Health Education Profession adopted

2005 Competency Update Project Results Released (1998-2004 study)

2006 Revised Framework Published

2007 Revised Study Guide Published

2007 CHES exam revised based on New Framework

2008 CHES Accredited by National Commission on Certifying Agencies (NCCA)

2010 Health Educator Job Analysis (HEJA) Results Released (2008-2009 study)

Significant progress has been made in the past 30 years in the Health Education Profession in role delineation, competency validation, and individual certifications.

7.6.8 Explain the role of credentialing in the promotion of the health education profession

Credentialing is an umbrella term that refers to several processes put in place to ensure that persons who deliver a given service have obtained a minimum level of competency (skills, ability, and knowledge). These processes include the accreditation of institutions and licensure or certification/registration of individuals (National Task Force on the Preparation and Practice of Health Education Specialists, 1985; Taub, Birch, Auld, Lysoby, & Rasar King, 2009). Certification is the method of individual credentialing for the profession.

The CHES certification was developed by, and for, the health education profession to demonstrate the mastery of a set of fundamental skills across all practice settings. It is a voluntary certification. The CHES credential has three components: academic preparation specifically in health education, successfully passing a written exam, and then continued professional development (continuing education) of a minimum of 75 credit hours over a five year period. In order to obtain and maintain the CHES credential, all three components must be met.

Key: ◻ Entry ⫼ Advanced – level information

As a result of the CUP and the HEJA-2010 findings, an advanced-level certification, MCHES will commence in 2010. The MCHES credential has four components: a combination of academic preparation and experience, successfully passing a written exam, and then continued professional development (continuing education) of a minimum of 75 credit hours over a five year period. "CHES" or "MCHES" after an educator's name is one indication of professional competence and a commitment to continued professional development.

NCHEC has committed to maintaining accreditation for the CHES certification through NCCA. Among the NCCA Standards for the Accreditation of Certification Programs is the requirement that a professional role delineation or job analysis be conducted and periodically validated. NCHEC has therefore committed to ongoing re-verification of the Responsibilities, Competencies and Sub-competencies of health education specialists which has implications beyond certification, including the areas of professional development and professional preparation in the field of health education.

In addition to individual certification, the health education profession has mechanisms for program approval or accreditation of institutions preparing health education specialists. The SOPHE/AAHE Baccalaureate Program Approval Committee (SABPAC) approves undergraduate programs. The Council on Education for Public Health (CEPH) currently primarily accredits graduate and some undergraduate programs. The National Council for Accreditation of Teacher Education (NCATE) and Teacher Accreditation Council (TEAC) both accredit undergraduate teacher preparation programs. Efforts have been made, and continue, to coordinate the system of quality assurance of health education programs under the guidance of three task forces starting with the National Task Force on Accreditation in Health Education (Allegrante, 2004; Taub et al., 2009).

7.6.9 Engage in professional development activities

Professional development activities are built into the CHES and/or MCHES certifications as continuing education credits are required to maintain and renew those professional credentials. The MCHES certification is specifically designed to recognize professional development with a minimum of five years of experience and demonstration of advanced-level practice required for eligibility for the certification. All health education specialists, whether certified or not, should make a commitment to ongoing continuing education and professional development. This publication includes two tools, a Self-Assessment for Health Education Specialists: Perceived Competence and Practice Questions to help assess knowledge and skills gaps that might direct those continuing education activities. The health education specialist, through job responsibilities or involvement with professional associations, can gain professional development through training, technical assistance, scholarly research and dissemination, and voluntary leadership and service.

7.6.10 Serve as a mentor to others

In order to grow the profession and elevate its importance in society, it is important for health education specialists to reach out to new and emerging health education specialists to help them develop and build their professional growth. Therefore, health education specialists are encouraged to become an official mentor or coach to someone in the profession and help them succeed by finding ways to use their strengths while developing new skills and

Key: ☐ Entry ⋀ Advanced – level information

knowledge. Take the opportunity to exchange skills. Many more seasoned health education specialists can upgrade their technology skills by working with, and learning from, "techno-native" colleagues. Collaborating on research or practice initiatives can contribute to the field as well as personal development.

7.6.11 Develop materials that contribute to the professional literature

From any practice setting, health education specialists can participate in research/practice collaboration, including participating on writing teams for publication in peer reviewed journals, electronic or print books. Participation as a member of a cross-disciplinary team in research or practice initiatives can enrich both health education literature and the other participating disciplines. Health education specialists staying current in reading one or more professional journals regularly can respond to articles in peer-reviewed journals in letters to the editor or commentary.

Practitioners can publish lessons learned and evaluation findings in "notes for the field" opportunities in research journals or by contributing to more practice-oriented journals (such as *Health Promotion Practice*). Practitioners and researchers can serve on dissertation or master's thesis committees, co-authoring articles with masters or doctoral candidates, and mentoring them to continue as contributors to the field. Research and practice collaborations can also lead to submission of theory-driven practice tested model programs, policies or practices to listings such as the Substance Abuse and Mental Health Services Administration's (SAMHSA) National Registry of Evidence-based Programs and Practices (NREPP) (SAMHSA, 2010).

All health education specialists can submit abstracts or presentations to local, state, and national meetings that can lead to them being included as a part of meeting proceedings. Volunteering to be a reviewer for such abstracts or for health education, health communication, health promotion, or related journals not only contributes to the professional literature of the field, but can also improve the health education specialist's own research and writing skills.

7.6.12 Engage in service to advance the health education profession

Previous sections have discussed service opportunities such as joining local, state, and national professional organizations and serving on committees or as an elected officer, and volunteering as a reviewer for conference abstracts or professional publications. Health education specialists can also contribute their skills and experience by serving on boards of local, state or national health and human service non-profit organizations. Recruiting the best and brightest of our students and colleagues to the profession of health education, engaging them in professional organizations, and mentoring them in our various roles and settings is a service that will continue to elevate all aspects of our profession.

Advocating for health education resources and making legislative visits to promote the inclusion of health education in state or federally funded health education, health communication and health promotion activities are other ways to serve. Running for public office at the local, state or federal level represents a long way to engage in service, thus working to reach the "Best in advocacy" (Galer-Unti et al., 2004). Seek positions of authority with responsibilities for making policy, and apply many of the health education skills discussed in this study guide to improve organizational effectiveness.

Key: ◻ Entry \\ Advanced – level information

AREA OF RESPONSIBILITY VII

The value of professional involvement and service is unquestionable. It is through service that a health education specialist can derive the greatest satisfaction. The struggles, accomplishments and networking that emerges from working with peers who share a similar interest will help health education specialists develop an appreciation for how much we can accomplish working collectively to achieve a common goal. More importantly than building resumes, service helps the educator to make connections, develop skills, and gain confidence in their abilities. All of these attributes yield rich rewards.

Key: ☐ Entry ◢◣ Advanced – level information

APPENDIX A

Code of Ethics for the Health Education Profession

The Code of Ethics for the Health Education Profession was developed by the Coalition of National Health Education Organizations (CNHEO). As the health education profession progresses and meets new challenges, the Code of Ethics is revised to reflect new realities. Therefore, it is important to note that at the same time the sixth edition of this manuscript was being developed, the Code of Ethics was being revised. The revised Code of Ethics will be released once it is approved by all CNHEO member organizations. Users of this companion guide are encouraged to remain attentive to the existing Code of Ethics and the revised Code of Ethics once made available.

PREAMBLE

The health education profession is dedicated to excellence in the practice of promoting individual, family, organizational, and community health. Guided by common ideals, health education specialists are responsible for upholding the integrity and ethics of the profession as they face the daily challenges of making decisions. By acknowledging the value of diversity in society and embracing a cross-cultural approach, health education specialists support the worth, dignity, potential and uniqueness of all people.

The Code of Ethics provides a framework of shared values within which health education is practiced. The Code of Ethics is grounded in fundamental ethical principles that underlie all health care services: respect for autonomy, promotion of social justice, active promotion of good, and avoidance of harm. The responsibility of each health education specialist is to aspire to the highest possible standards of conduct and to encourage the ethical behavior of all those with whom they work.

Regardless of job title, professional affiliation, work setting, or population served, health education specialists abide by these guidelines when making professional decisions (CNHEO, 1999).

Article I: Responsibility to the Public

A health education specialist's ultimate responsibility is to educate people for the purpose of promoting, maintaining, and improving individual, family, and community health. When a conflict of issues arises among individuals, groups, organizations, agencies, or institutions, health education specialists must consider all issues and give priority to those who promote wellness and quality of living through principles of self-determination and freedom of choice for the individual.

Section 1: Health education specialists support the right of individuals to make informed decisions regarding health, as long as such decisions pose no threat to the health of others.

Section 2: Health education specialists encourage actions and social policies that support and facilitate the best balance of benefits over harm for all affected parties.

Section 3: Health education specialists accurately communicate the potential benefits and consequences of the services and programs with which they are associated.

Section 4: Health education specialists accept the responsibility to act on issues that can adversely affect the health of individuals, families, and communities.

Section 5: Health education specialists are truthful about their qualifications and the limitations of their expertise and provide services consistent with their competencies.

Section 6: Health education specialists protect the privacy and dignity of individuals.

Section 7: Health education specialists actively involve individuals, groups, and communities in the entire educational process, so that all aspects of the process are clearly understood by those who may be affected.

Section 8: Health education specialists respect and acknowledge the rights of others to hold diverse values, attitudes, and opinions.

Section 9: Health education specialists provide services equitably to all people.

(CNHEO, 1999)

Article II: Responsibility to the Profession

Health education specialists are responsible for their professional behavior, for the reputation of their profession, and for promoting ethical conduct among others.

Section 1: Health education specialists maintain, improve, and expand their professional competence through continued study and education; membership, participation, and leadership in professional organizations; and involvement in issues related to the health of the public.

Section 2: Health education specialists model and encourage nondiscriminatory standards of behavior in their interactions with others.

Section 3: Health education specialists encourage and accept responsible critical discourse to protect and enhance the profession.

CODE OF ETHICS FOR THE
HEALTH EDUCATION PROFESSION

Section 4: Health education specialists contribute to the development of the profession by sharing the processes and outcomes of their work.

Section 5: Health education specialists are aware of possible professional conflicts of interest, exercise integrity in conflict situations, and do not manipulate or violate the rights of others.

Section 6: Health education specialists give appropriate recognition to others for their professional contributions and achievements.

(CNHEO, 1999)

Article III: Responsibility to Employers

Health education specialists accurately recognize the boundaries of their professional competence and are accountable for their professional activities and actions.

Section 1: Health education specialists accurately represent their qualifications and the qualifications of others whom they recommend.

Section 2: Health education specialists use the appropriate standards, theories, and guidelines as criteria when carrying out their professional responsibilities.

Section 3: Health education specialists accurately represent potential service and program outcomes to employers.

Section 4: Health education specialists anticipate and disclose competing commitments, conflicts of interest, and endorsement of products.

Section 5: Health education specialists openly communicate to employers expectations of job-related assignments that conflict with their professional ethics.

Section 6: Health education specialists maintain competence in their areas of professional practice.

(CNHEO, 1999)

Article IV: Responsibility in the Delivery of Health Education

Health education specialists promote integrity in the delivery of health education. They respect the rights, dignity, confidentiality, and worth of all people by adapting strategies and methods to meet the needs of diverse populations and communities.

Section 1: Health education specialists are sensitive to social and cultural diversity and are in accord with the law when planning and implementing programs.

Section 2: Health education specialists are informed of the latest advances in theory, research, and practice, and use strategies and methods that are grounded in, and contribute to, development of professional standards, theories, guidelines, statistics, and experience.

Section 3: Health education specialists are committed to rigorous evaluation of program effectiveness and the methods used to achieve results.

Section 4: Health education specialists empower individuals to adopt healthy lifestyles through informed choice rather than by coercion or intimidation.

Section 5: Health education specialists communicate the potential outcomes of proposed services, strategies, and pending decisions to all individuals who will be affected.

(CNHEO, 1999)

Article V: Responsibility in Research and Evaluation

Health education specialists contribute to the health of the population and to the profession through research and evaluation activities. When planning and conducting research or evaluation, health education specialists do so in accordance with federal and state laws and regulations, organizational and institutional policies, and professional standards.

Section 1: Health education specialists support principles and practices of research and evaluation that do no harm to individuals, groups, society, or the environment.

Section 2: Health education specialists ensure that participation in research is voluntary and is based upon the informed consent of the participants.

Section 3: Health education specialists respect the privacy, rights, and dignity of the research participants, and honor commitments made to those participants.

Section 4: Health education specialists treat all information obtained from participants as confidential unless otherwise required by law.

Section 5: Health education specialists take credit, including authorship, only for work they have actually performed and give credit to the contributions of others.

Section 6: Health education specialists who serve as research or evaluation consultants discuss their results only with those to whom they are providing service, unless maintaining such confidentiality would jeopardize the health or safety of others.

Section 7: Health education specialists report the results of their research and evaluation objectively, accurately, and in a timely fashion.

(CNHEO, 1999)

CODE OF ETHICS FOR THE
HEALTH EDUCATION PROFESSION

Article VI: Responsibility in Professional Preparation

Those involved in the preparation and training of health education specialists have an obligation to accord learners the same respect and treatment given other groups by providing quality education that benefits the profession and the public.

Section 1: Health education specialists select students for professional preparation programs based upon equal opportunity for all, and the individual's academic performance, abilities, and potential contribution to the profession and the public's health.

Section 2: Health education specialists strive to make the educational environment and culture conducive to the health of all involved, and free from sexual harassment and all forms of discrimination.

Section 3: Health education specialists involved in professional preparation and professional development engage in careful preparation; present material that is accurate, up-to-date, and timely; provide reasonable and timely feedback; state clear and reasonable expectations; and conduct fair assessments and evaluations of learners.

Section 4: Health education specialists provide objective and accurate counseling to learners about career opportunities, development, and advancement, and assist learners to secure professional employment.

Section 5: Health education specialists provide adequate supervision and meaningful opportunities for the professional development of learners.

(CNHEO, 1999)

APPENDIX B

The Certified Health Education Specialist (CHES) and Master Certified Health Education Specialist (MCHES) Examinations

To implement a certification program, it is necessary to develop examinations that accurately measure practice-related knowledge and skills. The National Commission for Health Education Credentialing, Inc. (NCHEC) utilizes the Certified Health Education Specialist (CHES) and the Master Certified Education Specialist (MCHES) examinations to assess the extent to which a candidate can possess, apply, and interpret knowledge relative to the Seven Areas of Responsibility; delineated from *A Competency-Based Framework for Health Education Specialists – 2010.*

Both the CHES and MCHES examinations are criterion-referenced tests that consist of a total of 165 (150 scored plus 15 pilot test) multiple-choice questions in paper-and-pencil format. The passing score for each exam is determined by a modified Angoff method and represents a fixed standard of knowledge, independent of candidate performance. Essentially, this method allows subject-matter experts to establish a level of knowledge that is expected of professionals who are minimally competent. This passing point is reviewed, and statistics are analyzed to ensure reliability and validity of both the CHES and MCHES exams. By using this methodology, there is no curve, and candidates do not compete against one another. There is also no penalty for guessing.

In constructing the exams, NCHEC works with Professional Examination Service (PES), a nonprofit, national testing organization with more than 50 years' experience in developing credentialing exams. Together, the organizations develop the examinations according to the process mentioned above. The percentage of questions in the exam pertaining to each Area of Responsibility is based on the results of the Health Educator Job Analysis 2010. The percent of questions coming from each Area of Responsibility for the current exams are presented in the tables below. When preparing for either the CHES or MCHES exams, it is recommended that a candidate take into account these percentages.

CHES Exam Seven Areas of Responsibility for Health Education Specialists

Area of Responsibility	Percentage of Questions
I. Assess Needs, Assets, and Capacity for Health Education	12%
II. Plan Health Education	15%
III. Implement Health Education	24%
IV. Conduct Evaluation and Research Related to Health Education	15%
V. Administer and Manage Health Education	11%
VI. Serve as a Health Education Resource Person	16%
VII. Communicate and Advocate for Health and Health Education	7%
TOTAL EXAM	**100%**

MCHES Exam Seven Areas of Responsibility for Health Education Specialists

Area of Responsibility	Percentage of Questions
I. Assess Needs, Assets, and Capacity for Health Education	10%
II. Plan Health Education	15%
III. Implement Health Education	20%
IV. Conduct Evaluation and Research Related to Health Education	16%
V. Administer and Manage Health Education	16%
VI. Serve as a Health Education Resource Person	15%
VII. Communicate and Advocate for Health and Health Education	8%
TOTAL EXAM	**100%**

APPENDIX C

Practice Examination Questions

The following practice examination questions address Sub-competencies identified as entry-level as defined by the Health Educator Job Analysis (refer to page 188) and outlined and addressed within this companion guide. The practice questions, written by health education specialists, may assist the user in preparing for the CHES examination and or to identify areas of concentration for professional development and training of practicing health education specialists. The questions are not on the current certification examination, nor have they been on any previous certification examination. These questions have not been subjected to the same rigorous psychometric testing procedures as questions appearing on the Certified Health Education Specialist (CHES) or Master Certified Health Education Specialist (MCHES) examinations. Specifically, a passing score on the practice examination questions does not in any way predict or guarantee a passing score on the CHES examination. The practice questions should only be used to direct study efforts.

The practice questions are meant to be challenging. Initially, the user may find that more than one answer appears to be correct. In these instances, the user is encouraged to conduct careful analysis of the questions and possible answers to identify the correct responses. It is recommended that the practice examination questions are answered under similar conditions in which the CHES examination is officially administered. For example, the user should allow no more than three hours to complete the examination. The user should not utilize or depend on resources such as the companion guide, textbooks, publications, or calculators to complete the examination.

An answer key is provided at the end of the practice examination questions. In addition to providing the user with the correct answer, the user will find at least one Area of Responsibility that aligns with the question identified. A review of the number of incorrect answers from any particular Area of Responsibility may help the user to target areas of weakness where more study would be beneficial. *It is strongly recommended that resources beyond the use of this companion guide are used to adequately prepare for the certification examination.*

For those preparing for the Master Certified Health Education Specialist (MCHES) examination or assessing additional professional development and training priorities for advanced-level practicing health education specialists, additional resources are available. A separate set of practice examination questions addressing sub-competencies identified as advanced-level as defined by the Health Educator Job Analysis (refer to page 188) are available for purchase as a supplement.

In closing, feedback from candidates who were successful in passing previous certification examinations and previous study guide users indicates that being part of a small group that allowed participants to "work through" the practice examination questions and discuss why answers were correct or incorrect can be beneficial.

APPENDIX C

1. Data compiled by others, which may or may not have been directly obtained from the individual or population being assessed, is known as:
   a. secondary.
   b. primary.
   c. tertiary.
   d. internal.

2. Sending a personally addressed letter advertising a new weight loss program is an example of:
   a. tailoring.
   b. targeting.
   c. marketing.
   d. mass mailing.

3. The health education specialist wishes to raise public awareness of an important health issue using such tools as a press release, Letter to the Editor, and interactive Web 2.0 resources. Awareness strategies using these tools would be considered:
   a. media advocacy.
   b. policy advocacy.
   c. legislative advocacy.
   d. public practice advocacy.

4. When presenting information to adults with less than a high school education, which method would be the best way to communicate statistical health information?
   a. Graphs
   b. Tables
   c. Handouts
   d. Technical discussions

5. Based on the chart below, what percentage of the population read at a below basic or basic level, resulting in difficulty with reading and comprehending health education materials?
   a. 29%
   b. 14%
   c. 43%
   d. 87%

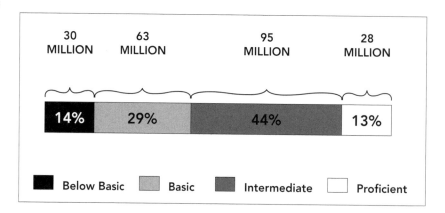

6. National surveillance data, hospital discharge data, and insurance claims data are all appropriate forms of which type of data:
   - a. secondary.
   - b. input.
   - c. descriptive.
   - d. primary.

7. Ongoing monitoring and assessment of program development and implementation is:
   - a. impact evaluation.
   - b. formative evaluation.
   - c. quantitative evaluation.
   - d. summative evaluation.

8. The first step in identifying a need for community health education programs should be to:
   - a. assess existing individual behaviors.
   - b. establish program objectives.
   - c. conduct a community analysis.
   - d. determine the poverty level.

9. Which of the following would be the primary incentive for a business or corporation to have a representative volunteer with a local health organization?
   - a. Meeting new people
   - b. Attending awards ceremonies
   - c. Facilitating meetings
   - d. Public recognition for volunteer contributions

10. The website that provides health information for consumers is:
   - a. MEDLINE.
   - b. Healthfinder.gov.
   - c. GEM.
   - d. National Center for Health Statistics.

11. Having a walking trail nearby is an example of which factor related to behavior change?
   - a. Predisposing
   - b. Reinforcing
   - c. Enabling
   - d. Fostering

12. Your advocacy efforts are starting to be successful in a town that has historically been pro-tobacco. The city council has voted 4-1 to hold a town hall meeting to discuss a clean indoor air ordinance. Which type of advocacy benchmark is this?
    a. Community or individual behavior
    b. Shifts in critical mass
    c. Changing definitions/reframing
    d. Institutional policy

13. Adolescents are often influenced by their peers when making health decisions. According to the Theory of Planned Behavior, which construct describes this phenomena?
    a. Attitudes
    b. Perceived Behavioral Control
    c. Intention
    d. Subjective norm

14. During a physical activity intervention session, a health education specialist asks participants to brainstorm ways to overcome barriers to physical activity. This session is focusing on which construct from Social Cognitive Theory?
    a. Self-efficacy
    b. Self-control
    c. Social support
    d. Reciprocal determinism

15. The process of managing the constant change that affects almost any organization is best reflected by conducting:
    a. a focus group.
    b. an evaluation.
    c. an assessment.
    d. a strategic planning session.

16. In considering the objective, "All youth participating in the after-school program will have a safe ride home at the end of the activity," the health education specialist recognizes that transportation is a tangible resource. In this scenario he/she is:
    a. writing behavioral objectives.
    b. assessing resources.
    c. designing a transportation intervention.
    d. assessing effectiveness.

PRACTICE EXAMINATION QUESTIONS

Please use the data set below for questions 17 and 18.

17. Assume that the health education specialist is analyzing following set of data.

Score   11 14 17 18 19 20 21 22 23 24 25
Frequency   2 1 5 8 6 12 13 10 15 9 8

These data most likely are characterized as:
      a. negatively skewed.
      b. positively skewed.
      c. normal.
      d. uniformly distributed.

18. In what situation will a health education specialist obtain a negative value for the variance?:
      a. A negative variance will never obtain.
      b. All observations are at the mean.
      c. The distribution is very negatively skewed.
      d. The distribution is positively skewed.

19. When searching online on behalf of a client, a health education specialist finds a list of article summaries on the effects of vaccination as a preventive measure for the spread of influenza. The type of source he/she found is classified as:
      a. secondary.
      b. tertiary.
      c. primary.
      d. null.

20. When collecting primary data, which of the following survey methods is most likely to save time and money?
      a. Face-to-face interviews
      b. Internet (E-mail)
      c. Mail
      d. Telephone

21. Health engineering strategies affect which of the following factors regarding where people live or work?
      a. Ecological
      b. Ergogenic
      c. Economical
      d. Environmental

22. A person is making a plan to quit smoking in the next month. This person would be in which stage of the Stages of Change?
      a. Preparation
      b. Precontemplation
      c. Action
      d. Contemplation

23. In order to justify additional funding for the program, the health education specialist, as project administrator, needs to measure whether the health education intervention caused the desired changes in the target audience. The role of this evaluation effort is:
    a. formative.
    b. monitoring.
    c. clinical.
    d. summative.

24. The board of a local health-related agency has hired a health education specialist to explore the possibility of developing a health promotion program. The initial task of the health education specialist is:
    a. setting program goals and objectives.
    b. conducting a needs assessment.
    c. creating the program.
    d. developing an evaluation plan.

25. A group of new immigrants in an urban community has an outbreak of measles among their children. They resist immunization. The health education specialist's job is to quickly develop an education and recruitment campaign to forestall a serious epidemic. Which of the following is the first step in the implementation process for this program?
    a. Gain acceptance for the program
    b. Specify tasks and estimate resources
    c. Develop plans for program activities
    d. Put the plans into action

26. If a researcher conducts a database search for information on harmful levels of certain chemicals in salt-water fish consumed in Florida, what combination of keywords would provide the best access to the information needed?
    a. Ocean, fish, Florida, chemicals
    b. Florida, fish, ocean, eating
    c. Fish, chemicals, Florida, consumption
    d. Morbidity, fishing industry, consumption, Florida

27. A health department wishes to create educational print materials for community members with language disorders and low literacy levels. Which of the following is most effective in determining the reading level of those written materials?
    a. Crisp Readability Formula
    b. FLASH
    c. SMOG
    d. Log-Gunning Index

28. Checking to see if an instrument is measuring concepts consistently is measuring its:
    a. reliability.
    b. utility.
    c. outcomes.
    d. internal bias.

29. Use of advocacy activities is the best implementation approach for which of the following health education interventions?
    a. Individual smoking cessation programs
    b. Interventions to persuade obese individuals to lose weight
    c. Work-related stress management techniques
    d. Legislation to restrict smoking in public places

30. Which of the following is an example of a learning objective?
    a. Individuals participating in the health education program will be able to identify three ways to protect their skin from the sun.
    b. Individuals in the program will increase their cardiovascular activity by 25 percent by the sixth week of the program.
    c. Seventy-five percent of individuals participating in the program will consume five to nine vegetables per day over the following three months.
    d. Program health education specialists will identify 10 new participants for each program period.

31. When the health education specialist creates and distributes a podcast regarding obesity prevention, they are utilizing:
    a. SMS (Short Message Service).
    b. communication technology.
    c. qualitative research.
    d. readiness assessment.

32. An after-school program was developed to help overweight and obese adolescents lose weight. In developing the program, the health education specialist considered the adolescents' attitude, beliefs and values regarding diet and physical activity. Knowing this information, the health education specialist helped to:
    a. institutionalize cultural knowledge.
    b. implement policies for youth.
    c. ensure the program was culturally appropriate and relevant.
    d. develop clear program goals and objectives.

33. The health education specialist working in a foreign country is working cross-culturally. One of the most important keys to culturally competent health promotion and understanding different health beliefs/practices is the health education specialist's understanding of that population's:
    a. food choices.
    b. value system.
    c. style of dress.
    d. health department organizational structure.

34. The local cancer control coalition is searching for evidence-based programs and policies for cancer prevention in their community. In the future, they also want to draft evidence-based policy and legislation. What would be the most appropriate resource to review?
    a. Decision-maker Matrix
    b. Benchmark Development Frameworks
    c. Advocacy Evaluation Resources
    d. Guide to Community Preventive Services

35. Which federal government agency is primarily responsible for Healthy People 2020?
    a. U.S. Consumer Product Safety Commission
    b. Office of Disease Prevention and Health Promotion
    c. National Institutes of Health
    d. Centers for Disease Control

36. Using the PRECEDE-PROCEED model for planning a community-wide physical activity program, the health education specialist first defines the quality of life of the target population. This phase is referred to as what type of assessment?
    a. Social
    b. Ecological
    c. Epidemiological
    d. Administrative

37. A health education specialist at a neighborhood health clinic socially interacts with a client's partner. The educator mentions the client's response to a prescribed medication. Which of the following responsibilities of the Health Education Profession's Code of Ethics did the health education specialist violate?
    a. Respect of clients' rights
    b. Respect of clients' confidentiality
    c. Respect of clients' dignity
    d. Respect of clients' cultural diversity

38. In order to support a team effort of a planning committee, it is important for the health education specialist to:
    a. understand group dynamics and team building.
    b. acquire as many resources as possible to recruit committee members.
    c. identify only community leaders as stakeholders.
    d. target only volunteer committee members.

39. Which section of the health education program evaluation report might contain a description of how the results agree or disagree with current literature?
    a. Literature review
    b. Methodology
    c. Results
    d. Discussion/conclusion

40. A health education specialist is tasked with evaluating the impact of policy decisions regarding the implementation of a new obesity prevention program. Specifically related to policy development, they are focusing on policy:
    a. outcomes.
    b. content.
    c. process.
    d. action.

41. All of the following are possible consequences of poor health literacy except:
    a. poor health outcomes.
    b. self-management of a chronic condition.
    c. improper use of medicines.
    d. inappropriate usage of health care services.

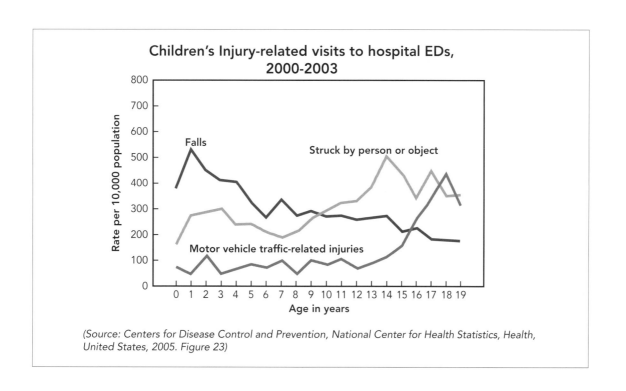

(Source: Centers for Disease Control and Prevention, National Center for Health Statistics, Health, United States, 2005. Figure 23)

42. According to Graph 1.2, during 2000-2003, which of the following is true?
    a. The number of visits related to falls decreased in direct proportion to age.
    b. Between 300 and 400 visits were by seven year olds who sustained falls.
    c. Over 100 visits per 10,000 population were from two year olds who sustained falls.
    d. The number of visits per 10,000 population related to motor vehicle traffic-related injuries increased in direct proportion to age.

43. According to Graph 1.2, during 2000-2003, among those struck by a person or object:
    a. those ages one-four had a lower rate of visits than those ages six-eight.
    b. those ages 13-14 had the highest rate of visits.
    c. the rate of visits increased as age increased.
    d. the greatest rate of visits was among children age 15.

44. According to Graph 1.2, which groups had the highest rate of visits?
    a. 14 year olds for being struck by person or object and 18 year olds for motor vehicle traffic-related injuries
    b. One year olds for falls and 14 year olds for being struck by person or object
    c. 14 and 17 year olds for struck by person or object
    d. This graph does not provide adequate information to determine the answer

45. Based on the information in this graph, which type of prevention program would be the best for health education specialists to implement?
    a. Violence prevention for adolescents
    b. Highway safety for people transporting infants and small children
    c. Injury from falls for adolescents
    d. Anger management for children under 10 years of age

46. According to the Diffusion of Innovations, which of the following groups is the most difficult to reach?
    a. Late Majority
    b. Innovators
    c. Early Adopters
    d. Laggards

47. An agency needs volunteers at a local health awareness event. Before the recruitment campaign can begin, the first step is to:
    a. create the volunteer newsletter.
    b. determine the volunteer reward/incentive system.
    c. develop a volunteer job description.
    d. plan the volunteer recognition banquet.

48. A sample in which each person in a population of interest has an equal likelihood of selection is said to be:
    a. non-probability.
    b. non-randomized.
    c. probability.
    d. randomized.

49. A health education specialist is implementing a substance abuse prevention program. Currently, participants are discussing how family patterns elicit acceptance and approval of certain behaviors. Which of the following best describe the concept being addressed?
    a. Physical
    b. Social/cultural
    c. Mental
    d. Community

50. The short term effects of health education interventions are most often directed toward:
    a. achieving changes in health knowledge, attitudes, skills or behavior.
    b. reducing health care costs.
    c. decreasing recidivism rates.
    d. decreasing morbidity and mortality rates.

51. Communication strategies are most often used in health education to:
    a. identify the target audience.
    b. insure a program is culturally sensitive.
    c. reinforce a message about health related behaviors.
    d. mobilize a community.

52. A health education specialist is asked to find evidence-based strategies for physical activity. The most appropriate bibliographic database to search is:
    a. CHID.
    b. EBMR.
    c. MEDLINE.
    d. PsychInfo.

53. The data analysis conducted to ascertain results that are generalizable to the population is known as what type of analysis?
    a. Inferential
    b. Interpretational
    c. Descriptive
    d. Process

54. Which of the following data collection methods is likely to increase interviewer bias?
    a. Mail
    b. E-mail
    c. Face-to-face
    d. Telephone

55. When a health education specialist exchanges information, alters activities, shares resources and enhances capacity to achieve a common purpose, he or she is:
    a. cooperating.
    b. coordinating.
    c. networking.
    d. collaborating.

56. Which of the following are elements of conducting an effective employee/staff appraisal?
    a. Present your appraisal in writing, without allowing an opportunity for discussion.
    b. Present your appraisal verbally and in writing without allowing an opportunity for discussion.
    c. Have the employee complete a form to submit to you for your signature.
    d. Provide specific examples to support your evaluation and focus on work-related behaviors.

57. Types of factors that influence a person's health such as compliance, consumption patterns, coping, preventive actions, and self-care, are known as:
    a. genetic.
    b. environmental.
    c. individual.
    d. behavioral.

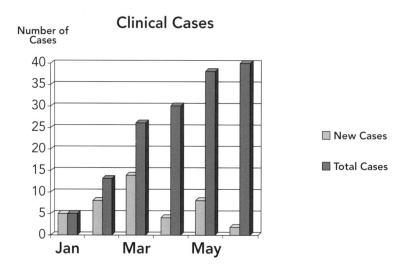

58. To depict the number of infections among a cohort of 113 women, a health education specialist presented existing data in the form of a graph (1.1). The graph reveals the number of new cases each month of a diagnosed asymptomatic infection and the cumulative number of cases at the end of six months. From the following statements, chose the best account regarding what is represented in the graph.
    a. Incidence is higher every month.
    b. Prevalence has risen steadily each month.
    c. Prevalence is variable every month.
    d. The identified infectious cases appear to have been cured.

59. A clinic director has asked a health education specialist to develop an appropriate education program to address this situation shown in Graph 1.1. The best initial approach by the health education specialist to this request is to:
    a. assure the director that a request for the program funding will be in the budget for next year.
    b. secure epidemiological and target group data to determine if this increase is an episodic chance occurrence or a new trend.
    c. gather data to identify the existence of a behavioral component that can be addressed with education.
    d. begin to develop an education program as requested.

60. Program goals and objectives should be determined:
    a. at the beginning of the planning process.
    b. after program participants are selected.
    c. after program activities are created.
    d. immediately before the outcome evaluation.

61. In health education presentations, which of the following is an appropriate guideline to promote learning?
    a. Use passive learning methods, such as lectures.
    b. Establish the relevance of the information to learners.
    c. Do not repeat information in any planned learning activity.
    d. Present information that is unique to one setting or situation.

62. Which of the following is most essential for health education specialists when creating material that addresses participants with low health literacy?
    a. Present a lot of information to assist in learning
    b. Have a behavioral action
    c. Use simple terms
    d. Use a few headings

63. Which of the following educational techniques would be most appropriate for a prevention program that includes changing norms related to smoking among adolescents?
    a. Social networking sites
    b. Personal digital assistants
    c. Lecture
    d. Videos

64. The health education specialist needs to communicate a prevention message to a proactive, health information-seeking audience. According to the needs assessment, this audience wants to obtain their information in a self-paced format and wants instant updates as new information becomes available. Which health communication channel would best address this audience's needs?
    a. Radio
    b. Groups
    c. Internet
    d. Print newspapers

APPENDIX C

65. A published synthesis of comprehensive works or data collections on particular topics is defined as a:
    a. summative evaluation.
    b. primary data analysis.
    c. secondary data synthesis.
    d. systematic review.

66. A health education specialist in charge of coordinating his/her agency's new outreach program wishes to start the strategic planning process. Which is the best first step to take?
    a. Identify stakeholders
    b. Agree on a strategic planning process
    c. Clarify organizational mandates
    d. Develop the mission statement

67. A health education specialist is collaborating with the health department on a training effort to implement effective physical activity programs. The group asked the health education specialist which groups may have the greatest benefit from the training. Which of the competencies are they addressing?
    a. Setting objectives
    b. Preparing audiovisuals
    c. Selecting the priority population
    d. Determining the subject content

68. The strategic planning process is used to answer which of the following three key questions?
    a. Where are we now? Where do we want to be? How do we get there?
    b. Where are we now? What is our objective? When are we going to change?
    c. Who is our competition? Where are they now? Where are we now?
    d. How do we impact the program? When do we impact the program? And by whom?

69. The three key domains of evidence-based health policy include:
    a. process, content, outcomes.
    b. process, impact, outcome.
    c. formative, summative, impact.
    d. impact, surveillance, outputs.

70. Which of the following data collection methods utilizes participants who meet specific criteria to provide information about a specific health issue?
    a. Community forum
    b. Focus group
    c. Health risk appraisal
    d. Secondary data collection

71. Which of the following is the first step in designing a survey?
    a. Determining the objectives of the survey.
    b. Determining the questions to be used on the survey.
    c. Determining the types of scales to be used.
    d. Determining the specific data to be collected.

72. Prior to program participation, the participant is notified about the potential risks and benefits of the program. This is part of a process called:
    a. omission.
    b. commission.
    c. ethics.
    d. informed consent.

73. Developing a time line of achievement for health education program objectives is a task usually associated with which phase of implementation?
    a. Establishing a system for program management
    b. Putting the plan into action
    c. Gaining acceptance for the program
    d. Specifying program tasks and resources

74. Smoking bans are an example of which of the following strategies?
    a. Health-related community service
    b. Health-related educational
    c. Health policy and enforcement
    d. Health communication

75. A systematic method of evaluating statistical data based on results of several independent studies of the same problem is a:
    a. stratified sample.
    b. case control/comparison study.
    c. meta analysis.
    d. inferential analysis.

76. Which primary data collection method is used to gather data through direct surveillance of the population under study?
    a. Observation
    b. Surveys
    c. Community forum
    d. Nominal group process

77. Attempting to provoke change within society using tools such as educational activities, coalition building, lobbying and media communication is:

    a. cultural competence.

    b. advocacy.

    c. health literacy.

    d. consumer-driven health care.

78. Which is the most useful tool for assessing baseline measures of current relationships external to the organization?

    a. Administrative process analysis

    b. Stakeholder analysis

    c. Impact analysis

    d. Organizational assessment

79. A health education specialist has been asked to collect data from participants by conducting focus group interviews. Given the short period of time he/she has to collect this data, one limitation of using qualitative research is:

    a. people don't like to talk in groups.

    b. the amount of time it takes to collect data.

    c. it is not an accepted form of data collection.

    d. you cannot pilot test.

80. Which of the following is a component of informed consent for clients of a stress management program?

    a. Knowledge of Hans Selye's theory of stress

    b. Acceptance of the program requirement to attend all scheduled stress management sessions

    c. Awareness of any inherent risks or dangers associated with participation in the stress management program

    d. Understanding that there is only one acceptable method of stress management

81. Conducting a needs assessment focuses on the:

    a. setting of a health-related program.

    b. leaders from the target audience.

    c. available resources for the program.

    d. people whom programs are directed towards.

82. Which of the following is the most appropriate targeted marketing strategy for a healthy eating program for children?

    a. "Table tents" advertising the program placed at the local senior citizen lunch program

    b. Fliers posted in local health departments that describe healthy eating techniques

    c. Free samples of healthy foods, such as fruits and vegetables, at local school cafeterias

    d. E-mail descriptions of the program sent to local legislators

83. A sample divided into segments based on characteristics of relevance to research, such as gender, age, or social class is said to be:
    a. randomized.
    b. stratified.
    c. cohort.
    d. non-experimental.

84. The health education specialist is working as a liaison between the university health service center and the local health department. Where there is a lot of room for collaboration it is essential that the health education specialist:
    a. defines the parameters of the relationships.
    b. establishes internship opportunities for health education students.
    c. provides technical expertise.
    d. establishes a contract between the two agencies.

85. When searching for information for a client about the social issues surrounding child abuse and neglect, which is the best database to use?
    a. HEDIR
    b. Psychic
    c. ERIC
    d. Index Medicus

86. A worksite healthy lifestyle promotion program is being offered in increments that focus on fitness, stress management, nutrition, and blood pressure control. Each increment is offered one-at-a-time over an eight week period. This process is considered:
    a. assessing.
    b. phasing-in.
    c. implementing.
    d. piloting.

87. "There will be a ten percent decrease in diabetes-related emergency room visits in South County within the next five years" is an example of a:
    a. behavioral objective.
    b. learning objective.
    c. administrative objective.
    d. program objective.

88. Program planning begins with:
    a. identification of different practice settings.
    b. assessment of existing health needs and problems.
    c. measurement of social marketing process.
    d. evaluation of learning objectives.

89. A type of analysis that is exploratory in nature and designed to describe phenomena specific to a population is:
    a. qualitative research.
    b. formative evaluation.
    c. analytical analysis.
    d. descriptive analysis.

90. Which of the following contains detailed information about an organization's or program's purpose and scope?
    a. Vision statement
    b. Mission statement
    c. Goal statement
    d. Values statement

91. The highest level of classification in Bloom's taxonomy is:
    a. Analysis.
    b. Synthesis.
    c. Application.
    d. Evaluation.

92. The health education specialist is searching for a published, reliable instrument that is used to measure a psychosocial health construct for use in a program evaluation. The most appropriate bibliographic database to search is:
    a. CINAHL.
    b. MEDLINE.
    c. HaPI.
    d. CHID.

93. During the planning process, it is most important for a health education specialist to use which of the following?
    a. The program's evaluation data
    b. Healthy People 2020 goals and objectives
    c. Community feedback
    d. Needs assessment data

94. When a researcher wishes to draw conclusions about a population sample, he/she can refer to:
    a. impact indicators.
    b. inferential statistics.
    c. probability samples.
    d. secondary data.

95. A health care provider is talking with a patient. Which of the following is most important in keeping open lines of communication between the two?
    a. Be aware of patient's possible feelings of fear, embarrassment, or resentment
    b. Maintain an authoritarian attitude so that the patient takes the situation seriously
    c. Always use scientific/medical terminology
    d. Do not allow a patient to doubt a diagnosis or treatment plan

96. When prioritizing health problems, health education specialists are looking for programs that are:
    a. highly important and highly changeable.
    b. less important and highly changeable.
    c. highly important and less changeable.
    d. less important and less changeable.

97. The most common way to establish and maintain professional contacts is through:
    a. blogs.
    b. telephone interviews.
    c. Internet searches.
    d. networking.

98. A health agency has an educational program focused on family planning perspectives. Policies have been implemented to ensure that the program will continue and be maintained over the next five years. Which of the following is the element of organizational culture that is taking place?
    a. Values
    b. Cultural norms
    c. Peer support
    d. Sustainability

99. School teachers are working with health education specialists in search of ideas for new lesson plans that they could use to integrate their math lessons with school health content and skills. The best source to search is the:
    a. HEDIR.
    b. ERIC.
    c. HEALTHPROM.
    d. MEDLINE

100. What are the types of consultative relationships where the health education specialist interprets and responds to health information requests without a formal agreement?
    a. External
    b. Cardinal
    c. Permissive
    d . Internal

101. The following is an example of a questionnaire item for undergraduate students: "What is your student status?"
    1. Freshman 2. Sophomore 3. Junior 4. Senior 5. Transfer

    Which of the following most accurately describes this question?
    a. It is mutually exclusive but not exhaustive.
    b. It is exhaustive but not mutually exclusive.
    c. It is neither exhaustive nor mutually exclusive.
    d. It is both exhaustive and mutually exclusive.

102. When thinking theoretically about designing theory-based practice, the health education specialist is:
    a. altering program design.
    b. evaluating constructs.
    c. asking and answering questions.
    d. analyzing pilot feedback.

103. Pretesting participants' knowledge of effective weight management techniques may be most helpful in:
    a. determining intervention strategies.
    b. guaranteeing that all participants lose weight.
    c. achieving appropriate body composition.
    d. learning what causes obesity.

104. Which of the following is an example of phasing-in a health education program?
    a. Conducting the entire program on a small scale
    b. Serving participants who differ in demographic characteristics from the target audience
    c. Limiting the number of program offerings
    d. Offering the program at no cost

105. In terms of organizational culture, shared vision and sense of belonging are part of which of the following?
    a. Organizational climate
    b. Values
    c. Cultural norms
    d. Organizational support

106. If a health education specialist considers using an instrument, like the BRFSS, that has been validated and tested for reliability, they are:
    a. avoiding development of their own instrument.
    b. practicing unethical behavior by using another instrument.
    c. identifying useful existing data collection instruments.
    d. comparing their population's responses to research questions.

107. The specific helping relationship created when a health education specialist assists an organization, but does not ultimately make direct changes is referred to as:
    a. advisory.
    b. adversarial.
    c. technical.
    d. consultative.

108. A health education specialist is faced with a controversial issue in a health program. One of the first resources to consult would be:
    a. a community leader.
    b. the Health Education Profession Code of Ethics.
    c. a professional mentor.
    d. the Internet.

109. A health education specialist is designing a health communication campaign to increase physical activity among school-aged youth. The best group to work with to develop and pretest the campaign's message and educational materials is:

    a. other health education specialists in the school's local community.

    b. area medical and social service personnel.

    c. local mass media experts.

    d. school-aged youth.

110. A health education specialist was randomly assigning research participants to control and treatment groups. The educator felt like one participant would benefit from the experimental group and intentionally assigned him/her to that group. The educator violated which of the following responsibilities of health education practice?

    a. Legal

    b. Moral

    c. Financial

    d. Ethical

111. Which of the following is an example of qualitative data that can be used to compile community needs assessments?

    a. Census reports

    b. Focus groups

    c. Telephone surveys

    d. Mortality tables

112. A broad, future-oriented statement reflecting the aim of a program is a:

    a. project.

    b. mission.

    c. goal.

    d. behavioral objective.

113. A health education specialist specifically chooses an assessment tool with a high "test-retest" reliability to use in his/her program evaluation effort. Reliability refers to:

    a. operational forms of the construct.

    b. systematic progression of the research steps.

    c. consistency of the measurement process.

    d. degree to which the tool measures what it is intended to measure.

114. Developing a time line of achievement for health education program objectives is a task usually associated with which phase of implementation?

    a. Specifying program tasks and resources

    b. Gaining acceptance for the program

    c. Putting the plan into action

    d. Establishing a system for program management

APPENDIX C

115. Health agency personnel are ready to review and adopt their new program's strategic plan. Who also should be included in this process?
    a. The entire community in the geographic area covered by the agency
    b. No one, just agency representatives
    c. Key stakeholders of the agency
    d. Local health education specialists

116. Checking to see if a Web site has been updated recently evaluates the Web site's:
    a. domain.
    b. accuracy.
    c. currency.
    d. affiliations.

117. The health education specialist wishes to describe a community's perceptions of its health needs, as well as its members' opinions about the local health department. Which type of research method is best?
    a. Qualitative
    b. Documentary
    c. Quantitative
    d. Procedural

118. The levels of strategies common to ecological models are:
    a. interpersonal, institutional, state, federal
    b. individual, interpersonal, institutional or organizational, community, public policy
    c. intrapersonal, community, group, organizational, legislative
    d. individual, community, local, state, national

119. The process for influencing human behavior on a large scale, using marketing principles for the purpose of public benefit rather than profit is:
    a. health marketing.
    b. market strategy.
    c. health communication.
    d. social marketing.

120. A health education specialist should primarily use instructional technology to:
    a. secure funding support.
    b. ensure cultural sensitivity.
    c. identify objectives.
    d. reach the target audience.

121. In communicating evaluation findings to stakeholders, the health education specialist should produce a final report that is focused and:

    a. reader friendly.
    b. scientifically descriptive.
    c. meets the needs of the author.
    d. exciting and engaging.

122. The choice of a data-collection method for a health education program evaluation is best linked to:

    a. computerized databases.
    b. research or program objectives.
    c. accuracy of the published information.
    d. interpretation of the research findings.

123. In the social ecological model, a school or worksite would fall under which factor or level?

    a. Individual
    b. Interpersonal
    c. Institutional
    d. Community

124. When using electronic resources such as bibliographic databases or Web sites, the health education specialist should analyze the information for accuracy and quality. Which Web site extension for the sample domain name is most likely to contain valid information?

    a. Nutrition.com
    b. Nutrition.epi
    c. Nutrition.usa
    d. Nutrition.gov

125. In order to help account for milestones in health advocacy work or policy change, it is helpful to use:

    a. a list of challenges.
    b. benchmarks.
    c. historical accounts.
    d. standards.

126. The data collection and analysis plan for a needs assessment should:

    a. delimit approaches for assessment.
    b. focus on one sub-population.
    c. discount stakeholder bias.
    d. develop a comprehensive approach.

127. Adults with which literacy level are most likely getting health information from TV and radio?
     a. Proficient
     b. Below basic
     c. Intermediate
     d. Advanced

128. A client requests a specific health service. The best resource to use to respond to his/her information request is a:
     a. health professional or health organization.
     b. health-related Web site.
     c. health promotion database.
     d. health software package.

129. To create a partnership, a health education specialist begins to create a relationship with personnel from another agency. They work together on a small project before deciding to partner on a larger, grant-funded project. This is an example of which principle in creating effective partnerships?
     a. Using data effectively
     b. Acknowledging and celebrating programs
     c. Minimizing turf wars
     d. Building trust

130. A health education specialist is investigating a data collection instrument to determine if the concepts in that instrument relate to the concepts of the theory upon which the program is based. He/she is considering the instrument's:
     a. content validity.
     b. criterion validity.
     c. reliability.
     d. construct validity.

131. Identifying and assessing the strengths and weaknesses of the way a health education specialist implements a program is best described as what type of evaluation?
     a. Simulation
     b. Formative
     c. Summative
     d. Impact

132. A school health advisory team is selecting a health curriculum to be adopted and implemented in the school district. The first issue to consider is if:
     a. it will entertain students.
     b. the community supports the curriculum.
     c. the curriculum is evidence-based.
     d. the political environment supports the curriculum.

133. After a clean indoor air ordinance passes with the help of advocacy efforts, Big Tobacco attempts to overturn it. A community health coalition stops its campaign. Which type of advocacy benchmark is this?
    a. Changing definitions/reframing
    b. Shift in critical mass
    c. Holding the line
    d. Institutional policy

134. The local Kiwanis Club asked a health education specialist to make a "healthy snacking" presentation to its group. Which of the following represents the correct order to plan and implement the presentation?
    a. Develop goals/objectives, understand audience needs, select appropriate methods, gather resources to aid implementation, evaluate effectiveness
    b. Gather resources to aid implementation, develop goals/objectives, understand audience needs, select appropriate methods, evaluate effectiveness
    c. Understand audience needs, develop goals/objectives, select appropriate methods, gather resources to aid implementation, evaluate effectiveness
    d. Develop goals/objectives, understand audience needs, gather resources to aid implementation, select appropriate methods, evaluate effectiveness

135. A health education specialist has been asked to deliver a training program for individuals caring for patients with diabetes. With adequate funding and training expertise, he/she should:
    a. use a variety of methods.
    b. only use advanced technologies.
    c. avoid one-on-one interactions.
    d. simply hand out print materials.

136. This body functions to protect human subjects engaged in research studies:
    a. ISL.
    b. BIR.
    c. IRB.
    d. BBB.

137. A local hospital has hired a company to work with the staff on team building. Time schedules, fees, and written goals and objectives have been developed. Which one of the following best describes this consultation process?
    a. Voluntary
    b. Informal
    c. Formal
    d. Required

138. "Program participants will be able to correctly identify five sources of dietary fiber" is an example of a:
    a. behavioral objective.
    b. program objective.
    c. learning objective.
    d. mission statement.

139. To understand the three human subjects protection guidelines of respect for persons, beneficence, and justice, one would look to the:
    a. CHNEO Code of Ethics.
    b. Informed consent process.
    c. Belmont Report.
    d. Geneva Convention Treaty.

140. Which health education professional organization exists specifically to protect and promote the health of children and youth by supporting coordinated school health programs as a foundation for school success?
    a. American School Health Association (ASHA)
    b. Eta Sigma Gamma (ESG)
    c. American Association for Health Education (AAHE)
    d. American Public Health Association's School Health Education and Services Section (APHA-SHES)

141. Administering strategies, interventions, and programs relates to improvement of factors:
    a. within the organization/environment.
    b. within and outside the organization/environment.
    c. outside of the organization/environment.
    d. relative to the process, impact, and outcome of the organization/environment.

142. Which of the following is considered an example of a community mobilization strategy?
    a. Community advocacy
    b. Health fair
    c. Mailed pamplets
    d. Simulation activity

143. When facilitating groups of stakeholders in a project, the health education specialist encounters some conflict between the organizations. The most effective conflict management strategy to use is:
    a. confrontation/fight.
    b. avoidance.
    c. collaborative problem solving.
    d. proactive planning.

144. Data was collected from 20 samples of adults between 1987 and 2008, a health education specialist found that the average level of happiness reported by people less than 65 years old declined from 1987 to 1999. For this same group, the average level of happiness increased slightly from 2000 to 2008. In addition, the average level of happiness reported by people aged 65 and older increased from 1987 to 2008. (The) variable of interest in this study is(are):
    a. age.
    b. age 65.
    c. 2008.
    d. 1987-2008.

145. A training that allows participants to learn by experience and is relevant to personal or work life is an example of which approach to learning?
    a. Content-centered approach
    b. Expert approach
    c. Experiential approach
    d. Learner-centered approach

146. A health education specialist schedules a panel to discuss Gay, Lesbian, Bisexual, Transgender, and Queer issues and trends to his/her program staff. This is an example of what kind of strategy?
    a. Community organizing
    b. Educational
    c. Communication
    d. Administrative/Policy

147. In this type of consultative relationship, the health education specialist provides mostly technical assistance, or process-directed services to the client.
    a. Internal
    b. External
    c. Independent
    d. Strategic

148. In the process of selecting the most appropriate educational method to use in a health education program, which of the following guidelines should be used?
    a. Ensure that only one method is selected for implementation
    b. Recognize that the program location rarely affects method selected
    c. Consider the nature of the audience and the purpose of the program
    d. Realize that all methods are equally useful in any setting

149. If a person weighs their susceptibility to developing high cholesterol against his or her perceptions about the severity of high cholesterol, this describes two constructs in which theory or model?
    a. Social Cognitive Theory
    b. Health Belief Model
    c. Transtheoretical Model
    d. Diffusion of Innovations

150. Electronic mailing lists are used by health education specialists to send announcements and questions to others in the field. One example of an E-mailing list is:
    a. HEDIR.
    b. CDP.
    c. CHID.
    d. USDHHS.

151. If a child responded to a questionnaire, but did not understand the complex language, his/her answers will contain:
    a. social desirability bias.
    b. random error.
    c. systematic error.
    d. triangulation.

152. Brainstorming, simulation and case studies are common tasks of which of the following health education methods and techniques?
    a. Environmental interventions
    b. Educational activities
    c. Behavior modification
    d. Advocacy activities

153. In a logic model, a healthy cooking class would be considered an:
    a. input.
    b. outcome.
    c. output.
    d. assumption.

154. The local medical clinic administration charged its health education specialist with designing a brochure for their new diabetes prevention education campaign. The intended audience possesses generally low health literacy levels. Therefore, the characteristics of this brochure should include:
    a. few examples and graphics.
    b. many varied messages.
    c. few polysyllabic words.
    d. many main points.

155. In the strategic planning process, organizations define or refine a mission statement. The next step is to:
    a. list internal and external strengths and opportunities.
    b. list mandates and sources.
    c. identify key stakeholders.
    d. write a report.

156. The most recent 18-month project to validate the contemporary practice of entry-and advanced-level health education specialists was the:
    a. Competency Update Project (CUP)
    b. Health Educator Job Analysis (HEJA)
    c. 2006 Revised Framework
    d. National Commission on Certifying Agencies (NCCA)

157. If your agency has limited financial resources, the most reliable Web site to use as a source to find a wide variety of downloadable health education materials is:
    a. GMM.
    b. FREEWEB.
    c. CHID.
    d. HRSA.

158. Forgetting to have middle-aged, sedentary adults provide a physician's consent to exercise would be considered negligence of:
    a. commission.
    b. omission.
    c. aversion.
    d. beneficence.

159. Participants in a health education program are asked to state the number of times they have been arrested. At which level of measurement is this data?
    a. Nominal
    b. Ordinal
    c. Interval
    d. Ratio

160. Which of the following is a situational analysis tool?
    a. PRECEDE
    b. SWOT
    c. MATCH
    d. CDCynergy

161. A college population was instrumental in developing a program to encourage students to receive testing for sexually transmitted infections. This program involved what principle of community organizing?
    a. Eliminating bias
    b. Focusing on program evaluation
    c. Modeling similar programs
    d. Developing ownership by the priority population

162. The American Heart Association has created a pamphlet outlining heart disease death rates among Americans over the age of 40. This is an example of a:
    a. primary data source.
    b. tertiary data source.
    c. secondary data source.
    d. qualitative data source.

APPENDIX C

163. Which of the following approaches is the best to use when working with adult learners?
    a. Lecture with technical information and include statistical analyses
    b. Use only distance-learning techniques
    c. Have small groups work together to solve problems
    d. Use the latest technological tools

164. Which of the following statements indicates a positive relationship between variables X and Y?
    a. As the value of X increases, the value of Y decreases.
    b. As the value of Y increases, the value of X decreases.
    c. As the value of X increases, the value of Y remains unchanged.
    d.As the value of X decreases, the value of Y decreases.

165. A health education specialist uses a deck of cards to help people visualize a serving of meat in a weight loss program. This is an example of assisting people with:
    a. oral literacy.
    b. conceptual knowledge.
    c. numeracy.
    d. print literacy.

STUDY GUIDE ANSWER KEY

1. a Area I	43. b Area I	85. b Area VI	127. b Area III
2. b Area III	44. b Area I	86. b Area III	128. a Area VI
3. a Area VII	45. a Area I	87. d Area II	129. d Area V
4. a Area VI	46. d Area III	88. b Area II	130. d Area IV
5. c Area II	47. c Area V	89. d Area IV	131. b Area IV
6. a Area IV	48. d Area IV	90. b Area V	132. c Area II
7. b Area IV	49. b Area III	91. d Area VI	133. c Area VII
8. c Area I	50. a Area II	92. c Area VI	134. c Area VII
9. d Area V	51. c Area III	93. d Area II	135. a Area III
10. b Area VI	52. b Area VI	94. b Area IV	136. c Area IV
11. c Area I	53. a Area IV	95. a Area VII	137. c Area VI
12. b Area VII	54. c Area I	96. a Area I	138. c Area II
13. d Area III	55. d Area III	97. d Area III	139. c Area III
14. a Area III	56. d Area V	98. d Area V	140. a Area VII
15. d Area V	57. d Area I	99. b Area VI	141. b Area V
16. b Area II	58. b Area IV	100. d Area VI	142. a Area II
17. a Area IV	59. c Area IV	101. b Area IV	143. c Area V
18. a Area IV	60. a Area II	102. c Area II	144. a Area IV
19. a Area VI	61. b Area II	103. a Area III	145. d Area III
20. b Area I	62. c Area VI	104. c Area III	146. b Area II
21. d Area II	63. a Area III	105. a Area V	147. b Area VI
22. a Area III	64. c Area VII	106. c Area IV	148. c Area II
23. d Area IV	65. d Area IV	107. d Area VI	149. b Area III
24. b Area I	66. a Area II	108. b Area III	150. a Area IV
25. a Area III	67. c Area VI	109. d Area VII	151. b Area IV
26. a Area VI	68. a Area V	110. d Area III	152. b Area II
27. c Area VII	69. a Area VII	111. b Area I	153. c Area III
28. a Area IV	70. b Area I	112. c Area II	154. c Area III
29. d Area III	71. a Area I	113. c Area IV	155. a Area V
30. a Area II	72. d Area III	114. d Area III	156. b Area VII
31. b Area III	73. a Area III	115. c Area V	157. d Area VI
32. c Area III	74. c Area II	116. c Area VI	158. b Area III
33. b Area V	75. c Area IV	117. a Area IV	159. d Area IV
34. d Area VII	76. a Area I	118. b Area III	160. b Area V
35. b Area I	77. b Area VII	119. d Area II	161. d Area II
36. a Area II	78. b Area V	120. d Area III	162. b Area VI
37. b Area III	79. b Area IV	121. a Area IV	163. c Area III
38. a Area II	80. c Area III	122. b Area IV	164. d Area IV
39. d Area IV	81. d Area I	123. c Area III	165. c Area VI
40. a Area VII	82. c Area III	124. d Area VI	
41. b Area VI	83. b Area IV	125. b Area VII	
42. c Area I	84. a Area VI	126. d Area I	

AUTHOR BACKGROUND INFORMATION

Chris Anne Rodgers Arthur, PhD, MPH, CHES
Professor, Department of Behavioral and
    Environmental Health
Jackson State University
Associate Professor, Department of Family Medicine
The University of Mississippi Medical Center
Jackson, Mississippi

Donna Beal, MPH, CHES
Regional Program Director
American Lung Association of California
San Maria, California

Cam Escoffery, PhD, MPH, CHES
Assistant Professor
Rollins School of Public Health
Atlanta, Georgia

Patricia A. Frye, DrPH, MPA, CHES
Project Manager
The Mississippi Institute for Improvement of
    Geographic
 Minority Health (MIGMH)
The University of Mississippi Medical Center
Jackson, Mississippi

Melissa Grim, PhD, CHES
Associate Professor, Health Education and Health
    Promotion
Department of Exercise, Sport, and Health
    Education
Radford University
Radford, Virginia

Leonard Jack, Jr, PhD, MSc, CHES
Associate Dean for Research
Director, Center for Minority Health &
Health Disparities Research and Education
Endowed Chair of Health Disparities Research
Professor, Division of Clinical and Administrative
    Sciences
College of Pharmacy
Xavier University of Louisiana
New Orleans, Louisiana

J. Dennis Kamholtz, PhD, CHES
Professor of Health Education
Department of Community Health Education
    and Recreation
University of Maine at Farmington
Farmington, Maine

Maurice "Bud" Martin, PhD, CHES
Assistant Professor of Community Health Education
Department of Community Health Education
    and Recreation
University of Maine at Farmington
Farmington, Maine

Angela D. Mickalide, PhD, CHES
Director of Education and Outreach
Home Safety Council
Washington, D.C.

Christopher N. Thomas, MS, CHES*
Public Health Advisor
Division for Heart Disease and Stroke Prevention
National Center for Chronic Disease Prevention
    and Health Promotion
Centers for Disease Control and Prevention
Atlanta, Georgia

Rebecca Reeve, PhD, CHES
Senior Advisor for Healthy Schools
North Carolina Department of Health
  and Human Services
Division of Public Health
Raleigh, North Carolina

Tung-Sung Tseng, DrPH, MS, CHES
Assistant Professor
Behavioral and Community Health Sciences
LSUHSC School of Public Health
New Orleans, Louisiana

Katherine M. Wilson, PhD, MPH, CHES*
Senior Public Health Educator
Division of Cancer Prevention and Control
National Center for Chronic Disease Prevention and
  Health Promotion
Centers for Disease Control and Prevention
Atlanta, Georgia

Kelly Wilson, PhD, CHES
Assistant Professor of Health Education
Department of Health and Human Performance
Texas State University
San Marcos, Texas

* The findings and conclusions presented in Chapter
  III by this author do not necessarily represent the
  official position of the Centers for Disease Control
  and Prevention.

Aday, L.A., & Cornelius, L.J. (2006). *Designing and conducting health surveys: A comprehensive guide (3rd ed.).* San Francisco, CA: Jossey-Bass.

Agency for Toxic Substances and Disease Registry (ATSDR). (n.d.). *A primer on health risk communication principles and practices.* Retrieved from http://www.atsdr.cdc.gov/HEC/primer.html

Ajzen, I. (1988). *Attitudes, personality, and behavior.* Chicago, IL: Dorsey Press.

Allegrante, J.P., Airhihenbuwa, C.O., Auld, M.E., Birch, D.A., Roe, K.M., & Smith, B.J., National Task Force on Accreditation in Health Education. (2004). Toward a unified system of accreditation for professional preparation in health education: Final report of the National Task Force on Accreditation in Health Education. *Health Education and Behavior, 31*(6), 668-83.

American Joint Committee on Standards for Educational Evaluation. (2008). *Program evaluation standards: Summary of the standards.* Retrieved from www.eval.org

American Psychological Association. (2002). Ethical principles of psychologists and code of conduct. *American Psychologist,* 57(12), 1060-73.

American School Health Association. (2009). *What is school health?* Retrieved from: http://www.ashaweb.org/i4a/pages/index.cfm?pageid=3278

Anderson, L.M., Brownson, R.C., Fullilove, M.T., Teutsch, S.M., Novick, L.F., Fielding, J., & Land, G.H. (2005). Evidence-based public health policy and practice: Promise and limits. *American Journal of Preventive Medicine,* 28(5S), 226-230.

Anspaugh, D.J., Dignan, M.B., & Anspaugh, S.L. (2000). *Developing health promotion programs.* Boston, MA: McGraw-Hill.

Atkins, D., Fink, K., & Slutsky, J. (2005). Better information for better health care: The evidence-based practice center program and the agency for healthcare research and quality. *Annals of Internal Medicine,* 142(12 pt 2), 1035-1041.

Authenticity Consulting. (2005). *Field guide to consulting and organizational development with nonprofits: A collaborative and systems approach to performance, change and learning.* Minneapolis, MN: Authenticity Consulting, LLC.

Baker, R., Crawford, S., & Swineheart, J. (2004). Development and testing of web questionnaires. In S. Presser, J.M. Rothgeb, M.P. Cuper, J.L. Lessler, E. Martin, J. Martin, & E. Singer (Eds.), *Methods for testing and evaluating survey questionnaires* (pp. 361-384). New York, NY: Wiley.

Bandura, A. (1986). *Social foundations of thought & action: A social cognitive theory.* Englewood Cliffs, NJ: Prentice Hall.

REFERENCES

Barnes, M.D., Penrod, C., Neiger, B.L., Merrill, R.M., Thackeray, R. Eggett, D.L., & Thomas, E. (2003). Measuring the relevance of evaluation criteria among health information seekers on the internet. *Journal of Health Psychology*, 8(1), 71-82.

Barr, D.A., (2002). *Introduction to U.S. health policy: The organization, financing, and delivery of health care in America*. San Francisco, CA: Pearson/Benjamin Cummings.

Bartholomew, L.K., Parcel, G.S., Kok, G., & Gottlieb, N.H. (2006). *Planning health promotion programs: An intervention mapping approach* (2nd ed.). San Francisco, CA: Jossey-Bass.

Bastida, E., Tseng, T., McKeever, C. & Jack, L., Jr. (2010). Ethics and community-based participatory research: Perspectives from the field. *Health Promotion Practice*, 11(16), 16-20.

Baumgartner, T.A., & Hensley, L.D. (2006). *Conducting and reading research in health and human performance* (4th ed.). Boston, MA: McGraw-Hill.

Beaulieu, L.J. (2002). Mapping assets of your community: A key component for building local capacity. In *Civic engagement* (Series No. 227). Retrieved from http://srdc.msstate.edu/publications/227/227.htm

Bennett, G.G., & Glasgow, R.E. (2009). The delivery of public health interventions via the Internet: Actualizing their potential. *Annual Review of Public Health*, 30, 273-292.

Bensley, L.B., Jr. (2009). Using theory and ethics to guide method selection and application. In R.J. Bensley & J. Brookins-Fisher (Eds.), *Community health education methods: A practical guide* (3rd ed.) (pp. 3-30). Sudbury, MA: Jones and Bartlett Publishers.

Berkman, N.D., DeWalt, D.A., Pignone, M.P., Sheridan, S.L., Lohr, K.N., Lux, L., Bonito, A.J. (2004). *Literacy and Health Outcomes. Evidence Report/Technology Assessment No. 87* Prepared by RTI International-University of North Carolina Evidence-based Practice Center under Contract No. 290-02-0016. (AHRQ Publication No. 04-E007-2). Rockville, MD: Agency for Healthcare Research and Quality.

Bringer, J.D., Johnston, L.H., & Brackenridge, C.H. (2006). Using computer-assisted qualitative data analysis software to develop a grounded theory project. *Field Methods*, 18(3), 245-266.

Brownson, R.C., Baker, E.A., Leet, T.L., & Gillespie K.N. (2003). *Evidence-based public health*. New York, NY: Oxford University Press.

Brownson, R.C., Chriqui, J.F., Stamatakis, K.A. (2009). Understanding evidence-based public health policy. *American Journal of Public Health*, 99(9), 1576-1583.

Brownson, R.C., Royer, C., Ewing, R., & McBride, T.D. (2006). Researchers and policy makers: Travelers in parallel universes. *American Journal of Preventive Medicine*, 30(2), 164-172.

REFERENCES

Butterfoss, F.D. (2007). *Coalitions and partnerships in community health*. San Francisco, CA: Jossey-Bass.

Butterfoss, F.D. (2009). Building and sustaining coalitions. In R.J. Bensley & J. Brookins Fisher (Eds.), *Community health education methods: A practical guide* (3rd ed.) (pp. 299-332). Sudbury, MA: Jones and Bartlett.

Butterfoss, F.D., Kegler, M.C., & Francisco, V.T. (2008). Mobilizing organizations for health promotion: Theories of organizational change. In Glanz, K., Rimer, B.K., & Viswanath, K. (Eds.), *Health behavior and health education: theory research and practice* (4th ed.) (pp. 335-362). San Francisco: Jossey-Bass.

Caira, N.M., Lachenmayr, S., Sheinfeld, J., Goodhart, F.W., Cancialosi, L., & Lewis, C. (2003). The health educator's role in advocacy and policy: Principles, processes, programs, and partnerships. *Health Promotion Practice*, 4(3), 303-313.

Centers for Disease Control and Prevention (CDC). (1999). Framework for program evaluation in public health. *Morbidity and Mortality Weekly Report, 48*, 11.

Centers for Disease Control and Prevention (CDC). (2000). Beyond the brochure (CDC Publication No. PDF-821K). Atlanta, GA:

Centers for Disease Control and Prevention (CDC). (2003a). *CDCynergy 3.0: Your guide to effective health communication (CD-ROM Version 3)*. Atlanta, GA: Author.

Centers for Disease Control and Prevention (CDC). (2003b). HIPAA privacy rule and public health. *Morbidity and Mortality Weekly Report, 52*, 1-24.

Centers for Disease Control and Prevention (CDC). Figure 23. (2005). National Center for Health Statistics, United States, 2005.

Centers for Disease Control and Prevention (CDC). (2006a). *Health marketing basics*. Retrieved from http://www.cdc.gov/healthmarketing/basics.htm.\

Centers for Disease Control and Prevention (CDC). (2006b). *Community guide: Public policy*. Retrieved from http://www.thecommunityguide.org/uses/policy_development.html

Centers for Disease Control and Prevention (CDC). (2010). *Introduction to program evaluation for public health programs*. Retrieved from http://www.cdc.gov/getsmart/program-planner/Step3.html

Chenoweth, D.H. (2007). *Worksite Health Promotion* (2nd ed.). Champaign, IL: Human Kinetics.

Cleary, M.J., & Neiger, B.L. (1998). *The certified health education specialist: A self-study guide for professional competency* (3rd ed.). Allentown, PA: National Commission for Health Education Credentialing, Inc. (NCHEC).

Coalition of National Health Education Organizations (CNHEO). (1999). *Code of ethics for the health education profession*. Retrieved from http://www.cnheo.org/PDF%20files/code2.pdf

REFERENCES

Coalition of National Health Education Organizations (CNHEO). (n.d.). *What does the Coalition do?* Retrieved from http://www.cnheo.org/index.html

Collins, D. (2003). Pretesting survey instruments: An overview of cognitive methods. *Quality of Life Research*, 12(3), 229-238.

Cottrell, R.R., Girvan, J.T., & McKenzie, J.F. (2009). *Principles and foundations of health promotion and education* (4th ed.). San Francisco, CA: Pearson/Benjamin Cummings.

DeCenzo, D.A., & Robbins, S.P. (1999). *Human resource management* (6th ed.). Danvers, MA: John Wiley and Sons.

Deeds, S.G. (1992). *The health education specialist: Self study for professional competence(p. 36)*. Los Alamitos, CA: Loose Cannon.

Dickert, N. & Sugarman, J. (2005). Ethical goals of community consultation in research. *American Journal of Public Health*, 95(7), 1123-1127.

DiClemente, R.J., Crosby, R.A., & Kegler, M.C. (2009). *Emerging theories in health promotion practice and research*. San Francisco, CA: Jossey-Bass.

Doak, C.C., Doak, L.G., Gordon, L., & Lorig, K. (2001). Selecting, preparing, and using materials. In K. Lorig (Ed.), *Patient education: A practical approach* (3rd ed.) (183-197). Thousand Oaks, CA: Sage Publications, Inc.

Doak, C.C., Doak, L.G., & Root, J.H. (1996). *Teaching patients with low literacy skills* (2nd ed.). Philadelphia, PA: JB Lippincott.

Doak, C.C., Doak, L.G., & Root, J.H. (Eds). (2002). *Pfizer health literacy principles: A handbook for creating patient education materials that enhance understanding and promote health outcomes*. New York, NY: Pfizer.

Dorfman, L. (2009). Using media advocacy to influence policy. In R.J. Bensley & J. Brookins-Fisher (Eds.). *Community health education methods: A practical guide* (3rd ed.) (pp. 361-389). Sudbury, MA: Jones and Bartlett.

Dougherty, A.M. (2008). *Psychological consultation and collaboration in school and community settings* (5th ed.). Florence, KY: Brooks Cole.

Doyle, E., Ward, S., & Oomen-Early, J. (2010). *The process of community health education and promotion*. Mountain View, CA: Mayfield Publishing Company.

Edberg, M. (2007). Social and Behavioral Theory in Public Health. Sudbury, MA: Jones and Bartlett.

Eysenbach, G., Powell, J., Kuss, O., & Sa, E. (2002). Empirical studies assessing the quality of health information for consumers on the World Wide Web: A systematic review. *JAMA, 287*(20), 2691-2700.

Fagen, M., Reed, E., Kaye, J., & Jack, L. (2009). Advocacy evaluation: What is it and where to find out more about it. *Health Promotion Practice, 10*(4), 482-484.

Fallon, L. F., & Zgodzinski. (2009). *Essentials of public health management.* Sudbury, MA: Jones and Bartlett.

Fitzpatrick, J.L., Sanders, J.R., & Worthen, B.R. (2004). *Program evaluation: Alternative approaches and practical guidelines* (3rd ed.). Boston, MA: Pearson, Allyn, & Bacon.

Fjeldsoe, B.S., Marshall, A.L., & Miller, Y.D. (2009). Behavior change interventions delivered by mobile telephone short-message service. *American Journal of Preventive Medicine, 36*(2), 165-173.

Fodor, J., Dalis, G., & Giarratano-Russell, S. (2002). *Health instruction: Theory and application for community, school, health care, and workplace settings* (6th ed.). Dubuque, IA: Kendall/Hunt.

Fottler, M.D., Hernandez, S.R., & Joiner, C.L. (1994). *Strategic management of human resources in health services organizations* (2nd ed.). Albany, NY: Delmar.

Freudenberg, N., Bradley, S.P., & Serrano, M. (2009). Public health campaigns to change industry practices that damage health: An analysis of 12 case studies. *Health Education and Behavior, 36*(2), 230-249.

Friere, P. (2000). *Pedagogy of the oppressed.* New York, NY: Continuum.

Friis, R.H., & Sellers, T.A. (2009). *Epidemiology for public health practice* (4th ed.). Sudbury, MA: Jones and Bartlett.

Gagne, R. M. (1985). *The conditions of learning and the theory of instruction* (4th ed.). New York, NY: Holt, Rinehart, and Winston.

Gagne, R.M., Briggs, L.J., & Wager, W.W. (1992). *Principles of instructional design.* Fort Worth, TX: Harcourt Brace & Company.

Galer-Unti, R., Tappe, M.K., & Lachenmayr, S. (2004). Advocacy 101: Getting started in health education advocacy. *Health Promotion Practice, 5*(3), 280-288.

Gazmararian, J.A., Baker, D.W., Williams, M.V., Parker, R.M., Scott, T., Green, D.C., . . . Koplan, J.P. (1999). Health literacy among Medicare enrollees in a managed care organization. *Journal of the American Medical Association, 281*(6), 545-551.

Gilbert, G.G., Sawyer, R.G., & McNeill, E.B. (2011). *Health education: Creating strategies for school and health* (3rd ed.). Sudbury, MA: Jones and Bartlett.

Gilmore, G.D., & Campbell, M.D. (2005). *Needs and capacity assessment strategies for health education and health promotion* (3rd ed.). Sudbury, MA: Jones and Bartlett.

REFERENCES

Gilmore, G.D., Olsen, L.K., Taub, A., & Connell, D. (2005). Overview of the national health educator competencies update project 1998-2004. *Health Education & Behavior, 32*(6):725-737.

Ginter, P.M., Swayne, L.M., & Duncan, W.J. (2002). *Strategic management of health care organization* (4th ed.). Malden, MA: Blackwell.

Giustini, D. (2006). How Web 2.0 is changing medicine. *British Medical Journal, 333*(7582), 1283-1284.

Glanz, K., Rimer, B.K., & Viswanath, K. (Eds.). (2008a) *Health behavior and health education: Theory research and practice* (4th ed.). San Francisco, CA: Jossey-Bass.

Glanz, K., Rimer, B.K., & Viswanath, K. (2008b). Theory, research and practice in health behavior and health education. In Glanz, K., Rimer, B.K., & Viswanath, K (Eds.) *Health behavior and health education: Theory research and practice* (4th ed.) (pp. 23-40). San Francisco, CA: Jossey-Bass.

Goldman, K.D. (2009). Social marketing concepts. In R.J. Bensley & J. Brookins-Fisher (Eds.). *Community health education methods: A practical guide* (3rd ed.) (pp. 103-128). Sudbury, MA: Jones and Bartlett Publishers.

Goldman, K.D., & Schmaltz, K.J. (2005). In K.D. Goldman & K.J. Schmaltz (Eds.), How great groups do it: Improving group effectiveness. *Health Education tools of the trade: Tools for tasks that didn't come with the job description* (pp.77-80). Washington, D.C: Society for Public Health Education.

Goodson, P. (2010). *Theory in Health Promotion Research and Practice: Thinking outside the box*. Sudbury, MA: Jones and Bartlett.

Green, L.W., & Kreuter, M.W. (2005). *Health program planning: An educational and ecological approach*. Boston, MA: McGraw-Hill.

Greenhalgh, T., Robert, G., MacFarlane, F., Bate, P., & Kyriakidou, O. (2004). Diffusion of innovation in service organizations: Systematic review and recommendations. *The Milbank Quarterly*, 82, 581-629.

Greenlick, M.R., Goldberg, B., Lopes, P., & Tallon, J. (2005). Health policy roundtable – view from the state legislature: Translating research into policy. *Health Services Research, 40*(2): 337-346.

Gronlund, N.E. (1995). *How to write and use instructional objectives* (5th ed.). Englewood Cliffs, NJ: Prentice Hall.

Guthrie, K., Louie, J., David, T., Foster, C.C. (2006). *The challenge of assessing policy and advocacy activities: Strategies for a prospective evaluation approach*. Los Angeles, CA: California Endowment.

Hartsfied, D., Moulton, A.D., & McKie, K.L. (2007). A review of model public health laws. *American Journal of Public Health*, 97, (supl1): S56-S61

Hastings, G. (2008). *Social marketing: Why should the devil have all the best tunes?* Burlington, MA: Butterworth-Heinemann.

Hayden, J. (2009). *Introduction to health behavior theory*. Sudbury, MA: Jones and Bartlett.

Healey, B.J., & Zimmerman, R.S. (2010). *The new world of health promotion: New program development, implementation, and evaluation*. Boston, MA: Jones and Bartlett.

Hellriegel, D., & Slocum, J.W. (2004). *Organizational behavior*. Quebec, Canada: Thomson South-western.

Henderson, R., & Rheault, W. (2004). Appraising and incorporating qualitative research in evidence-based practice. *Journal of Physical Therapy Education*, 18(3), 35-40.

Himmelman, A. T. (2002). *Collaboration for a change: Definitions, decision-making models, roles and collaborative process guide*. Retrieved from http://depts.washington.edu/ccph/pdf_files/4achange.pdf on 9-19-09

Hochbaum, G.M. (1958). *Public participation in medical screening programs: A socio-psychological study*. (PHS Publication No. 572). Washington, DC: US Public Health Service.

Houts, P., Doak, C.C., Doak, L.G., & Loscalzo, M.J. (2006). The role of pictures in improving health communication: A review of research on attention, comprehension, recall, and adherence. *Patient Education and Counseling*, 61(2), 173-190.

Hwang, S. (2008). Utilizing qualitative data analysis software. *Social Science Computer Review*, 26(4), 519-527.

Institute of Education Sciences, National Center for Education Statistics (IES). (2006). *The health literacy of America's adult: Results for the 2003 National Assessment of Adult Literacy*. (NCES Publication No. 2006-483). Washington, DC: U.S. Department of Education.

Institute of Medicine. (2002). *Speaking of health: Assessing health communication strategies for diverse populations*. Committee on Communication for Behavior Change in the 21st Century: Improving the Health of Diverse Populations. Washington, DC: National Academy Press.

Institute of Medicine. (2004). *Health literacy: A prescription to end confusion*. Washington, DC: National Academy Press.

Issel, L. M. (2009). *Health program planning and evaluation: A practical, systematic approach for community health*. (2nd ed.). Sudbury, MA: Jones and Bartlett.

Jack, L., Jr., Hayes, S., Scharalda, J.G., Stetson, B., Jones-Jack, N., Valliere, M., . . . LeBlanc, C. (2010). Appraising quantitative research in health education: Guidelines for public health educators. *Health Promotion Practice*, 11(2), 161-165.

Jacobson, K., Cucchi, P.S., & Morton, F. (2006). *Clear and effective patient education: A guide for improving health communications in the hospital setting*. Atlanta, GA: Rollins School of Public Health.

REFERENCES

Jeanfreau G. Scharalda, J.G., & Jack, L., Jr. (In-Press). Appraising qualitative research in health education: guidelines for public health educators. *Health Promotion Practice*.

Jennings, B., Kahn, J., Mastroianni, A.M., & Parker, L. (2003). *Ethics and public health: Model curriculum*. Retrieved from http://www.asph.org/UserFiles/ EthicsCurriculum.pdf

Johnson, B., & Turner, L.A. (2003). Data collection strategies in mixed methods research. In A. Tashakkori & Teddlie (Eds.). *Handbook of mixed methods in social and behavioral research* (pp. 297-320). Thousand Oaks, CA: Sage.

Johnson, D.W., & Johnson, F.P. (2005). *Joining together: Group theory and group skills*. Boston, MA: Allyn & Bacon.

Johnson, J., & Breckon, D. (2007). *Managing health education and promotion programs: Leadership skills for the 21st century*. Boston, MA: Jones and Bartlett.

Joint Committee on Health Education Terminology. (2002). Report of the 2000 joint committee on health education and promotion terminology. *Journal of School Health*, 72(1), 3-7.

Kemm, J., Parry, J., & Palmer, S. (2004). *Health Impact Assessment: Concepts, theory, techniques and applications*. New York, NY: Oxford University Press.

Kerlinger, F.N. (1986). *Foundations of Behavioral Research* (3rd ed.). New York, NY: Rinehart and Winston.

Kickbusch, I. (2001). Health literacy: Addressing the health and education divide. *Health Promotion International*, 16(3): 289-297.

Kirkpatrick, D.L., & Kirkpatrick. J.D. (2009). *Evaluating training programs: The four levels* (3rd ed.). San Francisco, CA: Berrett-Koehler.

Knowles, M.S., Holten III, E.F., & Swanson, R.A. (2005). *The adult learner: The definitive classic in adult education and human resource development*. (6th ed.). Burlington, MA: Butterworth-Heinemann.

Kreps, G., Barnes, M., Neiger, B. & Thackeray. (2009). Health Communication. In R.J. Bensley & J. Brookins-Fisher (Eds.) *Community health education methods: A practical guide* (3rd ed.) (p. 87). Sudbury, MA: Jones and Bartlett.

Kreuter, M.W., Farrell, D., Olevitch, L., & Brennan, L. (2000). *Tailoring health messages: Customizing communications with computer technology*. Mahwah, NJ: Lawrence Erlbaum and Associates.

Kreuter, M.W., Lezin, N.A., Kreuter, M.W., & Green, L.W. (2003). *Community health promotion ideas that work* (2nd ed.). Sudbury, MA: Jones and Bartlett.

Lachenmayr, S. (2009). Using advocacy to affect policy. In R.J. Bensley & J. Brookins-Fisher (Eds.), *Community health education methods: A practical guide* (3rd ed.) (pp. 333-360). Sudbury, MA: Jones and Bartlett.

REFERENCES

Last, J.M. (2001). *A dictionary of epidemiology/ edited for the International Epidemiological Association* (4th ed.). New York, NY: Oxford University Press.

Lawson, K. (2008). *The trainer's handbook: Updated edition* (3rd ed.). San Francisco, CA: Pfieffer.

Lefebvre, C. (2009). Integrating cell phones and mobile technologies into public health practice: A social marketing perspective. *Health Promotion Practice, 10*(4), 490-494.

Lindquist, A.M., Johansson, P.E., Petersson, G.I., Saveman, B., & Nilsson, G.C. (2008). The use of the Personal Digital Assistant (PDA) among personnel and students in health care: A review. *Journal of Medical Internet Research, 10*(4), doi:10.2196/jmir.1038.

Livet, M., Courser, M., & Wandersman, A. (2008). The prevention delivery system: Organizational context and use of comprehensive programming frameworks. *American Journal of Community Psychology, 41*(3-4), 361-378.

Livingood,W.C., & Auld, M.E. (2001).The credentialing of a population-based profession: Lessons learned from health education certification. *Journal of Public Health Management & Practice,*7(4), 38-45.

Longest, B.B., Jr. (2004). *Managing health programs and projects.* San Francisco, CA: Jossey-Bass.

Malterud, K. (2001). Qualitative research: Standards, challenges, and guidelines. *Lancet, 358,* 483-488.

Martin, M., & Vaughn, B. (2007). *Strategic diversity and inclusion management* (pp. 31-36). San Francisco, CA: DTUI Publication Division.

McDermott, R.J., & Sarvela, P.D. (1999). *Health education evaluation and measurement: A practitioner's perspective* (2nd ed.). Dubuque, IA: McGraw-Hill.

McKenzie, J.F., Neiger, B.L., & Thackeray, J. L. (2009). *Planning, implementing, & evaluating health promotion programs: A primer* (5th ed.). San Francisco, CA: Pearson/Benjamin Cummings.

McKenzie, J.F., Pinger, R.R., & Kotecki, J.E. (2008). *An introduction to community health* (6th. ed.). Sudbury, MA: Jones and Bartlett.

Minelli, M.J., & Breckon, D.J. (2009). *Community health education: Settings, roles, and skills for the 21st century* (5th ed.). Sudbury, MA: Jones and Barlett.

Minkler, M., & Wallertein, N. (2008). *Community-based participatory research for health from process to outcomes* (2nd ed.). San Francisco, CA: Jossey-Bass.

Modeste, N.N., & Tamayose, T.S. (2004). *The dictionary of public health promotion and education terms and concepts* (2nd ed.). San Francisco, CA: John Wiley and Sons.

REFERENCES

Montano, D.E., & Kasprzyk, D. (2008). Theory of reasoned action, theory of planned behavior, and the integrated behavioral model In Glanz, K., Rimer, B.K., & Viswanath, K. (Eds.) (2008) *Health behavior and health education: Theory research and practice* (4th ed.) (pp 67-96). San Francisco, CA: Jossey-Bass.

National Association of County and City Health Officials (NACCHO). (2010). *Mobilizing for action through Planning and Partnerships (MAPP)*. Retrieved from http://www.naccho.org/topics/infrastructure/MAPP/index.cfm

National Cancer Institute (NCI). (2005). *National cancer institute fact sheet: How to evaluate health information on the Internet – questions and answers*. Retrieved from http://www.cancer.gov/cancertopics/factsheet/Information/internet

National Cancer Institute (NCI). (2006). *Using what works: Adapting evidence-based programs to fit your needs*. Retrieved from http://cancercontrol.cancer.gov/use_what_works/start.htm

National Cancer Institute (NCI). (2008). *Making health communications work*. Retrieved from http://www.cancer.gov/pinkbook

National Center for Education Statistics (NCES). (2006). *The health literacy of America's adults: Results from the 2003 national assessment of adult literacy*. Retrieved from http://nces.ed.gov/pubs2006/2006483.pdf

National Commission for Health Education Credentialing, Inc. (NCHEC), Society for Public Health Education (SOPHE), American Association for Health Education (AAHE). (2010a). *A competency-based framework for health education specialist - 2010*. Whitehall, PA: Author.

National Commission for Health Education Credentialing, Inc. (NCHEC), Society for Public Health Education (SOPHE), American Association for Health Education (AAHE). (2010b). *Health educator job analysis -2010: Executive summary and recommendations*. Retrieved from http://www.nchec.org/news/what/

National Commission for the Protection of Human Subjects of Biomedical and Behavioral Research. (1979). *The Belmont report: Ethical principles and guidelines for the protection of human subjects of research*. Retrieved from http://ohsr.od.nih.gov/guidelines/belmont.html

National Library of Medicine. (2009). *Resources: A user's guide to finding and evaluating health information on the web*. Retrieved from http://www.mlanet.org/resources/userguide.html

National Task Force on the Preparation & Practice of Health Educators. (1985). *A framework for the development of competency-based curricula for entry-level health education specialists*. New York, NY: National Commission for Health Education Credentialing, Inc.

Neutens, J.J., & Rubinson, L. (2010). *Research techniques for the health sciences* (4th ed.). San Francisco, CA: Pearson/Benjamin Cummings.

REFERENCES

O'Donnell, M. (2002). *Health promotion in the workplace* (3rd ed.). Albany, NY: Delamar.

Office of Disease Prevention and Health Promotion (ODPHP). (n.d.). *Healthy people 2010: Health communication.* Retrieved from http://www.healthypeople.gov/document/HTML/Volume1/11HealthCom.htm

Office of Disease Prevention and Health Promotion, U.S. Department of Health and Human Services. (2009). *Healthy People 2010—The road ahead.* Retrieved from http://www.healthypeople.gov/HP2020/

Oldenburg, B., & Glanz, K. (2008). Diffusion of innovations. In K. Glanz, B.K. Rimer & K. Viswanath (Eds.). *Health behavior and health education: Theory research and practice* (4th ed.). San Francisco, CA: Jossey-Bass.

Olson, S.J. (2010). Partnerships and collaboration: Critical components to promoting health. In B.J. Healey & R.S. Zimmerman (Eds.). *The new world of health promotion: New program development, implementation and evaluation.* (pp. 283-213). Sudbury, MA: Jones and Bartlett.

Patton, M.Q. (2008). *Utilization-focused evaluation* (4th ed.). Thousand Oaks, CA: Sage.

Peters, E., Hibbard, J., Slovic, P., & Dieckmann, N. (2007). Numeracy skill and the communication, comprehension, and use of risk-benefit information. *Health Affairs, 26*(3), 741-748.

Piskurich, G.M., Beckschi, P., & Hall, B. (1999). *The ASTD handbook of training design and delivery.* New York, NY: McGraw Hill.

Plain Language Action and Information Network. (n.d.). *Federal Plain Language Guidelines: Improving communication from the federal government to the public.* Retrieved from http://www.plainlanguage.gov

Plomer, K.D. & Bensley, R.J. (2009). *Developing and selecting print materials.* In R.J. Bensley & J. Brookins Fisher (Eds.). *Community health education methods: A practical guide* (3rd ed.) (pp. 209-236). Sudbury, MA: Jones and Bartlett.

Poland, B. (2009). Settings for health promotion: An analytic framework to guide intervention design and implementation. *Health Promotion Practice, 10*(4): 505-516.

Presser, S., Couper, M.P., Lessler, J.T., Martin, E., Martin, J., Rothgeb, J.M., & Singer, E. (2004). Methods for testing and evaluating survey questions. *Public Opinion Quarterly, 68*(1): 109-130.

Prochaska, J. (2005). Stages of change, readiness, and motivation. In J. Kerr, R. Weitkunat & M. Moretti (Eds.). *ABC of behavior change: A guide to successful disease prevention and health promotion* (pp. 111-123). Edinburgh: Elsevier.

Prochaska, J., Redding, C., & Evers, K. (2008). The transtheoretical model and stages of change. In K. Glanz, B.K. Rimer & K. Viswanath (Eds.), *Health behavior and health education: Theory, research, and practice* (4th ed.) (pp. 170-222). San Francisco, CA: Jossey-Bass.Quinn, S., & Green, B. (2006). Eliminating racial and ethnic health disparities: A call for innovative research. *Health Education & Behavior,* 33(4): 437-439.

REFERENCES

Rees, K.S., & Goldsmith, M. (2009). Selecting presentation methods. In R.J. Bensley & J. Brookins-Fisher (Eds.), *Community health education methods: A practical guide* (3rd ed.) (pp. 265-298). Sudbury, MA: Jones and Bartlett.

Robbins, S. & Judge, T. (2008). *Essentials of organizational behavior* (8th ed.) Upper Saddle River, NJ: Prentice Hall.

Roe, K.M., Roe, K., & Strona, F.V. (2009). Facilitating groups. In R.J. Bensley & J. Brookins-Fisher (Eds.), *Community health education methods: A practical guide* (3rd ed.) (pp. 293-323). Sudbury, MA: Jones and Bartlett.

Rogers, E. (2003). *Diffusion of innovation* (3rd ed.). New York, NY: Free Press.

Rosenstock, I.M., Strecher, V.J., & Becker, M.H. (1988). Social learning theory and the health belief model. *Health Education Quarterly*, 15(2),175-183.

Rowitz, L. (2009). *Public health leadership: putting principles into practice* (2nd. ed.). Sudbury, MA: Jones and Bartlett.

Sallis, J.F., Owen, N., & Fisher, E.B. (2008). Ecological models of health behavior. In K. Glanz, B.K. Rimer & K. Viswanath (Eds), *Health behavior and health education: Theory, research, and practice* (4th ed.) (pp. 465-486). San Francisco, CA: Jossey-Bass.

Saris, W., van der Veld, W., & Gallhofer, I. (2004). Development and improvement of questionnaires using predictions of reliability and validity. In J.M. Presser, M.P. Rothgeb, J. L. Couper, E.M. Lessler, E. Martin, J. Martin & E. Singer (Eds.), *Methods for testing and evaluating survey questionnaires* (pp.275-298). New York, NY: Wiley.

Schiavo, R. (2007). *Health communication: From theory to practice*. San Francisco, CA: Jossey-Bass.

Schulz, A. (2004). Social determinants of health: Implications for environmental health promotion. *Health Education & Behavior*, 31(4), 455-471.

Schwartzberg, J., VanGeest, J., & Wang, C. (2005). *Understanding health literacy: Implications for medicine and public health*. Chicago, IL: American Medical Association.

Selden, C. R., Zorn, M., Ratzan, S., & Parker, R. M. (2000). *Health literacy, January 1990 through October 1999*. Bethesda, MD: National Library of Medicine.

Sengupta, S., Calman, N., & Hripcsak, G. (2008). A model for expanded public reporting in the context of HIPPA. *Journal of the American Medical Informatics Association*, 15(5), 569-574.

Sharma, M., & Romas, J. A. (2008). *Theoretical Foundations of Health Education and Health Promotion*. Sudbury, MA: Jones and Bartlett.

Sherow, S., Weinberg, J., Sloan, J., & Morin, E. (2002). *Planning for change: A coalition building technical assistance system*. Philadelphia, PA: Author.

Siegel, M. & Lotenberg, L.D. (2007). *Marketing public health: Strategies to promote social change* (2nd edition). Sudbury, MA: Jones and Bartlett.

Simons-Morton, B.G., Greene, W.H., & Gottlieb, N.H. (1995). *Introduction to health education and health promotion* (2nd ed.). Prospect Heights, IL: Waveland Press.

Simons-Morton, D.G., Simons-Morton, B.G., Parcel, G.S., & Bunker, J.F. (1988). Influencing personal and environmental conditions for community health: A multilevel intervention model. *Family and Community Health*, 11, 25-35.

STORE: Strategic Tobacco Retail Effort. (n.d.). Retrieved from http://www.tcsstore.org/stages/index.html

Substance Abuse and Mental Health Services Administration (SAMHSA). (2010). *National registry of evidence-based programs and practice.* Retrieved from http://www.nrepp.samhsa.gov/

Taub, A., Birch, D. A., Auld, M. E., Lysoby, L., & Rasar King, L. (2009). Strengthening quality assurance in health education: Recent milestones and future directions. *Health Promotion Practice*, 10(2), 192-200.

Taub, A., Kreuter, M., Parcel, G., & Vitello, E. (1987). Report from the AAHE/SOPHE Joint Committee on Ethics. *Health Education Quarterly*, 14(1), 79-90.

Teddlie, C., & Tashakkori, A. (2009). *Foundations of mixed methods research: Integrating quantitative and qualitative approaches in the social and behavioral sciences.* Thousand Oaks, CA: Sage.

Timmreck, T.C. (2003). *Planning, program development & evaluation: A handbook for health promotion, aging & health services.* Boston, MA: Jones and Bartlett.

Trochim, W.M., & Donnelly, J. (2008). *Research methods knowledge base* (3rd ed.)(pp. 6-8). Mason, OH: Atomic Dog.

Turnock, B.J. (2004). *Public health: What it is and how it works* (3rd ed.). Sudbury, MA: Jones and Bartlett.

United States Department of Health and Human Services (USDHHS), Office of Disease Prevention and Health Promotion (ODPHP). (2009). *Quick guide to health literacy.* Retrieved from http://www.health.gov/communication/literacy/quickguide/

USDHHS, National Institutes of Health (NIH), National Library of Medicine (NLM). (2000). In C.R. Selden, M. Zorn, S, Ratzan, S., et al. (Eds.). *Health Literacy, January 1990 through October 1999.* Bethesda, MD: National Library of Medicine.

USDHHS, Office of Minority Health. (2001). *National standards for culturally and linguistically appropriate services in health care final report.* Retrieved from http://raceandhealth.hhs.gov/templates/browse. aspx?lvl=3&lvlid=254

REFERENCES

U.S. Department of Health, Education and Welfare, Health Resources Administration, Bureau of Health Manpower (1978). *Preparation and practice of community, patient, and school health educators: Proceedings of the workshop on commonalities and differences.* Washington, DC: Division of Allied Health Professions.

United States Department of Justice (USDOJ). (2010). *Limited English proficiency: A federal interagency website.* Retrieved from http://www.justice.gov/crt/lep

United States Department of Labor, Bureau of Labor Statistics (2009). *Occupational outlook handbook, 2010-11 edition: Health educators.* Retrieved from http://www.bls.gov/oco/ocos063.htm

University of Kansas. (2009). *Community tool box: Overview of strategic planning or "VMOSA" (vision, mission, objectives, and action plans).* Retrieved from http://ctb.ku.edu/en/tablecontents/sub_section_main_1085.htm

University of Kansas. (2010). *Welcome to the community toolbox.* Retrieved from http://ctb.ku.edu

University of Wisconsin. (2009). *Enhancing Program Performance with Logic Models.* Retrieved from http://www.uwex.edu/ces/lmcourse

University of Wisconsin, Cooperative Extension, Program Development and Evaluation. (2002). *Logic models.* Retrieved from http://www.uwex.edu/ces/pdande/evaluation/evallogicmodel.html

Vaughn, E.J. (2008). Cultural competence and health education. In M.A Perez & R.R. Luquis (Eds.), *Cultural competence in health education and health promotion* (pp. 43-65). San Francisco, CA: Jossey-Bass.

Vernick, J.S. (1999). Lobbying and advocacy for the public's health: What are the limits for non-profit organizations? *American Journal of Public Health, 89*(9), 1425-1429.

Wagenschutz, H.M., & Rivas, J. (2009). Developing effective presentations. In R.J. Bensley, & J. Brookins-Fisher (Eds.), *Community health education methods: A practical guide* (3rd ed.) (pp. 183-208). Sudbury, MA: Jones and Barlett.

Wang, C., & Burris, M.A. (1997). Photovoice: Concept, methodology, and use for participatory needs assessment. *Health Education and Behavior, 24*(3), 369-387.

Weiss, C.H. (1998). *Evaluation: methods for studying programs and policies* (2nd ed.). Upper Saddle River, NJ: Prentice Hall.

Williams, M.V., Parker, R.M., Baker, D.W., Parikh, N.S., Pitkin, K., Coates, W.C., & Nurss, J.R. (1995). Inadequate functional health literacy among patients at two public hospitals. *Journal of the American Medical Association, 274*(21), 1677-1682.

Windsor, R., Clark, N., Boyd, N., & Goodman, R. M. (2004). *Evaluation of health promotion, health education, and disease prevention programs* (3rd ed.). Boston, MA: McGraw-Hill.

REFERENCES

W.K. Kellogg Foundation. (2004). *Logic model development guide*. Retrieved from http://www.wkkf.org/knowledge-center/Resources-Page.aspx

Workgroup for Community Health and Development (The University of Kansas). *The Community Tool Box*. Retrieved from http://ctb.ku.edu/en/tablecontents/chapter_1003.htm

Wurzbach, M.E. (Ed.). (2004). *Community health education and promotion: A guide to program design and evaluation* (2nd ed.). Gaithersburg, MD: Aspen Reference.

Zarcadoolas, C., Pleasant, A., & Greer, D.S. (2006). *Advancing health literacy: A framework for understanding and action*. San Francisco, CA: Jossey-Bass.

NOTES

NOTES

NOTES

NOTES